y

TOPICS IN MODERN MATHEMATICS

HOWARD M. NAHIKIAN

NORTH CAROLINA STATE UNIVERSITY AT RALEIGH

TOPICS IN
MODERN
MATHEMATICS

THE MACMILLAN COMPANY, NEW YORK

COLLIER–MACMILLAN LIMITED, LONDON

To Nancy

510
N153t

Second Printing, 1967

The author wishes to thank The University of Chicago
Press for its permission to use several of the text illustrations and problems from *A Modern Algebra for Biologists*
(1964) by Howard M. Nahikian.

Library of Congress catalog card number: 66–20822

THE MACMILLAN COMPANY, NEW YORK
COLLIER-MACMILLAN CANADA, LTD., TORONTO, ONTARIO

Printed in the United States of America

PREFACE

Not all modern mathematics is new mathematics. Most of the topics included in this book were known a full century ago. Probability theory, for example, had its early beginnings in the seventeenth century in the brilliant minds of Fermat (1601–1665) and Pascal (1623–1662). Matrix theory came into being in the nineteenth century out of the work of such men as Cayley (1821–1895), Sylvester (1814–1897), and Frobenius (1849–1917). Symbolic logic was initiated by Boole (1815–1864), and the theory of sets was developed in great part by Cantor (1845–1918). This is not to belittle the enormous amount of work and insight that has gone into these areas of mathematics during the ensuing years, for great strides have been made in all of these branches during this century, but simply to point out that modern science is the beneficiary of much from the past.

Why, then, "modern" mathematics, if it really is not new or recently discovered mathematics? Perhaps the adjective "relevant" would have been more appropriate than "modern" in the title of this book. These topics are relevant to modern problems in human affairs—warfare, transportation, economics, psychology, biology, and sociology, to name a few. Until recently many of the scientists working in these areas have found little use for mathematics, not because of a lack of problems, but because the mathematics that had been taught to them was inadequate for their problems.

The topics included in this book have been recommended by many of the

v

nation's leading mathematicians as an important segment of the necessary mathematical training for students of the life sciences and almost equally so for those whose chief interests may lie in the physical sciences. It is felt that this body of material should be made available to students very early in their careers. This is a part of the revolution that is under way in science education throughout the nation. Most of the topics were taught at the upper levels of college mathematics a decade or so ago. Now they are offered not only to first-year college students but to many advanced high school seniors.

At North Carolina State University a one-semester course based on most of the material in the first five chapters of this text is offered to freshmen and sophomores in the life sciences, textiles, economics, and forestry. These students have had traditional courses in algebra and trigonometry either in high school or during the first semester at the University. Some have had a semester course in polynomial calculus, but this is not prerequisite to the course in "modern topics."

The development of the material in this book is reasonably informal and in part expository. However, when a suitable occasion arises, a formal proof is not avoided. Although many of the topics are introductory in nature, a serious attempt has been made in each instance to present enough of the subject to make it not only interesting but useful. Throughout the discussion the common unifying thread is that of function and relation, naive set theory undergirding the entire development.

As in every writing project like this one, the author is indebted to many people. In particular he wishes to thank his long-time friend and colleague, Professor H. V. Park, for his careful reading of the manuscript and his many helpful suggestions. Others who have been of great service are Professors G. C. Watson and D. M. Peterson.

The author also wishes to offer sincere appreciation to the Macmillan staff for its wonderful cooperation in getting this book out in its final published form. In particular, he acknowledges with thanks the cooperation and many helpful suggestions of Arthur B. Evans, editor at The Macmillan Company, and Professor Carl B. Allendoerfer.

Especial thanks are due Adele Porter Covington for her careful typing of the final manuscript.

In spite of all this help there will be mistakes, for which the author takes full responsibility.

H. M. N.

Raleigh, N.C.

CONTENTS

TOPICS IN MODERN MATHEMATICS

CHAPTER 1

SETS AND SUBSETS

1.1 INTRODUCTION

It is not always easy to point to one area of mathematics and say with confidence that it is fundamental to the others. However, the theory of sets is basic to many of the mathematical topics to be considered in this course. In this chapter we shall discuss in some detail certain concepts in elementary set theory that will be needed later. We shall be concerned mainly with the vocabulary and the symbolism of set theory. The development of the subject is informal or naive rather than axiomatic.

1.2 SETS

A biologist classifies certain individuals having common characteristics as belonging to a *species*. A forester might be interested in a broad classification of various woods as hard or soft. A textile manufacturer might designate materials according as they are woven of synthetic, animal, or vegetable fibers. Within each such grouping several items might be placed. However, if each classification is *well defined*, it is possible to determine in general which object belongs to a specific category. In mathematics the word *set* is used rather than the words species, class, or category.

The early developments of set theory are credited to Georg Cantor (1845–1918), a German mathematician. His definition of a set may sound formidable. It is translated roughly as "the bringing together into a whole certain well-distinguished objects which are perceived or conceived." An object is an *element* of a set if it *is in* the set. We also say it *belongs* to the set or *is a member* of the set.

Note that Cantor's definition requires that the elements in a set be "well distinguished." Thus, given a set and an object one must be able to determine positively whether the object belongs or does not belong to the set. A set containing all of the even integers is well defined because it is possible to determine whether or not an integer belongs to the set according as the integer is or is not divisible by 2. On the other hand, a collection of the five best-dressed men on a faculty is not a well-defined set, because there is no objective standard that can be used in determining whether an individual belongs to the set or not. The same is true of such collections as the three greatest living Americans, the five greatest paintings, or even the four greatest mathematicians of all time.

In what follows sets are denoted by capital letters $A, B, C, \ldots$, and elements by small letters $a, b, c, \ldots$. The notation "$a \in A$" is interpreted "a belongs to set A." On the other hand, "$a \notin A$" is read "a does not belong to set A."

If the number of elements in a set is finite, we say that it is a *finite* set. Any set not finite is *infinite*.

The 26 people sitting at a conference table, the 402,315 books on the shelves of a library, the students of this class, the readers of this book, the letters of the English alphabet, the citizens of the United States who were living in the year 1910, and the members of the student council are all examples of finite sets.

Each of these sets is different from the others. No one is apt to assign to the set of library books an element from the set of people at the conference table. Although all the letters of the English alphabet may well be contained in some of the books of the library, they do not belong to the set whose elements are those books themselves. It is possible that an element belonging to the set of people at the conference table belongs also to the set of Americans living in 1910, but even if all of the elements of the first set belonged to the second set, these sets would be distinct.

Although the set of 26 people sitting in conference and the set of the letters of the English alphabet do not have any elements in common, these two sets do have a *property* in common, namely, the *number* of elements in each set. This fact may be established by *counting* the elements in each of these sets, since they are finite. However, there is another way that this information may be ascertained, which does not require counting and hence may be applied to infinite sets as well as finite ones. Suppose to each person in the conference there corresponds one and only one letter of the alphabet and that after the matching of individuals and letters there are no elements of either set left over; then it may be concluded that the two sets have the same number of elements.

It is apparent from the preceding example that it is not necessary to count the elements of two sets in order to determine whether or not they have the same number of elements. Whenever the elements of two sets can be matched in such a way that to each element of the first set there corresponds one and only one element of the second set, and conversely, the sets are said to be in *one-to-one correspondence*. Sets that can be placed in one-to-one correspondence are said to be *equivalent* and to have the same *cardinal number*.

Using these definitions, we may conclude that the sets $A = \{1, 2, \ldots, 100\}$ and $B = \{3, 6, \ldots, 300\}$ are equivalent and have the same cardinal number 100, because a one-to-one correspondence between A and B may be established in the obvious way $1 \leftrightarrow 3, 2 \leftrightarrow 6, \ldots, 100 \leftrightarrow 300$.

The *infinite* sets $Z^+ = \{1, 2, \ldots, n, \ldots\}$ and $G = \{3, 6, \ldots, 3n, \ldots\}$ also are equivalent, because the following one-to-one correspondence holds for all positive integers n: $1 \leftrightarrow 3, 2 \leftrightarrow 6, \ldots, n \leftrightarrow 3n$. In this connection, a set is said to have the cardinal number $\aleph_0$ (*aleph nought*) if it is equivalent to Z^+. Hence the set G has the cardinal number $\aleph_0$.

Some well-defined sets that occur in mathematics are

> The set C of all complex numbers.
> The set R of all real numbers.
> The set Q of all rational numbers.
> The set I of all integers including zero.
> The set F of all fractions that do not reduce to integers.
> The set Z^+ of all strictly positive integers.
> The set Z^- of all negative integers.

Although all the sets listed above are indeed infinite, one should not assume that only infinite sets are of importance in mathematics. In the chapters that follow will be found many examples of finite as well as infinite sets that are useful. For the present, however, we mention a few finite mathematical sets: the vertices of a triangle, the sides of a polygon, the faces of a cube, the integers greater than zero and less than ten, the primes greater than one and less than eighteen, and the right angles in a square.

If the number of elements in a finite set is comparatively small, the set may be designated by writing out explicitly all its elements in *any order* and enclosing them in braces, "{ }." For example, the set consisting of the letters "a," "b," and "c" may be written $\{a, b, c\}$, $\{a, c, b\}$, or $\{b, a, c\}$, and so on; the set of integers greater than zero and less than 5 may be written $\{1, 2, 3, 4\}$ or $\{3, 4, 1, 2\}$ or in any other order.

Whenever it is not convenient to list explicitly the elements of a given set, we may designate it by stating the *common property* that characterizes the elements that belong to the set. For example, the set A of integers greater than zero and less than 5 may be written

$$A = \{x \mid x \in I, 0 < x < 5\}. \tag{1.1}$$

The expression $0 < x < 5$ is called an *open statement*. The symbol x designates an *arbitrary* or *generic* element of the set A. The vertical line, $\mid$, is read "such that" or "for which." Since all the elements of A are integers, we indicate this by writing $x \in I$ as part of the description and follow this by $0 < x < 5$. Hence Equation 1.1 is read, "A is the set of integers x that are greater than zero and less than five."

As a further illustration, the set

$$B = \{x \mid x = 2n, n \in Z^+\} \tag{1.2}$$

is read, "B is the set of all positive even integers." This same set might be written alternatively

$$B = \{2, 4, 6, 8, \ldots\}, \tag{1.3}$$

where a sufficient number of elements of the set are listed so that the property that distinguishes them can be determined.

As a further illustration, the set

$$E = \{z \mid z \in C, |z| = 1\} \tag{1.4}$$

consists of all complex numbers z whose absolute value is 1. That is, if $z = a + bi$, then $|z| = \sqrt{a^2 + b^2} = 1$.

In general, the description of a set is given in terms of the elements of a larger set, U, which is called the *universal set*. In Equation 1.4 the universal set, out of which the elements of E are selected, is the set of all complex numbers C. Similarly, the universal set given in Equation 1.3 is the set I of all positive, negative, or zero integers. Thus it is clear that there are many universal sets that vary from application to application of set theory. In problems arising in sociology the universal set might be the rural population of a given state, or it might be the entire labor force of the steel industry in the United States. In an application of set theory to forestry, the universal set might well be a particular forest. In problems arising in cryptography the universal set is likely to be the alphabet used in the codes.

Just as it is convenient to have a universal set, or *superset*, to which to refer the set one is working with in a particular application, it is convenient to have a set *which contains no elements*. Such a set is called the *empty set* or *null set* and is denoted by $\varnothing$.

For example, the set of even integers which satisfy the equation $x^2 - 2x - 3 = 0$ is empty, because the only roots are the elements of the set $\{-1, 3\}$ and neither -1 nor 3 is an even integer.

Another example of an empty set is the set of all elements that are members of both $\{-1, 3, 5\}$ and $\{-2, 0, 2, 4\}$.

PROBLEMS

1. Which of the following are well-defined sets? The set of all _____
   (a) bugs
   (b) pretty girls
   (c) bushes
   (d) roses
   (e) praying mantises
   (f) handsome boys
   (g) good books
   (h) weeds
   (i) insects
   (j) smart kids

2. Which of the following sets are equivalent? Explain.
   (a) A set of children and the set of chairs they are using in a game of "musical chairs" in which the music has started.
   (b) The set of states of the U.S.A. and the set of integers divisible by 3 that are greater than zero and less than 151.
   (c) The set of primes greater than 1 and less than 9 and the set of positive odd integers less than 9.
   (d) The set of integers and the set of even integers.
   (e) The set of nonnegative even integers and the set of positive odd integers.
   (f) The set of students in a mathematics class and the set of quiz grades if the grades are all different.

3. Let R denote the set of all real numbers, I the set of all integers, and Z^+ the set of all positive integers. Write out explicitly the elements in each of the following sets.
   (a) $\{x \mid x \in Z^+, x^2 - 3x = 0\}$.
   (b) $\{x \mid x \in I, x^2 - 3x = 0\}$.
   (c) $\{x \mid x \in I, 2x^2 - 3x = 0\}$.
   (d) $\{x \mid x \in Z^+, 2x^2 - 3x = 0\}$.
   (e) $\{x \mid x \in R, 2x^2 - 3x = 0\}$.
   (f) $\{x \mid x \in Z^+, 2x - 5 < 6\}$.

4. Write the following sets symbolically in two ways.
   (a) The set of integers greater than -2 and less than or equal to 3.
   (b) The set consisting of the numbers 2/3 and -1.
   (c) The odd natural numbers less than 8.
   (d) The prime numbers greater than 1 and less than 12.

5. (a) Describe the set of rational numbers Q in terms of the elements of the set I of integers.
   (b) Describe the set of even integers E and the set of odd integers O in terms of the elements of the set of integers I.
   (c) Describe the set of rational fractions whose numerators are 1.

6. Which of the following are empty sets?
   (a) $\{x \mid x \in Z^+, x^2 - 3x - 4 = 0\}$.
   (b) $\{x \mid x \in Z^+, 2x^2 - x = 0\}$.
   (c) $\{x \mid n \in Z^+, x = 2n, x^2 - 3x = 0\}$.
   (d) $\{x \mid x$ a prime, $x = 2\}$.
   (e) $\{x \mid x \in I, x^2 = 4\}$.
   (f) $\{x \mid x \in I, x^2 - 5 = 0\}$.

7. Use set notation to describe the following.
   (a) The set of letters in the word *Constantinople*.
   (b) The set of vowels in the English alphabet.
   (c) The set of consonants in the word *consonant*.
   (d) The set of digits in 3.14159.
   (e) The set of positive integers divisible by 3.
   (f) The set of primes which divide 72.
   (g) The set of prime factors common to 300 and 504.

1.3 SUBSETS

If A and B are two sets such that every element of set A is also an element of set B, then A is said to be a *subset* of B. For example, the set of Buick automobiles is a subset of all automobiles. The set of Buicks which came off the assembly line last year is a subset of the set of all Buicks built during the past five years. The set of vowels is a subset of the alphabet. The set of integers is a subset of the rational numbers and at the same time is a subset of the real numbers and also of the set of complex numbers.

The definition of subset does not rule out the possibility of a set being considered a subset of itself. Certainly, every element of a given set B is an element of B, and this is the only stipulation of the definition. Whenever it is desirable to exclude this case, we shall state that A is a *proper subset* of B.

Notationally, we write $A \subset B$ only when A is a proper subset of B. The symbol "$\subset$" is known as the *inclusion symbol*, and the set A is said to be *included* in the set B. In all cases in which A is a subset of B but not necessarily a proper subset, we write $A \subseteq B$.

For example, if $B = \{-1, 2, 3, 5\}$ and $A = \{x \mid x^2 - 2x - 3 = 0\}$, then $A \subset B$. For in this case, $x \in A$ if and only if $x^2 - 2x - 3 = 0$; that is, $x = -1$ or $x = 3$. Although both of these elements belong to B, they do not constitute the entire set. Thus, A is a proper subset of B. On the other hand, if $C = \{-1, 3\}$ and $A = \{x \mid x^2 - 2x - 3 = 0\}$, it follows from the preceding discussion that A is not a proper subset of C, and we write $A \subseteq C$.

It can be shown logically that the empty set $\varnothing$ is a subset of every set, and we shall accept this result without proof. Thus, $\varnothing \subseteq A$, where A is an arbitrary set.

Let us note carefully the distinction between the symbols "$\in$" and "$\subseteq$." When we write $a \in A$, we indicate that a is an element which belongs to the set A. Since $\{a\}$ is a set whose element(s) belong to A, we have by definition that $\{a\}$ is a subset of A, and we write $\{a\} \subseteq A$. Thus the symbol "$\in$" relates an element to a set, whereas "$\subseteq$" relates a set to a set.

A special set closely related to any given set A is the set whose elements are all possible subsets of A. This set is called the *power set* of A and is denoted by the symbol 2^A. For example, if $A = \{a, b\}$, then $2^A = \{\varnothing, \{a\}, \{b\}, \{a, b\}\}$. The term *power set* stems from the result, which can be established, that when A has a finite number, n, of elements, there are 2^n elements in its power set (see Problem 5, this section). Of course, the notation of power set is not limited to finite sets. If A is an infinite set, then its power set 2^A is infinite also.

Two sets, A and B, are said to be *equal* (written $A = B$), if every element of A is an element of B and every element of B is an element of A. This definition implies that the defining property $P(x)$, which assigns the element x to the set A, and the defining property $Q(x)$, which assigns x to the set B, are equivalent in the sense that, although they may read differently, *they define exactly the same elements*. Because the definition of equality requires that every element of A must belong to B, we have $A \subseteq B$, and because every element of B must belong to A, we have $B \subseteq A$.

To prove that two sets A and B are equal, we first show that an arbitrary or generic element of set A belongs to set B, which establishes $A \subseteq B$, and then we show that a typical element of B belongs to set A, which proves that $B \subseteq A$. These results allow us to state that $A = B$.

For example, let $A = \{x \mid x \in I, (x - 1)(x + 2)(2x - 3) = 0\}$ and $B = \{1, -2\}$. If a is to be an element of set A, a must be an integer and it must satisfy the equation $(a - 1)(a + 2)(2a - 3) = 0$. The only integers that satisfy the given equation are $a = 1$ and $a = -2$, so we have at once $A \subseteq B$. Likewise, if $b \in B$, then $b = 1$ or $b = -2$. Since both elements belong to set A, we have $B \subseteq A$. By definition, $A = B$.

PROBLEMS

1. If $A = \{a_1, a_2, a_3, a_4\}$, which of the following are valid statements?
   (a) $a_2 \in A$.   (d) $\{a_3, a_4\} \in A$.
   (b) $\{a_2\} \in A$.   (e) $\{a_1, a_2, a_3\} \subset A$.
   (c) $\{a_3\} \subset A$.

2. Given $A = \{2, 0, -2\}$ and $B = \{x \mid x \in I, x^3 - 4x = 0\}$, write a logical proof that $A = B$.

3. Construct 2^A for $A = \{a_1, a_2, a_3\}$.

4. How many elements are there in the power set of a set with 4 elements? With 5 elements? Construct the power set of $A = \{w, x, y, z\}$.

5. Prove that there are 2^n elements in the power set of a finite set which has n elements.

6. If a set A has 2 elements, how many elements are there in the power set of 2^A? Construct this set for $A = \{a, b\}$.

7. Prove that $A = B$ if

$$A = \{x \mid x \text{ a prime, } 3 \leqslant x \leqslant 7\}$$

and $\qquad B = \{x \mid x = 2n + 1, n \in Z^+, 1 \leqslant n \leqslant 3\}.$

8. Prove that $A = B$ if $A = \{x \mid x \in Z^+, 1 \leqslant x \leqslant 6\}$ and $B = \{1, 2, 3, 4, 5, 6\}$.

9. Prove that, if $A \subseteq B$ and $B \subseteq C$, then $A \subseteq C$.

10. Which of the following pairs of sets are equal? Which are equivalent?
   (a) $\{3, 5, 7\}$, $\{2, 4, 6\}$.
   (b) $\{a, b, c\}$, $\{b, a, c\}$.
   (c) $\{5, 12, 17\}$, $\{17, 5, 12\}$.

1.4 SET OPERATIONS AND VENN DIAGRAMS

There are several ways of combining elements of two given sets to form other sets. The first of these *set operations* is called the *union* of two sets A and B and is denoted by "$A \cup B$." The union of sets A and B is the set which contains all of the elements that belong either to set A or to set B, or to both sets. Thus, $A \cup B = \{x \mid x \in A \text{ and/or } x \in B\}$. For example, if

$$A = \{-3, -1, 0, 1, 3\} \qquad \text{and} \qquad B = \{-2, -1, 0, 3, 4\},$$

then $A \cup B = \{-3, -1, 0, 1, 3, -2, 4\}$. Or again, if $C = \{$Tom, Dick, Harry$\}$ and $D = \{$Ike, Mike, Dick, Tom$\}$, and $C \cup D = \{$Tom, Dick, Harry, Ike, Mike$\}$.

The second set operation is called the *intersection* of two sets A and B and is denoted by "$A \cap B$." This set is formed from the elements that are common to both sets. Thus $A \cap B$ is the set whose elements belong *both* to set A *and* to set B; that is, $A \cap B = \{x \mid x \in A \text{ and } x \in B\}$.

In a previous illustration $A = \{-3, -1, 0, 1, 3\}$ and $B = \{-2, -1, 0, 3, 4\}$. The elements that belong to both sets A and B are contained in their intersection, $A \cap B = \{-1, 0, 3\}$, and the sets C and D of the second illustration have the intersection $C \cap D = \{$Tom, Dick$\}$.

We note that, if $X = \{x \mid x \in I, x^3 - 4x = 0\}$ and $Y = \{0, 2, 4\}$, it follows that $X \cup Y = \{-2, 0, 2, 4\}$ and $X \cap Y = \{0, 2\}$. On the other hand, if $Z = \{1, 3, 5\}$, then $X \cap Z = \varnothing$, and we say that set X and Z are *disjoint*; that is, two sets are disjoint if and only if they have no element in common.

Both union and intersection may be extended by definition to operations on a finite number, or even to operations on an infinite number, of sets. If $A_1, A_2, \ldots, A_n$ are sets, we write

$$\bigcup_{i=1}^{n} A_i = A_1 \cup A_2 \cup \cdots \cup A_n$$

to indicate their *union*, that is, to indicate the set containing all the elements that belong to A_1 or A_2 or $\cdots$ or A_n. Similarly, we indicate the *intersection* of the sets $A_1, A_2, \ldots, A_n$ by the symbol

$$\bigcap_{i=1}^{n} A_i = A_1 \cap A_2 \cap \cdots \cap A_n,$$

by which we mean the set of elements that are common to all the sets A_i.

For example, if $A_1 = \{-1, 0, 1, 2\}$, $A_2 = \{-4, -2, 0, 2\}$ and $A_3 = \{0, 1, 2, 3\}$, then

$$\bigcup_{i=1}^{3} A_i = A_1 \cup A_2 \cup A_3 = \{-4, -2, -1, 0, 1, 2, 3\}$$

and

$$\bigcap_{i=1}^{3} A_i = A_1 \cap A_2 \cap A_3 = \{0, 2\}.$$

The *complement* of a subset $A \subseteq U$ is the set of all elements in the universal set U that do not belong to A. We denote this set by A' or $\overline{A}$. Thus

$$\overline{A} = A' = \{x \mid x \in U, x \notin A\}.$$

If A and B are two subsets of the universal set U, the set of elements belonging to A that do not belong to B is called the *relative difference of A and B* and is denoted by $A - B$. It follows that $A - B = \{x \mid x \in A, x \notin B\}$.

For example, if $A = \{x \mid x \in I, x^3 - 4x = 0\}$ and $B = \{-2, -1, -\frac{1}{2}, 0, \frac{1}{2}, 1\}$, then $A - B = \{2\}$ and $B - A = \{-1, -\frac{1}{2}, \frac{1}{2}, 1\}$.

An important relation exists between these set operations: namely, $A - B = A \cap B'$. This can be established as follows. First assume that x is an arbitrary element of $A - B$. Then, because $x \in A - B$, we know that $x \in A$ and that also $x \notin B$. Because $x \notin B$, we must have $x \in B'$. Therefore, $x \in A \cap B'$, and we have shown that $A - B \subseteq A \cap B'$. Conversely, if $y \in A \cap B'$, then we have $y \in A$ and $y \in B'$. It follows that $y \in A$ and $y \notin B$. This is exactly what we mean when we say that $y \in A - B$. Because by assumption y is an arbitrary element in $A \cap B'$, we have proved that $A \cap B' \subseteq A - B$. Thus, by the definition of equal sets, we have $A - B = A \cap B'$.

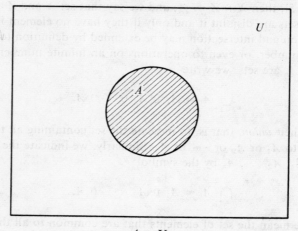

$A \subset U$.

FIGURE 1.1

Each of the sets $A \cup B$, $A \cap B$, A', $A - B$ can be represented geometrically by means of a device called a *Venn diagram*. It is customary to indicate the universal set U by the points inside a rectangle, and a subset $A \subset U$ by the points inside a circle within the rectangle (see Figure 1.1).

If A and B are subsets of U and $A \subset B$, the Venn diagram shows circle A lying within circle B, as in Figure 1.2.

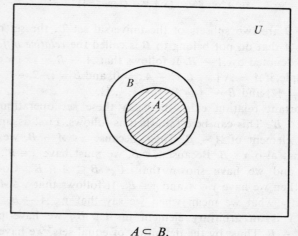

$A \subset B$.

FIGURE 1.2

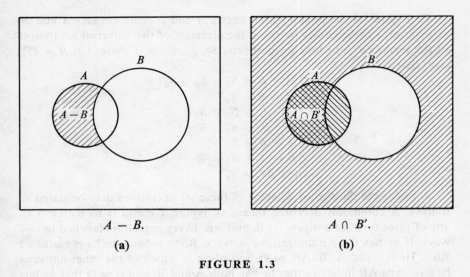

$A - B.$ $A \cap B'.$

(a)   (b)

FIGURE 1.3

In Figure 1.3, the points within the circles represent sets A and B, respectively. The set $A - B$ is represented by the hatched region in Figure 1.3 (a) while the set $A \cap B'$ is represented by the points of the cross-hatched region of Figure 1.3 (b). Since these regions are identical, the relationship $A - B = A \cap B'$ is verified for the case in which A and B are not disjoint (for other cases, see Problem 15, this section).

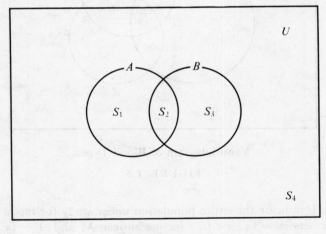

A Partition of U.

FIGURE 1.4

In Figure 1.4 the points within circles A and B represent sets A and B, respectively. These circles partition the elements of the universal set (points of the rectangle) into four disjoint sets, S_1, S_2, S_3, S_4 (where $A \cap B \neq \varnothing$), such that

$$A \cup B = S_1 \cup S_2 \cup S_3$$
$$A \cap B = S_2$$
$$A' = S_3 \cup S_4$$
$$B' = S_1 \cup S_4$$
$$A - B = S_1$$
$$B - A = S_3$$
$$(A \cup B)' = S_4$$

A biological illustration of some of these set operations may be stated as follows. A commonly accepted means of typing a blood is to match it to any of three types of antigen, A, B, and Rh. Every person is classified in two ways. If he has the Rh antigen, he is typed Rh$^+$; otherwise, he is classified Rh$^-$. He is typed A, B, AB, or O, according to which of the other antigens he has; type AB indicates that he has both A and B, and type O that he has neither A nor B.

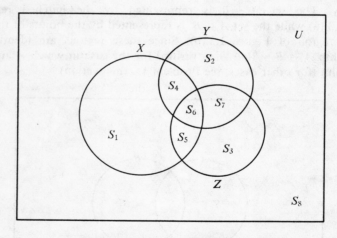

Venn Diagram of Blood Types.

FIGURE 1.5

We let U indicate the entire population under study for blood type and define the sets $X = \{x \mid x \in U, x$ having antigen A$\}$ and $Y = \{y \mid y \in U, y$ having antigen B$\}$ and $Z = \{z \mid z \in U, z$ having antigen Rh$\}$. In the general case a Venn diagram is drawn by partitioning the universal set U into eight disjoint subsets by means of three overlapping circles, X, Y, Z, as shown in Figure 1.5. The eight subsets have blood types as follows:

$$S_1 = X \cap Y' \cap Z' \qquad (\text{A, Rh}^-)$$
$$S_2 = X' \cap Y \cap Z' \qquad (\text{B, Rh}^-)$$
$$S_3 = X' \cap Y' \cap Z \qquad (\text{O, Rh}^+)$$
$$S_4 = X \cap Y \cap Z' \qquad (\text{AB, Rh}^-)$$
$$S_5 = X \cap Y' \cap Z \qquad (\text{A, Rh}^+)$$
$$S_6 = X \cap Y \cap Z \qquad (\text{AB, Rh}^+)$$
$$S_7 = X' \cap Y \cap Z \qquad (\text{B, Rh}^+)$$
$$S_8 = X' \cap Y' \cap Z' \qquad (\text{O, Rh}^-)$$

PROBLEMS

1. Simplify each of the following expressions.
   (a) $A \cup A$.   (e) $A \cup \varnothing$.
   (b) $A \cap A$.   (f) $A \cap U$.
   (c) $A \cap A'$.   (g) $A \cup A'$.
   (d) $A \cap \varnothing$.   (h) $A \cup U$.

2. The universal set and a subset is given in each of the following. Determine the complement in each case.
   (a) U is the set of natural numbers; $A = \{x \mid x \in U, x \text{ odd}\}$. What is A'?
   (b) U is the English alphabet; $A = \{a, e, i, o, u\}$. What is A'?
   (c) U is the set of rational numbers; $A = \{x \mid x \in I\}$. What is A'?
   (d) U is the set of real numbers; A is the set of integers. What is A'?

3. Given $U = \{0, 2, 4, 6, 8, 10\}$, $A = \{0, 4, 8\}$, $B = \{2, 4, 6, 8\}$, $C = \{0, 6, 10\}$, find A', B', C', $A \cup B$, $(A \cup B)'$, $A \cap B$, $(A \cap C)'$, $(A \cup B) \cap C$, $A' \cap B' \cap C'$, $A - B$, $(A - B)'$.

4. Let $V = \{a, e, i, o, u\}$, $A = \{a, r, t\}$, $B = \{b, o, a, t\}$, $C = \{c, e, n, t\}$, $D = \{d, o, g, m, a, t, i, c\}$. Find the following sets.
   (a) $A - B$.   (c) $B \cup C$.   (e) $(V \cap D) \cup A$.
   (b) $D - C$.   (d) $A \cap C$.   (f) $(B - C) \cap V$.

5. Draw Venn diagrams for the following situations.
   (a) $A \cup B$ for the case $A \cap B = \varnothing$.
   (b) $A \cup B$ for the case $A \subset B$.
   (c) $A \cap B$ for the case $A \supset B$.
   (d) $A - B$ for the case $A \supset B$.
   (e) $(A \cup B) \cap C$ for the case $A \cap B \subset C$, $A \nsubseteq C$, $B \nsubseteq C$.

6. Verify that $A \cup (B - A) = B$ when $A = \{a, b\}$ and $B = \{a, b, c, d\}$. Is it true that $B \cup (A - B) = A$? How about $A \cup (A - B)$?

7. Considering only two subsets of a population U, the set $X = \{x \mid x \in U, x \text{ has antigen A}\}$ and the set $Y = \{x \mid x \in U, x \text{ has antigen B}\}$, define the sets of people with blood types A, B, AB, and O in terms of X and Y.

8. Let S be the set consisting of the freshman class of the university. Denote by M the set of males in the class and by F the set of females. Let A be the set of administrative officers, D the set of deans, P the set of professors, c the chancellor, d one of the deans, and p one of the professors. State all the relationships you can think of, using $\in, \subset, \cup, \cap, -, \varnothing$.

9. Consider two sets A and B. Denote by the symbol $A \dotplus B$ the set of all the elements in A that do not belong to B and all the elements in B that do not belong to A. Express this set as one equation in terms of union, intersection, difference, and complementation.

10. A psychologist examining the qualifications of persons for a certain type of endeavor lists their qualifications in sets. Two individuals with sets A and B, respectively, are then compared by constructing the set $A \dotplus B$ (see Problem 9). If $A \dotplus B$ has few or no elements in it, the individuals are said to be "close together," and if $A \dotplus B$ has many elements in it, the individuals are correspondingly "far apart." Give an argument supporting or disagreeing with this psychological jargon.

11. In a certain situation there are three candidates with three sets of qualifications, respectively: $A = \{a, f, g, e, c\}$, $B = \{c, f, a, k, h\}$, and $C = \{a, e, h, f, k\}$. Determine the pair which is "closest together" and the pair which is "farthest apart" (see Problem 10).

12. Use Venn diagrams to demonstrate that the following relationships hold for sets X and Y.
    (a) $X \cup (X \cap Y) = X$.
    (b) If $X \cap Y = X$, then $X \subseteq Y$.
    (c) If $X \subseteq Y$, then $X \cap Y = X$.

13. Use Venn diagrams to demonstrate that the following relationships hold for sets X and Y and their complements, X' and Y', with respect to the universal set U.
    (a) $X' \cap Y' = (X \cup Y)'$.   (c) $(X')' = X$.
    (b) $X' \cup Y' = (X \cap Y)'$.   (d) $X' \cup X = U$.

14. Use Venn diagrams to verify that the following relationships hold for sets X, Y, and Z.
    (a) $X \cup (Y \cap Z) = (X \cup Y) \cap (X \cup Z)$.
    (b) $X \cap (Y \cup Z) = (X \cap Y) \cup (X \cap Z)$.

15. Use Venn diagrams to verify that $A - B = A \cap B'$ for sets A and B, when (a) $A \cap B = \varnothing$ and (b) $B \subset A$.

1.5 PRODUCT SETS

Until now, whenever we have considered a set of two elements a and b, we have not made any distinction between the two orders in which the elements could be listed. Thus, $\{a, b\} = \{b, a\}$ for any pair of elements a and b. However, in many applications it is necessary to take order into consideration. To this end we define an *ordered pair* of elements as (a, b), in which a is designated the *first*, and b the *second*, element, and such that $(a, b) = (c, d)$ if and only if $a = c$ and $b = d$.

Let A and B be any two sets. The *product set*, or *Cartesian product* $A \times B$, of A and B is defined by the open statement

$$A \times B = \{x \mid x = (a, b), a \in A, b \in B\}.$$

That is, $A \times B$ denotes the set whose elements are all possible ordered pairs (a, b) formed by choosing the first element of the pair from the set A and the second element from the set B. For example, if $A = \{a, b\}$ and $B = \{1, 2, 3\}$, then

$$A \times B = \{(a, 1), (a, 2), (a, 3), (b, 1), (b, 2), (b, 3)\}.$$

Again, if $C = \{$Carl, Pete, Tom$\}$, $D = \{$Dottie, Sarah$\}$, then the set of all possible couples that can be formed from these boys and girls is the product set

$C \times D = \{$(Carl, Dottie), (Carl, Sarah), (Pete, Dottie), (Pete, Sarah),

$\qquad\qquad\qquad\qquad\qquad$ (Tom, Dottie), (Tom, Sarah)$\}$.

If two coins are tossed together, the set of possible pairs of "heads" and "tails" is the product set

$$S_1 \times S_2 = \{(h, H), (h, T), (t, H), (t, T)\},$$

where $S_1 = \{h, t\}$ and $S_2 = \{H, T\}$.

A well-known geometrical example of the concept of a product set is that of locating points in the Cartesian plane. In this case, the set of real numbers is associated with the points of a horizontal line and of a vertical line, respectively, these lines being the axes of the Cartesian reference frame. Denoting the points of the horizontal and vertical axes by the sets of real numbers X and Y, respectively, all the points of the plane are then identified by the product set

$$X \times Y = \{(x, y) \mid x \in X, y \in Y\}.$$

Here x denotes the coordinate of the orthogonal projection of the point (x, y) on the X-axis and y denotes the coordinate of the corresponding projection on the Y-axis (see Figure 1.6).

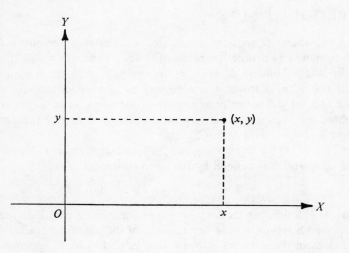

Product Set in the Cartesian Plane.

FIGURE 1.6

Product sets also are defined for more than two sets. Thus, in the general case of n sets $A_1, A_2, \ldots, A_n$ (where n is any positive integer), the product set $A_1 \times A_2 \times \cdots \times A_n$ is the set of *ordered n-tuples* of the type $(a_1, a_2, \ldots, a_n)$, where $a_1 \in A_1, a_2 \in A_2, \ldots, a_n \in A_n$. We write

$$A_1 \times A_2 \times \cdots \times A_n = \{(a_1, a_2, \ldots, a_n) \mid a_i \in A_i, i = 1, 2, \ldots, n\}.$$

To illustrate this concept, assume the sets are

$$A_1 = \{0, 1, 2\}, \quad A_2 = \{a_1, a_2\}, \quad A_3 = \{b_1, b_2\}.$$

Then

$$
\begin{aligned}
A_1 \times A_2 \times A_3 = \{&(0, a_1, b_1), (0, a_1, b_2), (0, a_2, b_1), (0, a_2, b_2) \\
&(1, a_1, b_1), (1, a_1, b_2), (1, a_2, b_1), (1, a_2, b_2) \\
&(2, a_1, b_1), (2, a_1, b_2), (2, a_2, b_1), (2, a_2, b_2)\}.
\end{aligned}
$$

In three-dimensional geometry one may designate the position of a point by means of a reference frame consisting of three mutually perpendicular axes. Associating the set of real numbers with the points of each of these lines, we have the three identical sets X, Y, and Z. Corresponding to each point in three-space is an ordered triple, (x, y, z), which is an element of the product set $X \times Y \times Z$ (see Figure 1.7).

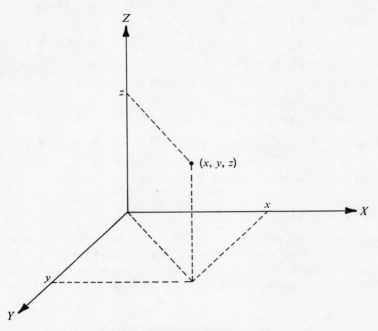

Product Set in Three Dimensions.

FIGURE 1.7

An example of a product set involving four sets is $X \times Y \times Z \times T$, in which the first three sets are real numbers designating space coordinates and T is the set of real numbers indicating time. The element (x, y, z, t) then corresponds to a point on a space-time graph.

PROBLEMS

1. Denoting by X and Y the sets of real numbers corresponding to the horizontal and vertical axes, plot the following subsets of $X \times Y$.
   (a) $\{(-1, -3), (0, 2), (2, 2), (-3, 0)\}$.
   (b) $\{(-2, 4), (0, 1), (2, -2), (4, -5)\}$.

2. Given $A = \{a_1, a_2\}$ and $B = \{b_1, b_2, b_3\}$, find $A \times B$, $A \times A$, and $B \times B$.

3. Given $A = \{1, 2\}$ and $B = \{1, 2, 3\}$, find $A \times B$, $B \times A$, $A \times A$, and $B \times B$.

4. If A contains m elements and B contains n elements, how many elements are contained in $A \times B$, $B \times A$, $A \times A$, $B \times B$?

5. Given A and B, the sets in Problem 3, find (a) $(A \times B) \cup (A \times A)$ and (b) $(A \times B) \cap (A \times A)$.

6. Given $A = \{1, 2\}$, $B = \{-1, 0, 1\}$, and $C = \{2, 3\}$, find $A \times B \times C$.

7. Construct the sets $A \times A$ and $A \times A \times A$, where $A = \{0, 1\}$.

8. Given $X = \{0, 1\}$ and $Y = \{0, 1\}$, evaluate the expression
$$f = xy + 2x - 3y$$
for all ordered pairs $(x, y) \in X \times Y$.

9. Given $X = \{0, 1\}$, $Y = \{0, 1\}$, and $Z = \{0, 1\}$, find the value of
$$f = xyz + xy - 2xz + 2y + z$$
for all ordered triples $(x, y, z) \in X \times Y \times Z$.

1.6 RELATIONS

In many applications of product sets we find that our interest lies in a subset rather than the whole set. For example, we may wish to indicate only those elements of the product set $X \times Y$ which correspond to the points of the vertical line $x = 3$, and we write $\{(x, y) \mid x \in X, y \in Y, x = 3\}$ (see Figure 1.8).

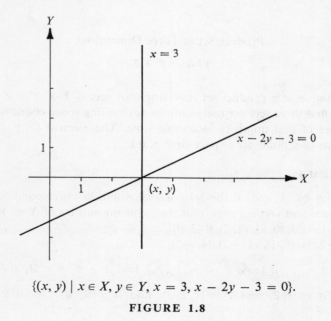

$$\{(x, y) \mid x \in X, y \in Y, x = 3, x - 2y - 3 = 0\}.$$

FIGURE 1.8

Similarly, the set $\{(x, y) \mid x \in X, y \in Y, x - 2y = 3\}$ is the subset of $X \times Y$ corresponding to the points of the straight line $x - 2y - 3 = 0$ (see Figure 1.8).

On the other hand, we may wish to designate by a set all points of the Cartesian plane that lie on or to the right of the line $x - 2y - 3 = 0$ and, at the same time, on or to the left of the line $x = 3$. In this case, we write

$$\{(x, y) \mid x \in X, y \in Y, x - 2y - 3 \geqslant 0, x \leqslant 3\}$$

and indicate the points of this set by the shaded part of the graph, as in Figure 1.9.

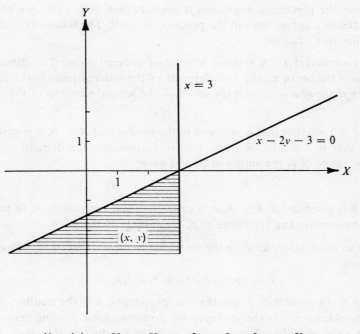

$$\{(x, y) \mid x \in X, y \in Y, x - 2y - 3 \geqslant 0, x \leqslant 3\}.$$

FIGURE 1.9

Although the last two examples were drawn from analytical geometry, we can find many illustrations of such subsets elsewhere. If, for example, we consider two sets, M the set of all raw materials and I the set of all industries, then $M \times I$ is the set of all ordered pairings, (m, i), of materials and industries. Clearly, in this case many of the pairs are not of any interest, because a particular industry has no use for many of the raw materials.

As another example, let W be the set of all living women in a certain nation; then $W \times W$ is the set of all pairs of women in that universe. Contained in this set is the subset S of pairs (a, b), such that "a is the daughter of b." In this case, the set S does not contain the element (a, a), since a is never the daughter of itself. Further, the element (b, a) cannot be in the set if (a, b) is in the set, since b is not the daughter of a if it is already established that a is the daughter of b. Of course, there will be many pairs ruled out, simply because the relationship defined by "is the daughter of" is very restrictive. For example, we know that if $(a, b) \in S$ and $(a, c) \in S$, then $b = c$, because an individual cannot be a daughter of two mothers (unless we allow adoptions).

From the preceding discussion it appears that quite often we are more interested in a subset than in the product set itself. The following definitions formalize this situation.

DEFINITIONS 1.1 A *relation* is a set of ordered pairs. The *domain of a relation* is the set of all the first elements of the ordered pairs in the relation, and the *range of a relation* is the set of all the second elements of the ordered pairs.

If R is a relation that is included in the product set $A \times B$, it is customary to say that R is *a relation from A to B*. In this case the domain of R is A and the range of R is a subset of B, and we write

$$R \subseteq \{(a, b) \mid a \in A, b \in B\}.$$

If R is a subset of $A \times A$, it is called a *binary relation in A*. In this case both the domain and the range of R are subsets of the set A.

As an illustration, let B be the set whose elements are certain officers of a company:
$$B = \{p, v_1, v_2, v_3, a, b, d, f, o, m, s\}$$

Here p is the president, v_i are the vice-presidents, a is the auditor, b is the head bookkeeper, d is the manager for domestic sales, f is the manager for foreign sales, o is the office manager, m is the production manager, and s is in charge of shipping and traffic. Assume that R is a binary relation in B and is defined by the statement "$(x, y) \in R$ if x is the superior of y, where x and y are elements of B." It may be seen from the organizational chart, Figure 1.10, that the relation R is the set of ordered pairs,

$$R = \{(p, v_1), (p, v_2), (p, v_3), (v_1, a), (v_1, b), (v_2, d), (v_2, f), (v_3, o), (v_3, m), (v_3, s)\}.$$

Strictly speaking, p is the superior of all of the personnel. However, we are assuming that he is a topflight executive who communicates only with his three vice-presidents. Note, too, that certain elements of $B \times B$ are eliminated

ORGANIZATIONAL CHART

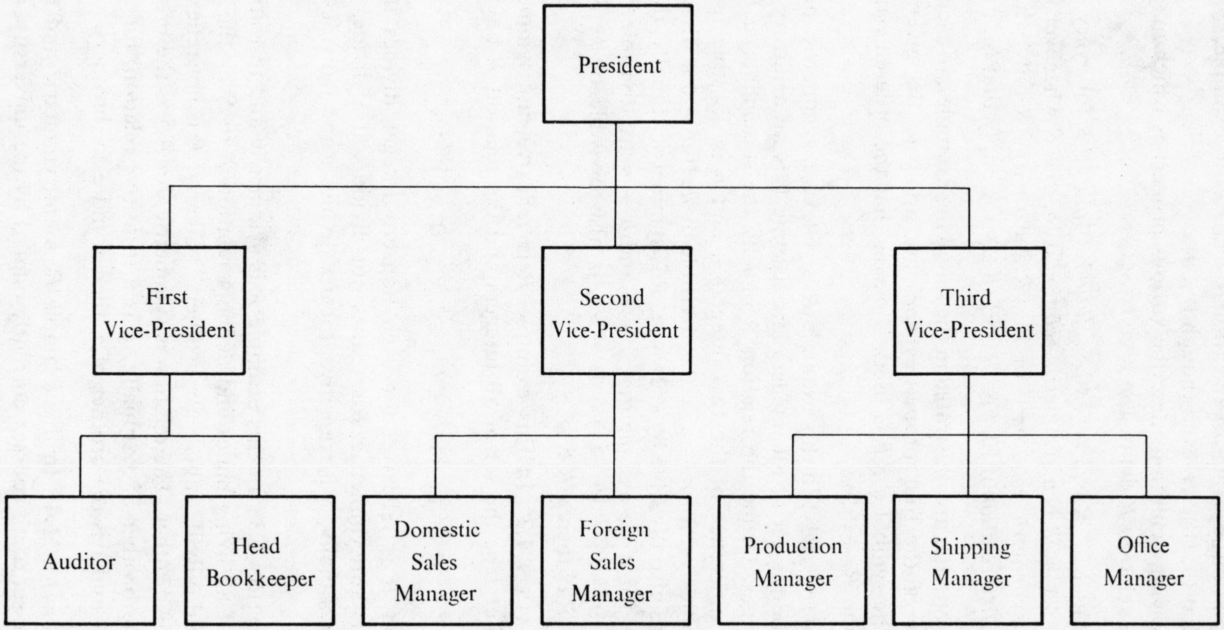

FIGURE 1.10

from the relation by the organizational chart; for example, $(v_1, v_2) \notin R$. Note also that $(a, v_1) \notin R$, even though $(v_1, a) \in R$.

The following definitions describe various properties which may be valid for a binary relation R defined in a given set A.

DEFINITION **1.2** R is a *reflexive relation* if $(a, a) \in R$ for every element a of the given set A. R is a *symmetric relation* if $(b, a) \in R$ whenever $(a, b) \in R$. R is an *antisymmetric relation* if $(a, b) \in R$ and $(b, a) \in R$ only when $a = b$. R is a *transitive relation* if $(a, b) \in R$ and $(b, c) \in R$ imply that $(a, c) \in R$.

These properties are illustrated in the following examples, in each of which at least one of the four properties does not apply to the given relation. Whenever the symbol $a\,R\,b$ is used, it means that the ordered pair (a, b) is in the relation R.

ILLUSTRATION **1.1**   In this example R is reflexive, symmetric, and transitive. Let I be the set of all integers and assume k is an arbitrary but fixed positive integer. Define the relation R in I by the statement "$a\,R\,b$ if and only if the difference of the two integers a and b is divisible by k." The relation is reflexive, for $a - a = 0$ is divisible by k. If $a - b$ is divisible by k, then $b - a$ is also divisible by k. Hence, R is symmetric. Finally, the relation is transitive, for if we assume that $a - b$ and $b - c$ are divisible by k, then their sum, $(a - b) + (b - c) = (a - c)$, is also divisible by k. That is, if $a\,R\,b$ and $b\,R\,c$, then $a\,R\,c$.

ILLUSTRATION **1.2**   In this example R is reflexive, antisymmetric, and transitive. Let I be the set of all integers and the relation R be defined as the set

$$R = \{(x, y) \mid x \in I, y \in I, x \neq 0, x \text{ divides } y\}.$$

The relation R is reflexive, for each nonzero integer divides itself. The relation R is antisymmetric, for y does not divide x if x divides y, except when $x = y$. Finally, R is transitive, for if x divides y and y divides z, then x divides z.

ILLUSTRATION **1.3**   In this example R is symmetric and transitive. Let S be the set of all living males and define a relation R in S by the statement "$x\,R\,y$ if and only if x and y are brothers." Clearly, R is not reflexive, for x cannot be his brother. The relation is symmetric, for if x is the brother of y, then y is the brother of x. Finally, R is a transitive relation, for if x is the brother of y and y is the brother of z, then x and z are brothers.

ILLUSTRATION **1.4**   In this example R is antisymmetric and transitive. Let S be the set of all courses currently offered by the university, and let R be the relation in S defined by "$a\,R\,b$ if and only if course a is a prerequisite of course b." R is certainly not reflexive, for a course is never its own prerequisite. R is not symmetric, for if a is the prerequisite of b, then b cannot be the prerequisite of a. The antisymmetric property does apply. (Why?) Finally, R is transitive, for if a is a prerequisite of b and b is a prerequisite of c, then a is a prerequisite of c.

PROBLEMS

1. Let I be the set of positive, negative, and zero integers, and let the binary relation R be defined as "(x, y) is in R if and only if $x - y$ is positive."
   (a) Determine the properties of R.
   (b) What are the properties of R if $x - y$ may be positive or zero?

2. Let A be a set of stimuli and B a set of responses, and assume that (a, b) is in a relation defined as "b is the response of a biological organism to a stimulus a." What properties, if any, does such a relation possess?

3. Sketch the graph of each of the following relations, in which it is assumed that X and Y are both sets of real numbers.
   (a) $\{(x, y) \mid x \in X, y \in Y, x - y = 2\}$.
   (b) $\{(x, y) \mid x \in X, y \in Y, x - y \leqslant 2\}$.
   (c) $\{(x, y) \mid x \in X, y \in Y, x = -1\}$.
   (d) $\{(x, y) \mid x \in X, y \in Y, x^2 + y^2 = 4\}$.

4. Sketch the graph of each of the following relations, assuming that X and Y are sets of real numbers.
   (a) $\{(x, y) \mid x \in X, y \in Y, x \geqslant -1, x + 2y \leqslant 4\}$.
   (b) $\{(x, y) \mid x \in X, y \in Y, x^2 + y^2 \leqslant 4\}$.
   (c) $\{(x, y) \mid x \in X, y \in Y, x^2 = 4, y^2 = 4\}$.
   (d) $\{(x, y) \mid x \in X, y \in Y, y = |x|\}$.

5. Determine the properties of the following relations.
   (a) "Within 10 minutes of the same time" for a set of clocks.
   (b) "In the same block" for a set of houses on Main Street.
   (c) "Is the brother of" for a given population of both sexes.
   (d) "Is less than or equal to" defined in the set of real numbers.
   (e) "Has a common divisor other than unity" for the set of natural numbers greater than 1.

1.7 EQUIVALENCE RELATIONS

The equals relation possesses the three properties *reflexivity* ($a = a$), *symmetry* (if $a = b$, then $b = a$), and *transitivity* (if $a = b$ and $b = c$, then $a = c$). This is certainly the most common relation possessing all three of these properties. However, many other relations satisfy these conditions, and they play an important role throughout mathematics.

A relation that is simultaneously reflexive, symmetric, and transitive is called an *equivalence relation*. We have already seen that the equals relation, $=$, has all of the required properties. Other examples of equivalence relations that come to mind are congruence in the set of plane geometric figures, similarity in the set of triangles, plane figures with equal areas, and equivalent sets.

The following examples demonstrate that the three conditions (or postulates) required of an equivalence relation are *independent*. We shall exhibit relations that satisfy two of the requirements but not the remaining one.

Consider the set of all straight lines in a plane. Let two lines be in relation if they have no points in common. Clearly, a line cannot be in relation to itself. Hence, this relation is not reflexive. However, it is symmetric and transitive.

The relation "greater than or equal to," $\geqslant$, defined in the set of real numbers, is both reflexive and transitive, but it fails the symmetry test (for example, $5 \geqslant 3$, but $3 \not\geqslant 5$). Therefore, it is not an equivalence relation.

Assume that A is the set of plane angles, and define a relation R in A by the open statement

$$R = \{(a, b) \mid a \in A, b \in A, |a - b| \leqslant 3°\}.$$

In this example, R is both reflexive and symmetric, but it is not transitive. As a counterexample, let a, b, and c be angles in the set such that $a - b = 2°$ and $b - c = 2°$; then $a - c = 4°$. That is, $a \, R \, b$ and $b \, R \, c$ do not imply $a \, R \, c$ in this case.

A set S is said to be *partitioned* by a set $\{S_1, S_2, \ldots, S_t\}$ of its subsets, provided that:

(a) the union of these subsets is equal to S.

(b) the subsets are disjoint in pairs.

For example, the set of all triangles is partitioned by the subset of all triangles that do not contain a right angle and by the subset of all right triangles. The set of integers is partitioned by three subsets: S_0, whose elements are exactly divisible by 3, S_1, whose elements are those integers that yield a remainder of 1 when divided by 3, and S_2, whose elements are the integers that yield a remainder of 2 when divided by 3. The set of people in a given community might be partitioned into subsets according to their religious affiliations.

Let R be an equivalence relation defined in a set A. An *equivalence class*, $[a]$, is the subset of S that contains all elements that are in the relation R with a. Thus, any two elements of S that are in an equivalence relation R

belong to the same equivalence class, and any two elements that are not in the relation R are in different classes.

For example, if S is the set of all integers and R is the equivalence relation "$a R b$ if and only if a and b are even integers," the respective equivalence classes are the set of all even integers and the set of all odd integers.

The *equals* relation defined in any set partitions the set into subsets or equivalence classes, each consisting of a single element. Such subsets are called *singletons*.

Let A be a set with subsets $S_1, S_2, \ldots, S_n$. Then, according to the previous definition, the set A is *partitioned* by the subsets $S_1, S_2, \ldots, S_n$ if and only if $A = \bigcup_{i=1}^{n} S_i$ and $S_i \cap S_j = \varnothing$, where $i \neq j$. Clearly, *an equivalence relation R partitions the set A on which it is defined*, for if we let S_1 be the subset containing the elements of A which are in the relation R and $S_2 = A - S_1$, then $A = S_1 \cup S_2$ and $S_1 \cap S_2 = \varnothing$.

The converse is also true; namely, *every partition of a given set A defines an equivalence relation R on A*. Let A be partitioned by subsets $S_1, S_2, \ldots, S_n$, and define a relation R as follows:

$$R = \{(a, b) \mid a \in S_i, b \in S_i\}.$$

That is, two elements of A are in relation R if and only if they belong to the same subset S_i, where i is arbitrary but fixed. We shall prove that R is an equivalence relation by showing that it is reflexive, symmetric, and transitive:

Reflexive Property: Let $a \in A$; then $a \in S_i$ for some $i = 1, 2, \ldots, n$. Furthermore, $a \notin S_j$ where $j \neq i$, because A is partitioned by $S_1, S_2, \ldots, S_n$ and, by definition, these subsets are disjoint.

Symmetric Property: If $(a, b) \in R$, then $a \in S_i$ and $b \in S_i$; hence $(b, a) \in R$.

Transitive Property: If $(a, b) \in R$ and $(b, c) \in R$, then $a \in S_i$, $b \in S_i$, and $c \in S_i$; hence $(a, c) \in R$.

We summarize these results in the following theorem.

THEOREM **1.1**   *A relation R defined on a set A is an equivalence relation if and only if it partitions A.*

To illustrate these concepts better, we introduce an important relation R in the set of integers, called a *congruence*. Let a, b, and m be integers. We define the concept formally as follows: "a is congruent to b, modulo m, if and only if the difference $(a - b)$ is divisible by m." This relation is denoted by the symbol "$\equiv$" and written $a \equiv b \pmod{m}$.

Theorem **1.2**   *Congruence is an equivalence relation on the set of integers.*

Proof.   From the definition of congruence, $a \equiv b \pmod{m}$ may be written $a - b = km$, where k is an integer. That is, $a \equiv b \pmod{m}$ is equivalent to the statement "There exists an integer k such that the difference $(a - b)$ is km." With this in mind, we now establish that the relation $\equiv$ has the three properties reflexivity, symmetry, and transitivity, which identify it as an equivalence relation.

Reflexive Property: Taking $k = 0$, we have $a - a = 0 \cdot m$, whence $a \equiv a \pmod{m}$.

Symmetric Property: If $a \equiv b \pmod{m}$, then $a - b = km$, and hence we may write $b - a = (-k)m$; therefore, $b \equiv a \pmod{m}$.

Transitive Property: Assume $a \equiv b \pmod{m}$ and $b \equiv c \pmod{m}$; then $a = k_1 m + b$ and $b = k_2 m + c$, whence $a = (k_1 + k_2)m + c$. Now it is assumed that k_1 and k_2 are integers; therefore, $k_1 + k_2$ is also an integer, and we have $a \equiv c \pmod{m}$.

Theorem **1.3**   *Any element in an equivalence class can be used to represent the class.*

Proof.   Assume that R is an equivalence relation defined on a given set S. As we have shown in Theorem 1.1, it is possible to assign to a particular subset all the elements $x \in S$ that are equivalent to the same element a. Earlier we called a subset of this type an *equivalence class*, denoting by $[a]$ that subset of S which consisted of elements equivalent to a. We note that if $x \in [a]$ and $y \in [a]$, then by definition $x R a$ and $a R y$, from which it follows that $x R y$, since R is transitive. Therefore, $x \in [y]$.

For example, the equivalence classes of the set of integers defined by the congruence relation $x \equiv a \pmod{3}$ are $[0] = \{\ldots, -6, -3, 0, 3, 6, \ldots\}$, $[1] = \{\ldots, -5, -2, 1, 4, 7, \ldots\}$, and $[2] = \{\ldots, -4, -1, 2, 5, 8, \ldots\}$. That is, any one of the integers in the first set is congruent to 0 (mod 3), and any pairs of these elements are congruent to each other. Thus, $[0] = [3] = [6]$, and so on. Similarly, $[-5] = [-2] = [1] = [4]$, and $[-4] = [-1] = [2]$, and so on.

The set of all equivalence classes determined by a relation R defined on a set S is called a *factor set* and is denoted by the symbol S/R. Thus, the factor set I/R, where I is the set of integers and R is the relation $x \equiv a \pmod{3}$, consists of the three elements $[0]$, $[1]$, $[2]$, which are themselves sets.

P r o b l e m s

1. In each of the following cases determine whether or not the relation defined on the specified set is an equivalence relation. If the given relation

fails to satisfy one or more of the properties of an equivalence relation, give a counterexample.

(a) "Has the same color of eyes" for a set of girls.
(b) "Is a divisor of" for a set of integers.
(c) "Has the same area as" for a set of bounded plane figures.
(d) "Has a common divisor other than unity" for a set of integers greater than 1.
(e) "Within five minutes of the same time" for a set of watches.
(f) "Lost the same number of points as" for the set of stocks listed at a stock exchange on a given day.
(g) "Is an element of" for the sets of a power set.
(h) "Is perpendicular to" for the set of all straight lines in a plane.
(i) "Is the same weight as" for a set of people.
(j) "Is parallel to" for a set of lines in the Cartesian plane.
(k) "Is not equal to" for the set of real numbers.
(l) "Is at war with" for the nations of the world in 1918.

2. Let I be the set of all integers and zero. Construct the equivalence classes, using the congruence relation, modulo 4.

3. Denoting the elements of the factor set I/R by [0], [1], [2], [3], [4], where R is defined by the statement "Integers a_1 and a_2 are in R, if and only if their difference is divisible by 5." Write out five elements in each class.

4. Let U be a population of persons in a given community. Partition U into subsets according to the following blood types: those people who have blood type A but not type B, those who have blood type B but not type A, those who have both A and B, and those who have neither A nor B. Draw a Venn diagram showing the corresponding equivalence classes. Other partitions might be made according to sex, age group, height, and so forth.

1.8 CORRESPONDENCES AND FUNCTIONS

As we look about us, we find many sets whose elements are associated in some manner with the elements of other sets, and it is to this topic that we now turn our attention. Consider the set of all species of insects on the earth and the set of all conceivable names, or the set of stocks listed on the New York stock exchange on a given day and the set of final quotations, or a set of students and a set of grades, or a set of mathematics instructors and a set of students.

Concerning the first example, it should be noted that, although the set of insect species is very large, it is finite. Similarly, the set of all *conceivable* names is finite, but its cardinal number is considerably larger than the first set. Because ordinarily a given species is paired with one and only one name (limiting our selection to its scientific name), it seems reasonable to state that, even when every insect species is named, only a *subset* of the name set will be needed for this correspondence. If the correspondence is carried out properly, however, only one name is paired with each species and, conversely, to each name in the *subset* there will correspond *one* and *only one* species. Such a correspondence is said to be *one-to-one*.

A somewhat similar situation arises in the second example: there is a finite number of stocks in the first set, and the final quotations which are paired with the stocks belong to a subset of the infinite set of positive rational numbers. As we shall see, however, there is an important difference between the two examples. In the first, not only does each species have one and only one name, but each name corresponds to one and only one species. In the

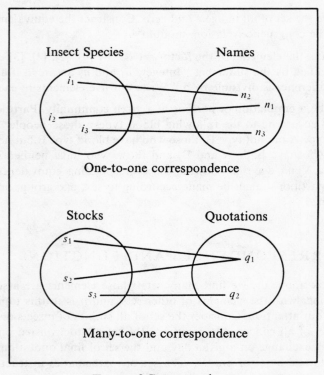

Types of Correspondence.

FIGURE 1.11

second example, it is quite probable that on any given day there will be several stocks listed with the same final quotation, yielding a *many-to-one correspondence*. We illustrate these points for two simple cases (see Figure 1.11).

The principal difference between the third example and the second lies in the fact that the set of grades that corresponds to the students is a subset of a finite set, namely, the integers from zero to 100.

The fourth example is radically different from the others. For the situation, in which the set of mathmatics instructors has few elements compared to the set of students taking mathematics, *each* member of the teacher set is associated with *several* members of the student set. Such correspondence is said to be *one-to-many* (see Figure 1.12). Although it is interesting and useful, we shall not study this type of correspondence in this text.

The correspondences discussed in the first three examples are called *functions*, which we define formally as follows.

DEFINITION **1.3**   If D and R are any two sets (not necessarily distinct), a *function f* with *domain D* and *range R* is a correspondence that pairs each element $x \in D$ with one and only one element $y \in R$. We indicate this fact by writing $f: D \to R$.

Every function is a relation, but not every relation is a function. First, we note that the definition requires that *each* element of the *domain* be included in the correspondence. Second, the definition stipulates that each element of the domain shall have a *unique partner*, or *image*, in the range. Another way

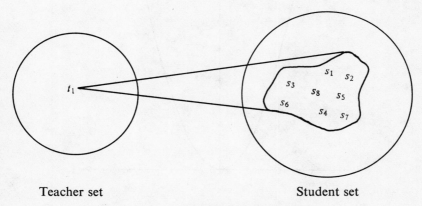

Teacher set   Student set

One-to-Many Correspondence

FIGURE 1.12

of stating this last requirement is: if the ordered pairs (x, a) and (x, b) are in a relation that is known to be a function, then $a = b$.

ILLUSTRATION 1.5 Let D be the set of all children in a certain community, and let R be the set of all adults in the same community. Define the relation f as that subset of $D \times R$ of ordered pairs (x, y) in which the first element x is a child and the second element y is the natural father of x. This is a function, because each child x has a father y. On the other hand, two different elements in f cannot have the same first element; that is, a child cannot have two different natural fathers. We note in passing that there may be several ordered pairs in f with the same second element, because a father may have more than one child.

We sometimes refer to the element $x \in D$ as an *argument* in the function and the corresponding $y \in R$ as the *value of the function at x*, written $y = f(x)$. There is an important distinction to be made between these two terms. A

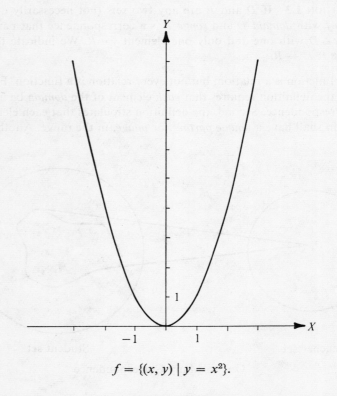

$$f = \{(x, y) \mid y = x^2\}.$$

FIGURE 1.13

function is a set of ordered pairs, but the value of a function at x is the corresponding image $y = f(x)$ defined by the function f.

Throughout this book it may be assumed that the domain and range of a function are subsets of the universal set of real numbers, unless explicitly stated otherwise.

DEFINITION **1.4**   The *graph of the relation R* whose domain and range are subsets of the set of real numbers, respectively, is the set G of all points in the Cartesian plane whose coordinates (x, y) belong to R.

We shall follow the established custom of representing the elements of the domain of the function or of the relation by points of the horizontal axis; those of the range, by points of the vertical axis. In drawing the graph of the relation, we shall plot a representative set of points, and in those regions where it is permissible we shall interpolate the other points, which are infinite in number, by drawing a smooth curve through this set. When a relation consists of a *finite* set of ordered pairs, however, its graph actually consists of a finite set of isolated points which are *not connected* by a curve.

ILLUSTRATION **1.6**   The function

$$f = \{(x, y) \mid y = x^2\}$$

has the set of real numbers for its domain, and its range is the set of non-negative real numbers (see Figure 1.13). If the domain of the function f is defined as the finite set $\{-3, -2, -1, 0, 1, 2, 3\}$, consisting of just seven integers, rather than the entire set of real numbers, then the range of f, which is determined by the open statement $y = x^2$, is limited to the finite set $\{0, 1, 4, 9\}$. In this case the function is the finite set of ordered pairs:

$$f = \{(-3, 9), (-2, 4), (-1, 1), (0, 0), (1, 1), (2, 4), (3, 9)\}.$$

The graph of f consists of seven isolated points and is shown in Figure 1.14.

ILLUSTRATION **1.7**   In the function

$$f = \{(x, y) \mid y = |x|\}$$

the open statement $y = |x|$ is read "y is equal to the *absolute value* of x." Its mathematical interpretation is

$$y = |x| = \begin{cases} x \text{ when } x \geqslant 0, \\ -x \text{ when } x < 0. \end{cases}$$

Hence the range of the function f is the set of nonnegative real numbers (see Figure 1.15).

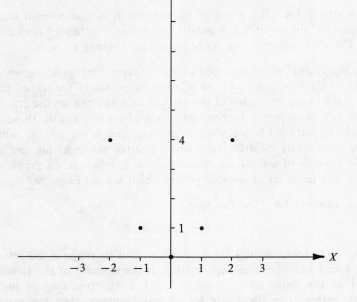

$$f = \{(-3, 9), \ (-2, 4), \ (-1, 1), \ (0, 0), \ (1, 1), \ (2, 4), \ (3, 9)\}.$$

FIGURE 1.14

ILLUSTRATION **1.8**   In the function

$$f = \{(x, y) \mid y = [x]\}$$

the open statement $y = [x]$, "y equals bracket x," is read "y is equal to the greatest integer not exceeding x" (see Figure 1.16). For example, $[2.35] = 2$, $[0.47] = 0$, while $[-1.56] = -2$. To determine the range of this function, let us first limit the domain to the subset of real numbers, $\{x \mid a \leqslant x < a + 1, \ a \in I\}$. The open statement $a \leqslant x < a + 1$, $a \in I$ is read "x is greater than or equal to the integer a but is less than the integer $a + 1$." That is, x lies in a *unit interval* which includes the left end-point but does not include the right end-point. We say that the interval is *closed on the left* and *open on the right*.

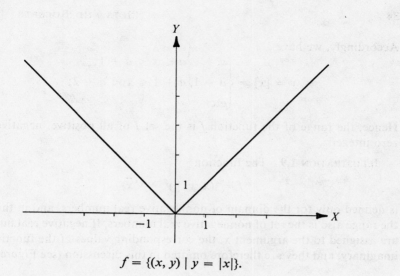

$$f = \{(x, y) \mid y = |x|\}.$$

FIGURE 1.15

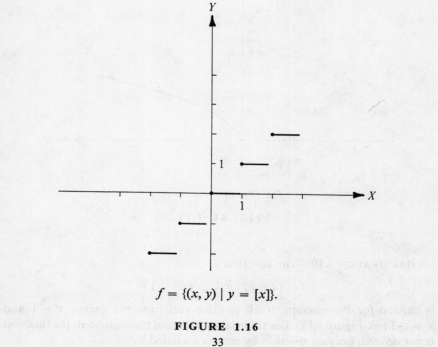

$$f = \{(x, y) \mid y = [x]\}.$$

FIGURE 1.16

Accordingly, we have

$$y = [x] = \begin{cases} a, & a \leqslant x < a + 1; \\ a + 1, & a + 1 \leqslant x < a + 2; \\ \text{etc.} \end{cases}$$

Hence, the range of the function f is the set I of all positive, negative, and zero integers.

ILLUSTRATION **1.9**   The function

$$f = \{(x, y) \mid y = \sqrt{x}\}$$

is defined only for the domain of nonnegative real numbers, and in this case the range also is the set of nonnegative real numbers. If negative real numbers are assigned to the argument x, the corresponding values of the function are imaginary, and they are therefore omitted in this discussion (see Figure 1.17).

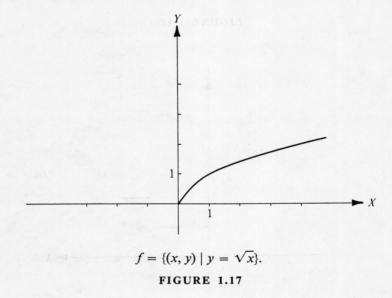

$$f = \{(x, y) \mid y = \sqrt{x}\}.$$

FIGURE **1.17**

ILLUSTRATION **1.10**   The function

$$f = \{(x, y) \mid y = 2/(x^2 - 1)\}$$

is defined for the domain of all positive real numbers except $x = 1$ and $x = -1$ (see Figure 1.18). For these latter values of the argument, the function *is not defined*, because division by zero is excluded.

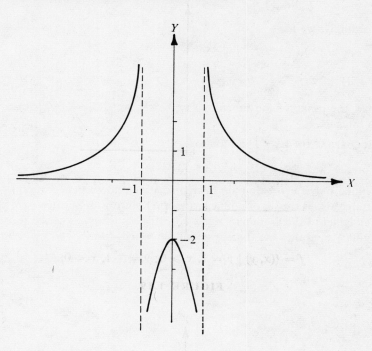

$$f = \{(x, y) \mid y = 2/(x^2 - 1)\}.$$

FIGURE 1.18

ILLUSTRATION **1.11**   The function

$$f = \{(x, y) \mid y = 1 \text{ when } x \geqslant 0, \ y = -1 \text{ when } x < 0\}$$

has the set of all real numbers for its domain (see Figure 1.19). The range of f is the set $\{-1, 1\}$. This function is said to be *piecewise constant* (in Illustration 1.8 the function has this property also).

ILLUSTRATION **1.12**   The function

$$f = \{(x, y) \mid y = x + 1\}$$

with domain $\{-3, -1, 0, 1, 4\}$ has the range $\{-2, 0, 1, 2, 5\}$. The given function is equal to $\{(-3, -2), (-1, 0), (0, 1), (1, 2), (4, 5)\}$ (see Figure 1.20).

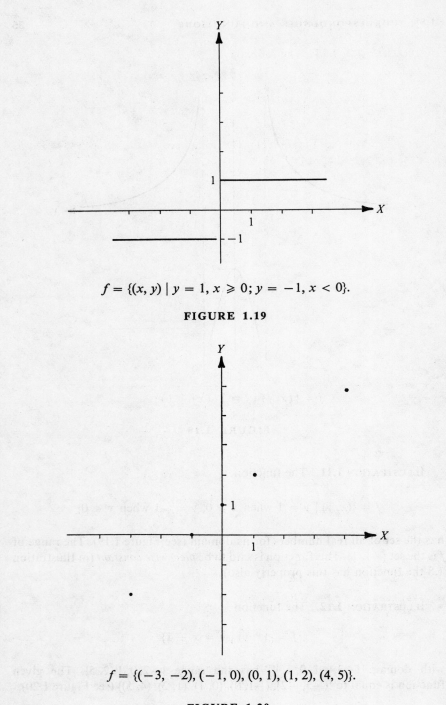

$f = \{(x, y) \mid y = 1, x \geqslant 0; y = -1, x < 0\}.$

FIGURE 1.19

$f = \{(-3, -2), (-1, 0), (0, 1), (1, 2), (4, 5)\}.$

FIGURE 1.20

ILLUSTRATION **1.13**   The function

$$f = \left\{ (x, y) \left| \begin{array}{l} y = -1, \ -3 \leqslant x < -1; \\ y = x, \ -1 \leqslant x < 2; \\ y = 2, \ 2 \leqslant x \leqslant 5. \end{array} \right. \right\}$$

is *piecewise linear* (see Figure 1.21). The domain of f is the set $\{x \mid -3 \leqslant x \leqslant 5\}$, and the range is the set $\{y \mid -1 \leqslant y \leqslant 2\}$.

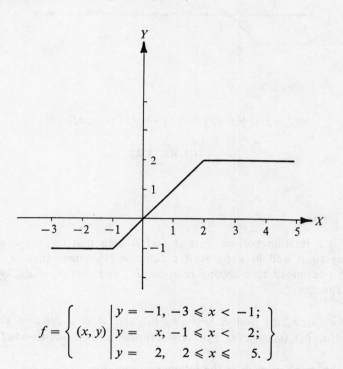

$$f = \left\{ (x, y) \left| \begin{array}{l} y = -1, \ -3 \leqslant x < -1; \\ y = \ \ x, \ -1 \leqslant x < \ \ 2; \\ y = \ \ 2, \ \ \ 2 \leqslant x \leqslant \ \ 5. \end{array} \right. \right\}$$

FIGURE 1.21

ILLUSTRATION **1.14**   The function

$$f = \left\{ (x, y) \mid y = \frac{x^2 - 1}{x - 1} \right\}$$

is defined for the domain of all real numbers except $x = 1$ (because division by zero is not possible), and the range of f is the set of all real numbers except $y = 2$ (see Figure 1.22).

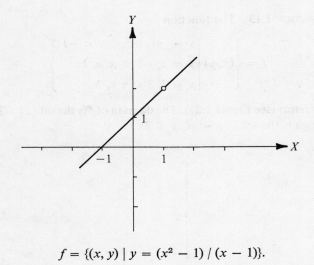

$$f = \{(x, y) \mid y = (x^2 - 1) / (x - 1)\}.$$

FIGURE 1.22

PROBLEMS

1. If R is a relation between sets A and B such that (a_1, b_1) and (a_1, b_2) belong to R and $b_1 \neq b_2$, is R a function? Suppose that (a_1, b_1) and (a_2, b_1) belonged to a second relation, R', and that $a_1 \neq a_2$. Would R' be a function?

2. If $A = \{a_1, a_2, a_3\}$ and $B = \{b_1, b_2, b_3\}$ and R is a relation such that $R = \{(a_1, b_1), (a_2, b_1), (a_3, b_2)\}$, is R a function? Is it one-to-one?

3. Plot the graph of each of the following functions.
   (a) $f = \{(-2, 2), (-1, 5), (0, 2), (3, -3), (5, 0), (6, 4)\}$.
   (b) $f = \{(-2, 0), (-1, \sqrt{3}), (0, 2), (1, \sqrt{3}), (2, 0)\}$.
   (c) $f = \{(0, 0), (1, 1), (2, \sqrt{2}), (3, \sqrt{3}), (4, 2)\}$.
   (d) $f = \{(-1, 0.4), (0, 1), (1, 2.7), (2, 7.4)\}$.

4. Plot the graph of each of the following functions.
   (a) $f = \{(x, y) \mid y = 1 - x^2, -3 \leqslant x \leqslant 3\}$.
   (b) $f = \{(x, y) \mid y = 1 + x^2, -3 \leqslant x \leqslant 3\}$.

(c) $f = \{(x, y) \mid y = x^2 + 2x + 1, -3 \leqslant x \leqslant 3\}$.
(d) $f = \{(x, y) \mid y = (x - 1)(x + 2), -3 \leqslant x \leqslant 3\}$.

5. Plot the graph of each of the following functions.
  (a) $f = \{(x, y) \mid y = -|x|, -2 \leqslant x \leqslant 2\}$.
  (b) $f = \{(x, y) \mid y = 1 - |x|, -2 \leqslant x \leqslant 2\}$.
  (c) $f = \{(x, y) \mid y = 2|x|, -2 \leqslant x \leqslant 2\}$.

6. Plot the graph of each of the following functions.
  (a) $f = \{(x, y) \mid y = -[x], -2 \leqslant x \leqslant 2\}$.
  (b) $f = \{(x, y) \mid y = 1 - [x], -2 \leqslant x \leqslant 2\}$.
  (c) $f = \{(x, y) \mid y = x + [x], -2 \leqslant x \leqslant 2\}$.

7. Plot the graph of each of the following functions where defined on the given interval.

  (a) $f = \left\{(x, y) \mid y = \dfrac{1}{x - 1}, -2 \leqslant x \leqslant 4\right\}$.

  (b) $f = \left\{(x, y) \mid y = \dfrac{x^2 - 1}{x - 1}, -2 \leqslant x \leqslant 4\right\}$.

  (c) $f = \left\{(x, y) \mid y = \dfrac{x^2}{x - 1}, -2 \leqslant x \leqslant 4\right\}$.

  (d) $f = \left\{(x, y) \mid y = \dfrac{x^2}{x^2 - 1}, -4 \leqslant x \leqslant 4\right\}$.

8. Plot the graph of each of the following functions.

  (a) $f = \left\{(x, y) \,\middle|\, \begin{array}{l} y = -x + 1, -4 \leqslant x < 0; \\ y = 1, x = 0; \\ y = x + 1, 0 < x \leqslant 4. \end{array}\right\}$.

  (b) $f = \left\{(x, y) \,\middle|\, \begin{array}{l} y = -2x - 2, -2 \leqslant x < -1; \\ y = 0, -1 \leqslant x < 1; \\ y = -2x + 2, 1 \leqslant x \leqslant 4. \end{array}\right\}$.

1.9 THE INVERSE OF A FUNCTION

In Section 1.8 the concept of function was defined and discussed. It will be recalled that a correspondence is a function if each element of the domain is paired with a unique element of the range. It was pointed out that sometimes the function is such that the pairing is one-to-one; that is, to each element of the range, which is the image of an element in the domain, there corresponds a *unique pre-image*, or correspondent, in the domain.

The importance of a one-to-one correspondence becomes apparent when the following problem is proposed. *Given a value of the function, determine the corresponding argument at which the function takes on this value.* Quite often there will be several arguments that yield the same value of the function, and in these cases the reversed relation is one-to-many and is *not* a function. However, when no two ordered pairs in a function f have the same second element, there exists a new function f^{-1}, closely related to f, called the *inverse function* of f.

If the function $f: A \to B$ consists of the ordered pairs (a_1, b_1), (a_2, b_2), ..., then the inverse function $f^{-1}: B \to A$ consists of the ordered pairs (b_1, a_1), (b_2, a_2), ... That is to say, the range of f becomes the domain of f^{-1}, and the domain of f becomes the range of f^{-1}.

ILLUSTRATION **1.15** Consider the function f defined by

$$f = \{(1, -2), (0, 2), (-2, 0), (-1, 1)\}.$$

To find the inverse function, f^{-1}, we interchange the first and second elements in each of the ordered pairs in f to obtain

$$f^{-1} = \{(-2, 1), (2, 0), (0, -2), (1, -1)\}.$$

When the function f is defined by an open statement

$$f = \{(x, y) \mid y = f(x)\}$$

the corresponding inverse function f^{-1}, when it exists, is likewise defined by an open statement:

$$f^{-1} = \{(y, x) \mid x = f^{-1}(y)\}.$$

Whenever the domain and range of f are sets of real numbers, we shall retain the convention of denoting the argument or independent variable in f^{-1} by x and the corresponding value of the function or dependent variable by $y = f^{-1}(x)$. This can be done by switching the variables in the inverse function thus:

$$f^{-1} = \{(x, y) \mid y = f^{-1}(x)\}.$$

ILLUSTRATION **1.16** Let us determine the inverse of the function

$$f = \{(x, y) \mid y = 2x - 1, 0 \leqslant x \leqslant 3\}.$$

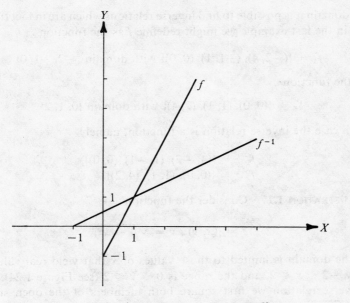

$$f = \{(x, y) \mid y = 2x - 1, 0 \leqslant x \leqslant 3\},$$
$$f^{-1} = \{(x, y) \mid y = \tfrac{1}{2}(x + 1), -1 \leqslant x \leqslant 5\}.$$

FIGURE 1.23

The defining statement, $y = 2x - 1$, is first solved for x in terms of y, yielding $x = \tfrac{1}{2}(y + 1)$. The domain of f^{-1} is the range of f and is therefore $-1 \leqslant y \leqslant 5$. Switching variables, we write the inverse of f as

$$f^{-1} = \{(x, y) \mid y = \tfrac{1}{2}(x + 1), -1 \leqslant x \leqslant 5\}.$$

The graphs of f and f^{-1} are given in Figure 1.23.

It frequently happens that the inverse of a given function is not itself a function. For example, the relation

$$f = \{(-2, 4), (-1, 1), (0, 0), (1, 1), (2, 4)\}$$

is a function, but the inverse of this relation is the set of ordered pairs

$$\{(4, -2), (1, -1), (0, 0), (1, 1), (4, 2)\}$$

which is not a function, because the ordered pairs $(4, -2)$, $(4, 2)$, and $(1, -1)$, $(1, 1)$ have the same first elements, respectively, but *different* second elements. On the other hand, by restricting the given function to selected subsets of the domain it is possible to find inverse relations which are in fact functions. Thus, in the last example we might redefine f as the function

$$f_1 = \{(-2, 4), (-1, 1), (0, 0)\} \text{ with domain } \{-2, -1, 0\}$$

or as the function

$$f_2 = \{(0, 0), (1, 1), (2, 4)\} \text{ with domain } \{0, 1, 2\}.$$

In each case the inverse relation is a function, namely

$$f_1^{-1} = \{(4, -2), (1, -1), (0, 0)\},$$
$$f_2^{-1} = \{(0, 0), (1, 1), (4, 2)\}.$$

ILLUSTRATION **1.17**   Consider the function

$$f = \{(x, y) \mid y = \sqrt{4 - x^2}\}$$

Here the domain is limited to those values of x that yield real values of y, namely $-2 \leqslant x \leqslant 2$, and the range is $0 \leqslant y \leqslant 2$ (see Figure 1.24). To find the inverse relation we first square both members of the open statement $y = \sqrt{4 - x^2}$, obtaining the equation

$$y^2 = 4 - x^2.$$

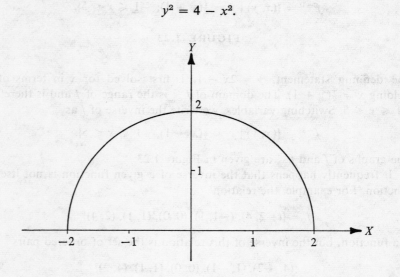

$$f = \{(x, y) \mid y = \sqrt{4 - x^2}\}.$$

FIGURE 1.24

Solving this equation for x, we have

$$x = \pm \sqrt{4 - y^2}, \qquad \text{with } 0 \leqslant y \leqslant 2,\ -2 \leqslant x \leqslant 2.$$

Switching variables, we have the inverse relation defined by

$$f^{-1} = \{(x, y) \mid y = \pm \sqrt{4 - x^2}\},$$

which is *not* a function, because there are two values of y for each value of x in the domain $0 \leqslant x \leqslant 2$ (except when $x = 2$). However, if we restrict f to either of the following,

$$f_1 = \{(x, y) \mid y = \sqrt{4 - x^2}\} \qquad \text{with domain } \ \ 0 \leqslant x \leqslant 2$$
$$\text{and range} \qquad 0 \leqslant y \leqslant 2,$$
$$f_2 = \{(x, y) \mid y = \sqrt{4 - x^2}\} \qquad \text{with domain } -2 \leqslant x \leqslant 0$$
$$\text{and range} \qquad 0 \leqslant y \leqslant 2,$$

then (see Figure 1.25) the respective inverse functions exist, namely

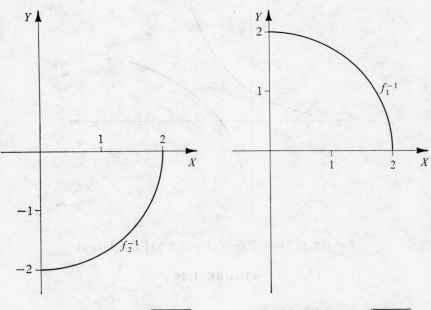

$$f_2^{-1} = \{(x, y) \mid y = -\sqrt{4 - x^2}\}. \qquad f_1^{-1} = \{(x, y) \mid y = \sqrt{4 - x^2}\}.$$

FIGURE 1.25

$$f_1^{-1} = \{(x, y) \mid y = \sqrt{4 - x^2}\} \qquad \text{with domain } 0 \leqslant x \leqslant 2$$
$$\text{and range} \quad 0 \leqslant y \leqslant 2,$$
$$f_2^{-1} = \{(x, y) \mid y = -\sqrt{4 - x^2}\} \qquad \text{with domain } 0 \leqslant x \leqslant 2$$
$$\text{and range} \quad -2 \leqslant y \leqslant 0.$$

ILLUSTRATION **1.18**   The function

$$f = \{(x, y) \mid y = 2^x\}$$

is defined for the domain $-\infty < x < \infty$, and the corresponding range is $0 < y < \infty$. The inverse of this function is defined by

$$f^{-1} = \{(x, y) \mid y = \log_2 x\}$$

with domain $0 < x < \infty$ and range $-\infty < y < \infty$ (see Figure 1.26).

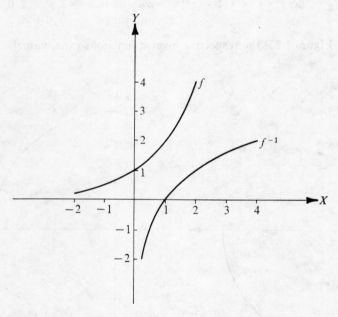

$$f = \{(x, y) \mid y = 2^x\}, \quad f^{-1} = \{(x, y) \mid y = \log_2 x\}.$$

FIGURE 1.26

ILLUSTRATION **1.19**   The function

$$f = \{(x, y) \mid y = \sin x\}$$

is defined for the domain $-\infty < x < \infty$ and has the range $-1 \leqslant y \leqslant 1$

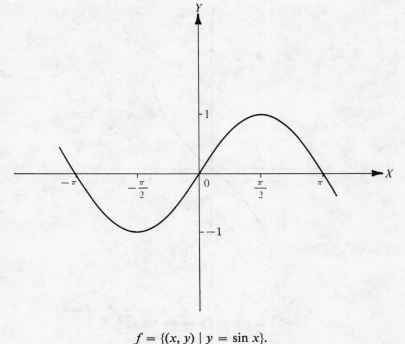

$$f = \{(x, y) \mid y = \sin x\}.$$

FIGURE 1.27

(see Figure 1.27). It will be recalled from trigonometry that sin x is periodic and that sin $(x + 2n\pi) = \sin x$ for all positive or negative integers n. If the domain of f is restricted to the interval $-\pi/2 \leqslant x \leqslant \pi/2$, the range namely $-1 \leqslant y \leqslant 1$, is unchanged. The correspondence between domain and range, however, is now one-to-one, and in consequence this new function has an *inverse which is a function*;

$$f^{-1} = \{(x, y) \mid y = \arcsin x\}$$

with the domain $-1 \leqslant x \leqslant 1$ and range $-\pi/2 \leqslant y \leqslant \pi/2$ (see Figure 1.28).

Our discussion of the inverse of a function shows that sometimes a correspondence between two sets is reversible, namely, when it is one-to-one. In what follows we shall see that in some instances two functions may be combined to produce a single function having the domain of the first and the range of the second.

Let us consider three sets, X, Y, and Z, not necessarily distinct. Assume

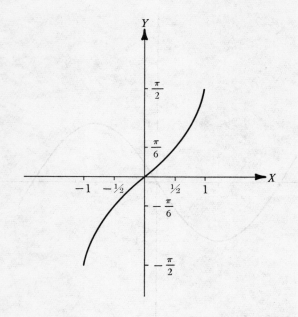

$$f^{-1} = \{(x, y) \mid y = \text{arc sin } x\}.$$

FIGURE 1.28

that there exist functions $f: X \to Y$ and $g: Y \to Z$, which are defined respectively by the open statements

$$f = \{(x, y) \mid y = f(x)\},$$
$$g = \{(y, z) \mid z = g(y)\}.$$

With f and g functions, we are assured by the definition of a function that to each element $x \in X$ there corresponds a unique image $y = f(x) \in Y$ and that to each element $y \in Y$ there corresponds a unique image $z = g(y) = g[f(x)] \in Z$. Thus, the two functions f and g establish a correspondence between the set X and the set Z, and because of the uniqueness of the image at each step the correspondence is a function with domain X and range a subset of Z (see Figure 1.29).

DEFINITION 1.5   The *composite* of two functions $f: X \to Y$ and $g: Y \to Z$ is the function $g[f]: X \to Z$, such that

$$g[f] = \{(x, z) \mid z = g[f]x = g[f(x)]\}$$

with domain X and range a subset of Z.

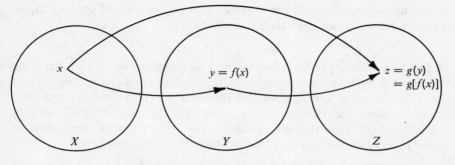

Composite Mapping $g[f]\colon X \to Z$.

FIGURE 1.29

ILLUSTRATION **1.20**   Let $f = \{(x, y) \mid y = x^2\}$ and $g = \{(y, z) \mid z = 1 - y\}$; then the composite of f and g is $g[f] = \{(x, z) \mid z = 1 - x^2\}$.

In general, the order in which the composite is formed is important. Thus, in Illustration 1.20, if $g = \{(x, y \mid y = 1 - x\}$ and $f = \{(y, z) \mid z = y^2\}$, then $f[g] = \{(x, z) \mid z = (1 - x)^2\} \neq g[f]$.

DEFINITION **1.6**   The *identity* function $i\colon X \to X$ is a one-to-one correspondence, whose domain and range sets are identical, and which maps each element $x \in X$ into itself; that is, $i = \{(x, y) \mid y = x\}$.

We now establish the following interesting and important result.

THEOREM **1.4**   *The composite of a function and its inverse is the identity function.*

Proof.   Let $f\colon X \to Y$ and $f^{-1}\colon Y \to X$ be defined respectively by

$$f = \{(x, y) \mid y = f(x)\},$$
$$f^{-1} = \{(y, x) \mid x = f^{-1}(y)\}.$$

Then, forming the composite function $f^{-1}[f]$, we have

$$f^{-1}[f] = \{(x, y) \mid y = f^{-1}[f(x)] = f^{-1}(y) = x\} = i,$$
$$f[f^{-1}] = \{(y, x) \mid x = f[f^{-1}(y)] = f(x) = y\} = i.$$

Hence, the theorem is established.

The concept of a function of a single argument may be extended in a natural way to that of a function of two or three or, in general, n arguments or variables. For example, a function $f\colon X \times Y \to Z$ of two variables is a correspondence that maps each ordered pair (x, y) of the domain $X \times Y$

into a unique element z of the range Z; that is, f is a set of ordered triples (x, y, z) defined by an open statement of the type

$$f = \{(x, y, z) \mid z = f(x, y)\}.$$

A function of this type from biology may be described as follows. Let X be the set of living males and Y the set of living females of a certain species, and let Z be the set of offspring of this species alive at an arbitrary but fixed moment. Read the relation $z = f(x, y)$ as "z is the only living offspring of parents (x, y)." Then this is a function, provided we restrict the domain to those ordered pairs (x, y) that have a single living offspring.

DEFINITION **1.7** *A function $f: X_1 \times X_2 \times \cdots \times X_n \to Z$ of n arguments* is a correspondence which maps each ordered n-tuple, $(x_1, x_2, \ldots, x_n)$, of the domain $X_1 \times X_2 \times \cdots \times X_n$ into a unique element z of the range Z; that is,

$$f = \{(x_1, x_2, \ldots, x_n, z) \mid z = f(x_1, x_2, \ldots, x_n)\}.$$

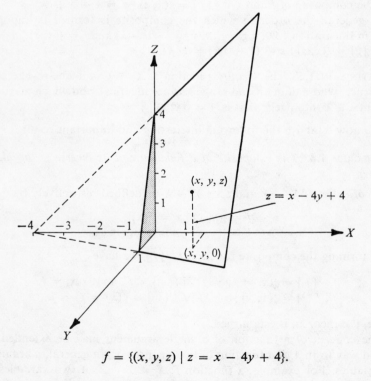

$$f = \{(x, y, z) \mid z = x - 4y + 4\}.$$

FIGURE **1.30**

ILLUSTRATION **1.21**   Let X, Y, and Z be sets of real numbers, and define $f : X \times Y \to Z$ as $f = \{(x, y, z) \mid z = x - 4y + 4\}$. This function may be interpreted geometrically as the set of all points (x, y, z) that lie in the plane $x - 4y - z + 4 = 0$ (see Figure 1.30).

ILLUSTRATION **1.22**   Assume X, Y, and Z are sets of real numbers, and consider the function

$$f = \{(x, y, z) \mid z = \sqrt{4 - x^2 - y^2}\}.$$

The range Z being limited to real numbers, we must choose as the domain of the function the subset of $X \times Y$ of ordered pairs (x, y) such that $4 - x^2 - y^2 \geqslant 0$. This set may be interpreted geometrically as the co-ordinates of all points that lie on and interior to a circle of radius 2 with center at the origin. The geometric representation of the given function may be shown to be a hemisphere of radius 2 with center at the origin (see Figure 1.31).

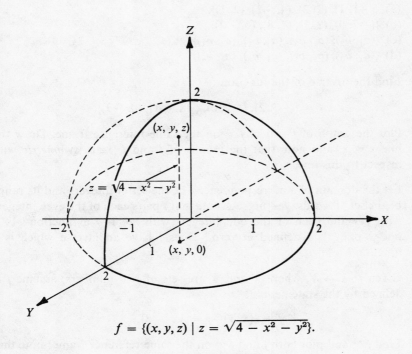

$$f = \{(x, y, z) \mid z = \sqrt{4 - x^2 - y^2}\}.$$

FIGURE 1.31

ILLUSTRATION **1.23**   A function of three variables is defined by

$$f = \{(x, y, z, w) \mid w = xy + yz\}$$

with domain $X \times Y \times Z$, where $X = Y = Z = \{0, 1\}$. We wish to find the images of all distinct triples (x, y, z) of the domain. We first form the domain, which is a finite set consisting of eight distinct triples:

$$X \times Y \times Z = \{(1, 1, 1), (1, 1, 0), (1, 0, 1), (1, 0, 0), (0, 1, 1),$$
$$(0, 1, 0), (0, 0, 1), (0, 0, 0)\}.$$

Referring to the function f, we determine the following images:

$$f(1, 1, 1) = 2, \quad f(1, 1, 0), = 1, \quad f(1, 0, 1) = 0, \quad f(1, 0, 0) = 0,$$
$$f(0, 1, 1) = 1, \quad f(0, 1, 0) = 0, \quad f(0, 0, 1) = 0, \quad f(0, 0, 0) = 0.$$

PROBLEMS

1. Determine the inverse relation defined by each of the following functions. Indicate whether or not the inverse relation is a function.
   (a) $\{(-1, 1), (2, 2), (4, -1), (2, 1)\}$.
   (b) $\{(-2, 0), (2, 1), (4, 8), (6, -2)\}$.
   (c) $\{(a_1, b_2), (a_2, b_3), (a_3, b_1), (a_4, b_4)\}$.
   (d) $\{(a_1, b_3), (a_2, b_1), (a_3, b_3), (a_4, b_4)\}$.

2. Find the inverse of the function

   $$f = \{(-3, 2), (-2, 0), (-1, -1), (0, -3)\}.$$

   Plot the graph of f and of f^{-1} on the same reference frame. Draw the line $y = x$, and note that the graphs of f and f^{-1} are *symmetric* with respect to this line.

3. Let the domain of a correspondence f be the set of integers and its range be the set of words {yes, no}. Assume that f pairs each of the even integers with *yes* and each of the odd integers with *no*. Is f a function? Is it one-to-one? Is f defined at zero? Does f have an inverse which is a function?

4. Given $f: X \to Y$, where X and Y are sets of real numbers, assume f is defined by the statement

   $$f = \{(x, y) \mid y = \tfrac{1}{2}x - 3\}.$$

   Find f^{-1} and plot both f and f^{-1} on the same reference frame; note that these graphs are symmetric with respect to the line $y = x$.

5. Given $f: X \to Y$, where X and Y are sets of real numbers, assume f is defined by the statement

$$f = \{(x, y) \mid y = x^2\}.$$

(a) What are the domain and the range of f?
(b) Draw the graph of f.
(c) Is the inverse relation a function?
(d) If the answer to (c) is negative, redefine f in such a way that the new function will have an inverse that is a function.

6. Let $f: X \to Y$, where X and Y are sets of real numbers and the function is defined by

$$f = \{(x, y) \mid y = |x|\}.$$

(a) What are the domain and range of f?
(b) Redefine f such that the inverse will be a function.
(c) Draw all graphs.

7. Let $f: X \to Y$, where X and Y are sets of real numbers and the function is defined by

$$f = \{(x, y) \mid y = [x]\}.$$

(a) Draw the graph of f.
(b) Explain why the inverse is not a function.
(c) Using the fact that a relation and its inverse are symmetric to the line $y = x$ when their graphs are plotted on the same reference frame, sketch the inverse of f.

8. Plot the graph of the function

$$f = \{(x, y) \mid y = 3^x\}$$

for the domain $-2 \leqslant x \leqslant 2$. Find the inverse function f^{-1} and plot its graph on the same reference frame.

9. Discuss the periodic function

$$f = \{(x, y) \mid y = \cos x\}.$$

Sketch its graph over the interval $-\pi \leqslant x \leqslant 2\pi$. Redefine f such that the inverse relation will be a function.

10. Discuss the periodic function

$$f = \{(x, y) \mid y = \tan x\}.$$

Sketch its graph over the interval $-\pi \leqslant x \leqslant \pi$. Redefine f such that the inverse relation will be a function.

11. (a) If $f: X \to Y$ and $g: Y \to Z$, where X, Y, and Z are sets of real numbers and

$$f = \{(x, y) \mid y = 1 - x\}, \qquad g = \left\{(y, z) \mid z = \frac{1}{y}\right\}.$$

What is the composite function $g[f]$?

(b) If $g = \left\{(x, y) \mid y = \frac{1}{x}\right\}$, and $f = \{(y, z) \mid z = 1 - y\}$, what is the composite $f[g]$?

12. (a) If $f = \{(x, y) \mid y = e^x\}$ and $g = \{(y, z) \mid z = \log_e y\}$, what is $g[f]$?

(b) If $g = \{(x, y) \mid y = \log_e x\}$ and $f = \{(y, z) \mid z = e^y\}$, what is $f[g]$?

13. (a) If $f = \{(x, y) \mid y = \tan x\}$ and $g = \{(y, z) \mid z = \arctan y\}$, what is $g[f]$?

(b) If $g = \{(x, y) \mid y = \arctan x\}$ and $f = \{(y, z) \mid z = \tan y\}$, determine the composite function $f[g]$.

14. If $X = Y = \{0, 1\}$ and $f: X \times Y \to Z$, where

$$f = \{(x, y, z) \mid z = x^2 - 2y^2\},$$

what are all the possible values of f?

15. If $X = Y = Z = \{0, 1\}$ and $f: X \times Y \times Z \to W$, where

$$f = \{(x, y, z, w) \mid w = x + 2y - z\},$$

what are all the possible values of f?

Supplementary Reading

ALLENDOERFER, C. B., and C. O. OAKLEY, *Principles of Mathematics*, 2nd ed., McGraw-Hill, New York, 1965.

BIRKHOFF, G., and S. MAC LANE, *A Brief Survey of Modern Algebra*, 3rd ed., Macmillan, New York, 1965.

BREUER, JOSEPH, *The Theory of Sets*, Prentice-Hall, Englewood Cliffs, N.J., 1959.

HALMOS, PAUL R., *Naive Set Theory*, Van Nostrand, Princeton, N.J., 1960.

NAHIKIAN, H. M., *A Modern Algebra for Biologists*, Univ. Chicago, Chicago, 1964.

2

BOOLEAN ALGEBRA

2.1 INTRODUCTION

Boolean algebra, or the algebra of logic, as it is sometimes called, is named in honor of the English mathematician George Boole (1815–1864). In 1848 Boole published his first volume on the subject, entitled *The Mathematical Analysis of Logic*. In 1854 he published his masterpiece, *An Investigation of the Laws of Thought*. These two works were concerned mainly with a detailed study of a method designed to place logic in a mathematical context. The latter publication also included a treatment of probability.

The symbolic logic of Boole was neglected by mathematicians for many years. In recent years, however, it has been used successfully in the investigation of certain subtle questions raised in studies of the foundations of mathematical thought. Boolean algebra has been applied also to the analysis of electrical networks, to the logic of electronic computers, to the social sciences, and to certain areas of biology, including a logical calculus for the investigation of the behavior of neural nets.

2.2 ABSTRACT BOOLEAN ALGEBRA

In this section we shall exhibit an axiomatic system called Boolean algebra. In developing it we shall state certain *definitions*. It is certainly conceivable that in some instances mathematical definitions are abstractions of natural phenomena, but it is not required that all mathematical definitions be of existential import. While it is not the concern of mathematics to justify the particular definitions selected, subsequent developments will demonstrate that these definitions make Boolean algebra particularly useful.

Accompanying these definitions are certain *axioms* or *postulates*, whose role is to place the entities of the system in relation to each other and to dictate the rules which must be followed in order that further conclusions or *theorems* that may exist in the system may be obtained by logical deduction.

We begin the axiomatic system with a set $B = \{a, b, c, \ldots\}$ of undefined elements in which an *equivalence relation*, $=$, is defined. That is to say, although we do not specify the elements of the set B, we do require that we shall be able to state whether $a = b$ or $a \neq b$ for every pair of elements in the set. Next, for future reference, we need the following definition.

DEFINITION **2.1** A *binary operation* ρ on a set B is a function of the product set $B \times B$ into B. That is, $\rho: B \times B \rightarrow B$.

Definition 2.1 indicates that every ordered pair of elements of the set B is mapped into a unique element of B by the binary operation ρ. We say that B is *closed* with respect to the given operation. Whenever we use "operation" in this connection, we shall mean binary operation. For example, the process of ordinary addition on the set of integers is a binary operation on that set, since it maps a pair of integers (a, b) into a unique integer $c = a + b$.

Moreover, if the elements of $B = \{S_1, S_2, \ldots\}$ are the subsets of some universal set U, then their union, $S_1 \cup S_2$, is a subset of U. Thus, union is a binary operation on the power set of U (the set of all subsets of U), as are also such set operations as intersection and relative difference, $S_1 \cap S_2$ and $S_1 - S_2$, respectively.

In abstract Boolean algebra there are two basic binary operations that may be applied to any ordered pair of elements of the set B to yield a unique third, not necessarily different, element of B. One of these operations is *union* and is denoted by the symbol " $\vee$ " (called a "wedge"). The second operation is *multiplication* and is denoted by the symbol " $\cdot$ ". In the subsequent development of the properties of these operations and their respective symbols, it will be noted that they bear a striking resemblance to union and intersection, " $\cup$ " and " $\cap$," in the algebra of sets.

Before proceeding with the development of this algebraic system, perhaps a brief remark concerning notational matters is in order. Every abstract algebraic system is structured on a set of undefined elements, which in this case we have denoted by B. For the system itself we use the notation $\mathscr{B} = \{B, \vee, \cdot\}$, which indicates the set and the operations which have been introduced up to this point.

The algebraic system $\mathscr{B}$ is developed by requiring the binary operations $\vee$ and $\cdot$ to satisfy certain axioms for all elements of $B = \{a, b, c, \ldots\}$.

THE COMMUTATIVE LAWS
- (a) $a \vee b = b \vee a$.
- (b) $a \cdot b = b \cdot a$.

THE ASSOCIATIVE LAWS
- (a) $a \vee (b \vee c) = (a \vee b) \vee c$.
- (b) $a \cdot (b \cdot c) = (a \cdot b) \cdot c$.

THE DISTRIBUTIVE LAWS
- (a) $a \cdot (b \vee c) = (a \cdot b) \vee (a \cdot c)$.
- (b) $a \vee (b \cdot c) = (a \vee b) \cdot (a \vee c)$.

Note that in each of the laws part (b) differs from part (a) only in that "$\cdot$" is everywhere interchanged with "$\vee$." The first distributive law states that multiplication distributes across union, and the second states that union distributes across multiplication.

SPECIAL ELEMENTS   It is postulated that a Boolean algebra $\mathscr{B}$ contains two special elements, 0 (zero) and 1 (one), which satisfy the following axioms for every element a in B:
- (a) $0 \vee a = a = a \vee 0$.
- (b) $1 \cdot a = a = a \cdot 1$.

DEFINITION 2.2   A *unary* operation α on a set B is a function of B into B, $\alpha: B \to B$.

A simple example of a unary operation on the set of real numbers is that of "forming the negative of a number." A unary operation on the set of nonnegative real numbers is "forming the square root of a number," and a unary operation on the set of complex numbers is "forming the conjugate of a number."

COMPLEMENTATION   There is postulated on the set B of a Boolean algebra $\mathscr{B}$ a unary operation "$'$" called *complementation*, which assigns to each element a of B an element a' of B such that
- (a) $a \vee a' = 1 = a' \vee a$.
- (b) $a \cdot a' = 0 = a' \cdot a$.

Although it is upon the preceding definitions and axioms that the other properties of a Boolean algebra will be developed, it must not be assumed that this is the only choice of axioms which will yield the same algebraic system. From this particular selection of postulates certain theorems may be logically deduced (Theorems 2.1 to 2.8, for example), but it is conceivable that the same system might be developed by selecting some of the foregoing axioms and some of the resulting theorems as a set of postulates. It should be clear, however, that if we were to specify more axioms than necessary, we should have to verify additional postulates in order to establish that the particular algebraic system is Boolean.

Before beginning the development of the theorems that are logical consequences of the foregoing postulates, we first call attention to the important fact that each postulate is of a *dual* nature and that each part is obtained from the other by replacing " $\vee$ " with " $\cdot$ " and " $\cdot$ " with " $\vee$," and "1" with "0" and "0" with "1." These pairs of symbols are called *duals*, and because of this duality it is possible to obtain a second, or dual, theorem from each one established by logical deduction from the axioms. This is set forth as follows.

THE PRINCIPLE OF DUALITY   If in a theorem established by logical deduction from Boolean axioms the symbols " $\vee$," " $\cdot$," "0," and "1" are replaced with their respective duals, the resulting statement is a valid theorem.

The proof of a dual theorem, although it is not written out formally, consists of the dual of each step in the proof of the original theorem. In most cases the application of the principle of duality yields a new theorem. However, if a theorem or statement is unchanged when dual replacements are made, it is said to be *self-dual*.

THEOREM **2.1** (*Uniqueness of* 0 *and* 1).   *In a Boolean algebra the special elements are unique.*

Proof.   Let us assume that there are two zero elements, 0 and 0_1, in $\mathscr{B}$. By the axiom of special elements (a) we must have, for all elements a in $\mathscr{B}$,

$$a \vee 0 = a \quad \text{and} \quad a \vee 0_1 = a.$$

Accordingly, since 0 and 0_1 are elements in B, we may write

$$0_1 \vee 0 = 0_1 \quad \text{and} \quad 0 \vee 0_1 = 0.$$

But, by the commutative law (a), $0 \vee 0_1 = 0_1 \vee 0$. Hence, $0_1 = 0$. The uniqueness of the special element 1 follows from this by application of the Principle of Duality.

THEOREM **2.2** (*Uniqueness of Complementation*).   *In a Boolean algebra each element, a, has a unique complement, a'.*

Proof.   Assume that a' and a'_1 are both complements of a. Then, in accordance with the laws listed previously,

$$
\begin{aligned}
a' &= a' \vee 0 & \text{Special elements (a)} \\
&= a' \vee (a \cdot a_1') & \text{Complementation (b)} \\
&= (a' \vee a) \cdot (a' \vee a_1') & \text{Distributivity (b)} \\
&= 1 \cdot (a' \vee a_1') & \text{Complementation (a)} \\
&= 1 \cdot a' \vee 1 \cdot a_1' & \text{Distributivity (a)} \\
&= a' \vee a_1'. & \text{Special elements (b)}
\end{aligned}
$$

Similarly, we can repeat each of the preceding steps, replacing a' with a_1' to obtain

$$
\begin{aligned}
a_1' &= a_1' \vee a' \\
&= a' \vee a_1'. \qquad \text{Commutativity (a)}
\end{aligned}
$$

Hence, by the transitivity of the equals relation, $a_1' = a'$.

THEOREM 2.3   *For each element, a, in a Boolean algebra, $(a')' = a$.*

Proof.   By definition of the complement of an element a,

$$
a \vee a' = 1 \qquad \text{and} \qquad a \cdot a' = 0.
$$

Applying the commutative laws to these expressions, we have

$$
a' \vee a = 1 \qquad \text{and} \qquad a' \cdot a = 0.
$$

Comparing these equations to

$$
a' \vee (a')' = 1 \qquad \text{and} \qquad a' \cdot (a')' = 0
$$

and recalling that the complement of an element is unique (Theorem 2.2), we conclude that $(a')' = a$.

THEOREM 2.4 (*Complement of 0 and 1*).   *For the special elements 0 and 1 of a Boolean algebra, $0' = 1$ and $1' = 0$.*

Proof.   Let $0'$ be the complement of 0. Then by complementation, (a) and (b), we have $0 \vee 0' = 1$ and $0 \cdot 0' = 0$. Referring to the axioms of special elements (a) and (b), we have

$$
\begin{aligned}
a \vee 0 = 0 \vee a = a & \qquad \therefore\ 0 \vee 1 = 1, \\
a \cdot 0 = 0 \cdot a = 0 & \qquad \therefore\ 0 \cdot 1 = 0.
\end{aligned}
$$

Hence, by the uniqueness of the complement (Theorem 2.2),

$$
0' = 1.
$$

Applying the principle of duality to this result, we have

$$
1' = 0.
$$

In the next theorem the *idempotent laws* are developed. These laws are in contrast to any laws of operation that apply to the algebra of complex numbers and account for many of the special properties that characterize Boolean algebras.

THEOREM **2.5** (*Idempotent Property*).   *For every element, a, in a Boolean algebra, $a \vee a = a$ and $a \cdot a = a$.*

Proof.   Let a be an arbitrary element in a Boolean algebra; then

$$
\begin{aligned}
a &= a \vee 0 & &\text{Special elements (a)}\\
&= a \vee (a \cdot a') & &\text{Complementation (b)}\\
&= (a \vee a) \cdot (a \vee a') & &\text{Distributivity (b)}\\
&= (a \vee a) \cdot 1 & &\text{Complementation (a)}\\
&= a \vee a. & &\text{Special elements (b)}
\end{aligned}
$$

Applying the principle of duality to $a \vee a = a$, we have $a \cdot a = a$.

THEOREM **2.6** (*Further Properties of* 0 *and* 1).   *For every element, a, in a Boolean algebra, $a \vee 1 = 1$ and $a \cdot 0 = 0$.*

Proof.   Let a be an arbitrary element in a Boolean algebra; then

$$
\begin{aligned}
1 &= a \vee a' & &\text{Complementation (a)}\\
&= a \vee (a' \cdot 1) & &\text{Special elements (b)}\\
&= (a \vee a') \cdot (a \vee 1) & &\text{Distributivity (b)}\\
&= 1 \cdot (a \vee 1) & &\text{Complementation (a)}\\
&= a \vee 1. & &\text{Special elements (b)}
\end{aligned}
$$

Applying the principle of duality to $a \vee 1 = 1$, we have $a \cdot 0 = 0$.

THEOREM **2.7** (*Absorption Property*).   *For each pair of elements, a and b, in a Boolean algebra, $a \vee (a \cdot b) = a$ and $a \cdot (a \vee b) = a$.*

Proof.   Let a and b be arbitrary elements in a Boolean algebra; then

$$
\begin{aligned}
a &= 1 \cdot a & &\text{Special elements (a)}\\
&= (1 \vee b) \cdot a & &\text{Theorem 2.6}\\
&= (1 \cdot a) \vee (b \cdot a) & &\text{Distributivity (a)}\\
&= a \vee (a \cdot b). & &\text{Special elements (b) and commutativity (b)}
\end{aligned}
$$

The relationship $a \cdot (a \vee b) = a$ is the dual of $a \vee (a \cdot b) = a$.

THEOREM **2.8** (*De Morgan's Laws*).   *For every pair of elements a and b in a Boolean algebra, $(a \cdot b)' = a' \vee b'$ and $(a \vee b)' = a' \cdot b'$.*

Proof. Consider first:

$$(a \cdot b) \cdot (a' \vee b') = (a \cdot b) \cdot a' \vee (a \cdot b) \cdot b' \qquad \text{Distributivity (a)}$$
$$= (a \cdot a') \cdot b \vee a \cdot (b \cdot b') \qquad \text{Associativity (b) and}$$
$$\text{commutativity (b)}$$
$$= 0 \cdot b \vee a \cdot 0 \qquad \text{Complementation (b)}$$
$$= 0 \vee 0 \qquad \text{Theorem 2.6}$$
$$= 0. \qquad \text{Special elements (a)}$$

Consider next:

$$(a \cdot b) \vee (a' \vee b') = [(a \cdot b) \vee a'] \vee b' \qquad \text{Associativity (a)}$$
$$= [(a \vee a') \cdot (b \vee a')] \vee b' \qquad \text{Distributivity (b) and}$$
$$\text{commutativity (a)}$$
$$= 1 \cdot (b \vee a') \vee b' \qquad \text{Complementation (a)}$$
$$= a' \vee (b \vee b') \qquad \text{Commutativity (a) and}$$
$$\text{associativity (a)}$$
$$= a' \vee 1 \qquad \text{Complementation (a)}$$
$$= 1. \qquad \text{Theorem 2.6}$$

By the definition of the complement and its uniqueness, we have from both considerations that $a' \vee b'$ is the complement of $a \cdot b$; that is, $(a \cdot b)' = a' \vee b'$. The dual of this result is $(a \vee b)' = a' \cdot b'$.

DEFINITION **2.3** A *partially ordered* set is a system consisting of a set and a relation, $\leqslant$ (less than or equal to), subject to the conditions:
(a) $a \leqslant b$ and $b \leqslant a$, if and only if $a = b$.
(b) If $a \leqslant b$ and $b \leqslant c$, then $a \leqslant c$.

We now partially order the elements of a Boolean algebra as indicated in the following definition.

DEFINITION **2.4** For all ordered pairs (a, b) of a Boolean algebra, $a \leqslant b$ if and only if $a \cdot b' = 0$.

THEOREM **2.9** *The relation given in Definition 2.4 is a partial ordering relation.*

Proof. The reasons for the following steps should be provided by the reader. We first establish Definition 2.3(a). Assume $a \leqslant b$; then

$$a \cdot b' = 0,$$
$$a' \vee b = 1,$$
$$a' \cdot a \vee b \cdot a = 1 \cdot a,$$
$$0 \vee b \cdot a = a,$$
$$b \cdot a = a.$$

In similar manner, starting with the assumption that $b \leqslant a$, we can show that $a \cdot b = b$. Hence we have

$$a = b \cdot a = a \cdot b = b.$$

To establish (b) of Definition 2.3 we assume $a \leqslant b$ and $b \leqslant c$ or, equivalently, $a \cdot b' = 0$ and $b \cdot c' = 0$. Now consider:

$$
\begin{aligned}
a \cdot c' &= (a \cdot c') \cdot 1 \\
&= (a \cdot c') \cdot (b \vee b') \\
&= (a \cdot c') \cdot b \vee (a \cdot c') \cdot b' \\
&= a \cdot (b \cdot c') \vee (a \cdot b') \cdot c' \\
&= a \cdot 0 \vee 0 \cdot c' \\
&= 0 \vee 0 \\
&= 0 \\
\therefore \ a &\leqslant c.
\end{aligned}
$$

THEOREM **2.10** *The following properties of the ordering relation* $\leqslant$ *are valid for arbitrary elements, a, b, c, of a Boolean algebra:*
(a) *If* $a \leqslant b$ *and* $a \leqslant c$, *then* $a \leqslant b \cdot c$.
(b) *If* $a \leqslant b$, *then* $a \leqslant b \vee c$ *for an arbitrary element c.*
(c) $a \leqslant b$ *if and only if* $b' \leqslant a'$.

Proof. (a) Let us assume $a \leqslant b$ and $a \leqslant c$. Then $a \cdot b' = 0$ and $a \cdot c' = 0$ by Definition 2.4; and it follows that

$$
\begin{aligned}
a \cdot (b \cdot c)' &= a \cdot (b' \vee c') &&\text{Theorem 2.8} \\
&= a \cdot b' \vee a \cdot c' &&\text{Distributive (a)} \\
&= 0 \vee 0 &&\text{(assumption)} \\
&= 0 &&\text{Special elements (a)} \\
\therefore \ a &\leqslant b \cdot c. &&\text{Definition 2.4}
\end{aligned}
$$

(b) Let us assume $a \leqslant b$ or, equivalently, $a \cdot b' = 0$. Let c be an arbitrary element; then,

$$
\begin{aligned}
a \cdot (b \vee c)' &= a \cdot (b' \cdot c') &&\text{Theorem 2.8} \\
&= (a \cdot b') \cdot c' &&\text{Associative (b)} \\
&= 0 \cdot c' &&\text{(assumption)} \\
&= 0 &&\text{Theorem 2.6} \\
\therefore \ a &\leqslant (b \vee c). &&\text{Definition 2.4}
\end{aligned}
$$

(c) Let us assume $a \leqslant b$, or, equivalently, $a \cdot b' = 0$; then,

$$
\begin{aligned}
0 &= a \cdot b' &&\text{(assumption)} \\
&= (a')' \cdot (b)' &&\text{Theorem 2.3} \\
&= b' \cdot (a')' &&\text{Commutative (b)} \\
\therefore \ b' &\leqslant a' &&\text{Definition 2.4}
\end{aligned}
$$

PROBLEMS

1. Assume x and y are elements of an abstract Boolean algebra, $\mathscr{B} = \{B, \vee, \cdot, '\}$. Use the axioms and theorems of this section to prove the following (do not use the Principle of Duality).
   (a) $(x' \cdot y')' = x \vee y$.
   (b) $x \vee (x \cdot y) = x$.
   (c) $x \vee (x' \cdot y) = x \vee y$.
   (d) $x \cdot (x' \vee y) = x \cdot y$.
   (e) $(x' \cdot y')' \vee (x' \cdot y)' = 1$.
   (f) $x \leqslant 0$ if and only if $x = 0$.

2. Write the dual of each relationship in Problem 1.

3. Assume x, y, and z are elements of an abstract Boolean algebra, $\mathscr{B} = \{B, \vee, \cdot, '\}$. Determine the complement of each of the following expressions, and simplify.
   (a) $x' \vee x$.
   (b) $(x \cdot y) \vee z'$.
   (c) $(x' \vee y) \vee z$.
   (d) $x \cdot [y \vee (z \cdot x')]$.

4. Take the algebraic system $\mathscr{B} = \{B, \vee, \cdot\}$, where $B = \{a, b, c, d\}$ and the binary operations $\vee$ and $\cdot$ are respectively defined by the following tables:

$\vee$	a	b	c	d
a	a	b	c	d
b	b	b	b	b
c	c	b	c	b
d	d	b	b	d

$\cdot$	a	b	c	d
a	a	a	a	a
b	a	b	c	d
c	a	c	c	a
d	a	d	a	d

   (a) Verify that the system $\mathscr{B}$ is commutative with respect to both operations.
   (b) Verify that the idempotent laws hold for this system.
   (c) How many triples (x, y, z) would have to be tested in order to verify that $x \vee (y \vee z) = (x \vee y) \vee z$ or that $x \cdot (y \cdot z) = (x \cdot y) \cdot z$?
   (d) Determine which of the elements of B have the properties of the special elements, 0 and 1, of a Boolean algebra. Verify that your choices satisfy the axioms $0 \vee x = x$ and $1 \cdot x = x$ for all elements $x \in B$.
   (e) Determine the complement, x', of each element $x \in B$.
   (f) Show that all pairs of elements of B except (c, d) satisfy the conditions of Definition 2.4 and Theorem 2.9.

5. Given a and b, arbitrary elements in an abstract Boolean algebra, prove the following relationships.
   (a) $a \leqslant b$ if and only if $a \cdot b = a$.
   (b) $a \leqslant b$ if and only if $a \vee b = b$.
   (c) $0 \leqslant a \leqslant 1$.

2.3   A SIMPLE MODEL OF A BOOLEAN ALGEBRA

A remarkably simple algebraic system that satisfies the axioms of a Boolean algebra is $\mathscr{B} = \{B, \vee, \cdot\}$, where $B = \{0, 1\}$ and the binary operations $\vee$ and $\cdot$ are defined in Tables 2.1.

TABLES 2.1

$\vee$	0	1
0	0	1
1	1	1

$\cdot$	0	1
0	0	0
1	0	1

To establish that any algebraic system is a Boolean algebra, it must be demonstrated that all the axioms we have stipulated in the preceding section are satisfied by the system. Before we attempt a formal demonstration that the algebraic system $\{B, \vee, \cdot\}$, introduced above is Boolean, we shall find it convenient to define the following important concept.

DEFINITION 2.5   A *Boolean function* is a mapping, $\beta: B \times B \times \cdots \times B \to B$, where B is the set of elements of a Boolean algebra $\mathscr{B}$.

Such a function involves a finite number of arguments, each with domain B, the binary operations $\vee$, $\cdot$, and the unary operation $'$. If the number of arguments in the function is n, the function maps each ordered n-tuple, $(x_1, x_2, \ldots, x_n)$, into a unique image, $x_i \in B$.

If there are k elements in B, then there are k^n distinct n-tuples obtained by assigning the k elements of B to the n components, x_j, in all possible ways. In particular, when $B = \{0, 1\}$, there are $2^2 = 4$ ordered pairs: $(0, 0)$, $(0, 1)$, $(1, 0)$, and $(1, 1)$. If $B = \{0, 1\}$, then there are $2^3 = 8$ distinct ordered triples: $(0, 0, 0)$, $(0, 0, 1)$, $(0, 1, 0)$, $(0, 1, 1)$, $(1, 0, 0)$, $(1, 0, 1)$, $(1, 1, 0)$, and $(1, 1, 1)$.

We shall say that two Boolean functions are *equal* if and only if each of the distinct n-tuples is mapped into the same image by both functions for all k^n cases. In general, when B has a finite number of elements, a valid proof of a theorem consists in verifying that it is true for all possible cases. A convenient device for systematically examining all cases is the so-called *truth table*, which we use to verify that the various axioms hold for the algebraic system $\{\{0, 1\}, \vee, \cdot\}$ of this section.

THEOREM 2.11   *The algebraic system $\{\{0, 1\}, \vee, \cdot\}$ is commutative with respect to the binary operations $\vee$ and $\cdot$*

Proof. We shall prove $a \vee b = b \vee a$ and ask the reader to verify $a \cdot b = b \cdot a$ (see Problem 1 of this section). In the first two columns of Table

2.2 are listed the $2^2 = 4$ distinct ordered pairs (a, b). In columns 3 and 4 are listed the corresponding values of the functions $a \vee b$ and $b \vee a$, obtained from Tables 2.1, in which the binary operation $\vee$ is defined. We conclude that $a \vee b = b \vee a$ for this system, because columns 3 and 4 are identical for all possible entries listed in columns 1 and 2.

TABLE 2.2

$a \vee b = b \vee a$

a	b	$a \vee b$	$b \vee a$
0	0	0	0
0	1	1	1
1	0	1	1
1	1	1	1
(1)	(2)	(3)	(4)

THEOREM **2.12** *The algebraic system* $\{\{0, 1\}, \vee, \cdot\}$ *is associative with respect to the binary operations,* $\vee$ *and* $\cdot$.

Proof. We shall prove that $a \vee (b \vee c) = (a \vee b) \vee c$ and ask the reader to verify $a \cdot (b \cdot c) = (a \cdot b) \cdot c$ (see Problem 2, this section). Table 2.3 lists the $2^3 = 8$ distinct ordered triples (a, b, c) in the first three columns and the corresponding values of the functions $a \vee (b \vee c)$ and $(a \vee b) \vee c$ (columns 5 and 7). We conclude that $a \vee (b \vee c) = (a \vee b) \vee c$, because columns 5 and 7 are identical for all possible entries in columns 1, 2, and 3.

TABLE 2.3

$a \vee (b \vee c) = (a \vee b) \vee c$

a	b	c	$b \vee c$	$a \vee (b \vee c)$	$a \vee b$	$(a \vee b) \vee c$
0	0	0	0	0	0	0
0	1	0	1	1	1	1
0	0	1	1	1	0	1
0	1	1	1	1	1	1
1	0	0	0	1	1	1
1	1	0	1	1	1	1
1	0	1	1	1	1	1
1	1	1	1	1	1	1
(1)	(2)	(3)	(4)	(5)	(6)	(7)

THEOREM **2.13**   *The algebraic system* $\{\{0, 1\}, \vee, \cdot\}$ *is distributive with respect to the binary operations* $\vee$ *and* $\cdot$.

Proof.   We shall prove that $a \vee (b \cdot c) = (a \vee b) \cdot (a \vee c)$ and ask the reader to verify $a \cdot (b \vee c) = (a \cdot b) \vee (a \cdot c)$ (see Problem 3, this section). In columns 1, 2, and 3 of Table 2.4 are listed the $2^3 = 8$ distinct ordered triples (a, b, c). In columns 5 and 8 are listed the corresponding values of the functions $a \vee (b \cdot c)$ and $(a \vee b) \cdot (a \vee c)$. We conclude that $a \vee (b \cdot c) = (a \vee b) \cdot (a \vee c)$, because columns 5 and 8 are identical for all possible entries listed in columns 1, 2, and 3.

TABLE 2.4

$a \vee (b \cdot c) = (a \vee b) \cdot (a \vee c)$

a	b	c	$(b \cdot c)$	$a \vee (b \cdot c)$	$(a \vee b)$	$(a \vee c)$	$(a \vee b) \cdot (a \vee c)$
0	0	0	0	0	0	0	0
0	1	0	0	0	1	0	0
0	0	1	0	0	0	1	0
0	1	1	1	1	1	1	1
1	0	0	0	1	1	1	1
1	1	0	0	1	1	1	1
1	0	1	0	1	1	1	1
1	1	1	1	1	1	1	1
(1)	(2)	(3)	(4)	(5)	(6)	(7)	(8)

The reader is asked to prove, by truth tables, the following result (see Problem 4, this section).

THEOREM **2.14**   *The elements* 0 *and* 1 *of* $\{\{0, 1\}, \vee, \cdot\}$ *satisfy the relationships* $0 \vee a = a$ *and* $1 \cdot a = a$.

THEOREM **2.15**   *In the algebraic system* $\{\{0, 1\}, \vee, \cdot\}$, $0' = 1$ *and* $1' = 0$. *Furthermore*, $a \vee a' = 1$ *and* $a \cdot a' = 0$.

Proof.   Table 2.5 lists the truth values of the functions $a \vee a'$ and $a \cdot a'$ for all possible values of the arguments. It may be seen from columns 3 and 4 that $a \vee a' = 1$ and $a \cdot a' = 0$.

THEOREM **2.16**   *The relation* $\leqslant$, *as defined in Definition* 2.4, *applies to the algebraic system* $\{\{0, 1\}, \vee, \cdot\}$.

TABLE 2.5

$$a \vee a' = 1, \ a \cdot a' = 0$$

a	a'	$a \vee a'$	$a \cdot a'$
0	1	1	0
1	0	1	0

Proof.   Table 2.6 lists the ordered pairs (a, b); for each ordered pair it may be seen that $a \cdot b' = 0$, and so $a \leqslant b$.

TABLE 2.6

$$a \leqslant b$$

a	b	b'	$a \cdot b'$
0	0	1	0
0	1	0	0
1	1	0	0

Having verified that the algebraic system $\{\{0, 1\}, \vee, \cdot\}$ fulfills all the axioms that define a Boolean algebra, we may conclude that this system is a Boolean algebra. It follows that all the results (Theorems 2.1 to 2.10) developed logically from the axioms now apply to the algebraic system $\{\{0, 1\}, \vee, \cdot\}$ without need of further proof.

Problems

The algebraic system referred to in the following problems is $\{\{0, 1\}, \vee, \cdot\}$. Construct truth tables to prove the following.

1. $a \cdot b = b \cdot a$.

2. $a \cdot (b \cdot c) = (a \cdot b) \cdot c$.

3. $a \cdot (b \vee c) = (a \cdot b) \vee (a \cdot c)$.

4. $a \vee a = a$ and $a \cdot a = a$.

5. $(a \vee b)' = a' \cdot b'$ and $(a \cdot b)' = a' \vee b'$.

6. $a \cdot b = a$ if $a \leqslant b$.

7. $a \leqslant b$ if $a \cdot b = a$.

8. $a \vee b = b$ if $a \leqslant b$.

9. $a \leqslant b$ if $a \vee b = b$.

2.4 AN ALGEBRA OF SETS

In this section we shall study an algebraic system, $\mathscr{B} = \{2^U, \cup, \cap\}$, in which 2^U is the power set of a universal set U and the binary operations are set union, $\cup$, and set intersection, $\cap$. We shall demonstrate that this system, along with the unary operation of set complementation, $'$, and the binary relation, $\subseteq$, is a Boolean algebra.

For a convenient comparison of set algebra and abstract Boolean algebra the basic entities, operations, and relations of these two systems are listed in parallel columns in Table 2.7.

TABLE 2.7

Boolean Algebra	Set Algebra
1. Set B of undefined elements, $\{a, b, c, \dots\}$	1. The power set of a universal set U
2. Binary operation, union, $\vee$	2. Set union, $\cup$
3. Binary operation, multiplication, $\cdot$	3. Set intersection, $\cap$
4. Unary operation, complementation, a'.	4. Set complementation, $A' = U - A$.
5. Special element, 1	5. Universal set, U
6. Special element, 0	6. Empty set, $\varnothing$
7. Relation, $a \leqslant b$	7. Subset relation, $A \subseteq B$

In verifying that the algebra $\{2^U, \cup, \cap, '\}$ is Boolean we shall have to show that the axioms defining an abstract Boolean algebra (Section 2.2) are valid also for this system. In establishing each axiom it will be necessary to prove the equality of certain sets. For example, to show that the commutative law holds for set algebra, we must prove that sets $A \cup B$ and $B \cup A$ are equal.

Because the axioms defining a Boolean algebra are of a dual character, the verification that a particular postulate is satisfied in the algebra of sets is developed for one of the parts while the second part is left to the reader to prove.

THEOREM **2.17** *The algebra of sets is commutative with respect to the binary operations of union,* ∪, *and intersection,* ∩.

Proof. Assume $x \in A \cup B$. Then $x \in A$ and/or $x \in B$; but this implies $x \in B \cup A$.

$$\therefore \ A \cup B \subseteq B \cup A. \tag{2.1}$$

Now let $y \in B \cup A$. Then $y \in B$ and/or $y \in A$. Hence $y \in A \cup B$.

$$\therefore \ B \cup A \subseteq A \cup B. \tag{2.2}$$

Combining Equations 2.1 and 2.2, we have

$$A \cup B = B \cup A.$$

The reader will supply the proof that $A \cap B = B \cap A$ (Problem 1, this section).

In the proof of the next theorem a somewhat modified version of the truth table is introduced, in contrast to the logical argument developed in the proof of Theorem 2.17:

THEOREM **2.18** *The algebra of sets is associative with respect to the binary operations* ∪ *and* ∩.

Proof. At the top of each column in Table 2.8 is listed the set under consideration. In each row the letter **y** indicates that an arbitrary (but fixed) element is in the set listed at the top of each column while the letter **n** indicates that the element is not in the set. The first three columns give the $2^3 = 8$ distinct ordered triples that can be formed from the set {**y**, **n**} thus exhausting

TABLE 2.8

$$A \cup (B \cup C) = (A \cup B) \cup C$$

A	B	C	$B \cup C$	$A \cup (B \cup C)$	$A \cup B$	$(A \cup B) \cup C$
y	y	y	y	y	y	y
y	y	n	y	y	y	y
y	n	y	y	y	y	y
y	n	n	n	y	y	y
n	y	y	y	y	y	y
n	y	n	y	y	y	y
n	n	y	y	y	n	y
n	n	n	n	n	n	n
(1)	(2)	(3)	(4)	(5)	(6)	(7)

all possible cases. Each triple indicates whether or not an arbitrary element x occurs in set A and/or set B and/or set C. Using the definition of the binary operation of set union, $\cup$, one can determine very quickly whether or not the element belongs to $A \cup (B \cup C)$ and $(A \cup B) \cup C$. Columns 5 and 7 are identical in all cases, and it follows that $A \cup (B \cup C) = (A \cup B) \cup C$.

THEOREM **2.19** *The algebra of sets is distributive with respect to the binary operations* $\cup$ *and* $\cap$.

Proof. The proof that $A \cup (B \cap C) = (A \cup B) \cap (A \cup C)$ is based on the truth table (Table 2.9), in which it is demonstrated that the sets $A \cup (B \cap C)$ and $(A \cup B) \cap (A \cup C)$, columns 5 and 8, respectively, are identical for all of the $2^3 = 8$ distinct cases that arise.

The reader is asked to prove the dual, namely that $A \cap (B \cup C) = (A \cap B) \cup (A \cap C)$ in Problem 3, this section.

TABLE 2.9
$$A \cup (B \cap C) = (A \cup B) \cap (A \cup C)$$

A	B	C	$B \cap C$	$A \cup (B \cap C)$	$A \cup B$	$A \cup C$	$(A \cup B) \cap (A \cup C)$
y	y	y	y	y	y	y	y
y	y	n	n	y	y	y	y
y	n	y	n	y	y	y	y
y	n	n	n	y	y	y	y
n	y	y	y	y	y	y	y
n	y	n	n	n	y	n	n
n	n	y	n	n	n	y	n
n	n	n	n	n	n	n	n
(1)	(2)	(3)	(4)	(5)	(6)	(7)	(8)

The reader is asked to supply the proofs of Theorem 2.20 and Theorem 2.21 (Problems 4 and 5, this section).

THEOREM **2.20** *For every element A in the algebra of sets the special elements, U and $\varnothing$, have the following properties:*
(a) $\varnothing \cup A = A$.
(b) $U \cap A = A$.

THEOREM **2.21** *To each element A in the algebra of sets there exists a unique complement, $A' = U - A$, such that* (a) $A \cup A' = U$ *and* (b) $A \cap A' = \varnothing$.

THEOREM **2.22**   *The relation* $\subseteq$ *in the algebra of sets is reflexive, anti-symmetric, and transitive.*

Proof.   Reflexive property: Because every set is a subset of itself, we have $A \subseteq A$ for every element A.

Antisymmetric property: If $A \subseteq B$ and $B \subseteq A$, then, by definition of equal sets, $A = B$.

Transitive property: If $A \subseteq B$, then every element of A belongs to B, and if $B \subseteq C$, every element of B belongs to C. Therefore, every element of A belongs to C, and we may conclude that $A \subseteq C$.

THEOREM **2.23**   *In the algebra of sets,* $A \subseteq B$ *if and only if* $A \cap B' = \varnothing$.

Proof.   Assume x is an arbitrary element in set A. Let $A \subseteq B$; then $x \in B$, and hence $x \notin B'$. Therefore, $A \cap B' = \varnothing$. Conversely, let $A \cap B' = \varnothing$; then if $x \in A$, we must conclude that $x \notin B'$. Therefore, $x \in B$. An arbitrary element belonging to A also belongs to B, and it follows that $A \subseteq B$.

With the completion of Theorem 2.23 we have verified that the algebraic system $\{2^U, \cup, \cap, '\}$, where 2^U is the power set of a universal set $\cup$, satisfies all the axioms of the abstract Boolean algebra defined in Section 2.2. We say that the two algebraic systems are *isomorphic* with, or abstractly equal to, each other. All the theorems obtained by logical deduction from the axioms of the abstract Boolean algebra are true for the algebra of sets without further need of proof. However, several of these results are given as problems in this section and are to be developed independently.

PROBLEMS

In all of the following problems the algebraic system to which they refer is $\{2^U, \cup, \cap, '\}$.

1. Prove that $A \cap B = B \cap A$.

2. Prove that $A \cap (B \cap C) = (A \cap B) \cap C$.

3. Prove that $A \cap (B \cup C) = (A \cap B) \cup (A \cap C)$.

4. Prove Theorem 2.20.

5. Prove Theorem 2.21.

6. Prove that $(A \cup B)' = A' \cap B'$.

7. Prove that $(A \cap B)' = A' \cup B'$.

8. Prove that $(A')' = A$.

9. Prove that $\varnothing \subseteq A \subseteq U$.

10. Prove that $A \cup A = A$ and $A \cap A = A$.

2.5 THE ALGEBRA OF LOGICAL PROPOSITIONS

In this section we shall discuss briefly the application of Boolean algebra to symbolic logic. It is not the purpose of this discussion to develop the topic completely, but rather to show its relation to Boolean algebra and at the same time to give the reader a sufficient background for further study in this area.

It will be recalled that we began our study of abstract Boolean algebra with a set of undefined elements and certain binary and unary operations on the set, defined by axioms, and then proceeded to deduce logically the properties of this system. In developing the algebra of sets we started with a set of elements consisting of subsets of a universal set, and the binary and unary operations were the set operations of union, intersection, and complementation. After establishing that this system satisfied all the axioms of abstract Boolean algebra we were able to apply, without further proof, all the theorems which had been logically deduced in the Boolean algebra.

In the algebra of propositions we begin with a set, $B = \{p, q, r, \ldots\}$, whose elements are undefined *statements*, or *logical propositions*. By a "logical proposition" we shall mean any declarative sentence that is free from ambiguity and has the property of being true or false but not both simultaneously. For example, the following are logical propositions:

> Set A has the same cardinal number as set B.
> The number x is an integer.

On the other hand, the following sentence is not a logical proposition, because it is *false* if it is assumed to be true and it is *true* if it is assumed to be *false*:

> This sentence which you are reading is false.

Each logical proposition $x \in B$ is mapped into the set $\{0, 1\}$ according to the following rule:

> (a) If x is true, then x is mapped into 1;
> (b) If x is false, then x is mapped into 0.

Thus, we say that x has a *truth value* of 1 or 0, respectively, and we may freely interchange the words *true* and *false* with the corresponding symbol.

Defined on the set B of logical propositions are two binary operations, called *connectives*. The first of these is *disjunction*, symbolized by " ∨ " (the symbol denoting union in abstract Boolean algebra). If p and q are logical propositions, then $p \vee q$ is read "p or q." By the disjunction " ∨ ," we shall mean "or" in an inclusive sense; that is, $p \vee q$ means either p or q, or both p and q.

Consider, for example, the statement "A rose looks or smells beautiful." Here we may let p and q stand for the statements:

> p: A rose looks beautiful.
> q: A rose smells beautiful.

Then the given statement, $p \vee q$, does not exclude the case in which the rose both looks and smells beautiful. On the other hand, $p \vee q$ does not guarantee this case either.

The second binary operation defined on the set B of logical propositions is the connective *conjunction*, which we denote by " ∧ ." For arbitrary logical propositions p and q the symbol "$p \wedge q$" is read "p and q."

In addition to the binary operations we define a *unary* operation, called *negation*, which is denoted by placing a prime, ', to the right of the proposition. Thus, if p is a statement which is true, then p' is the negation of p and is therefore a false statement. For example, if p is the statement "There is snow on the mountain," then p' is the statement "There is no snow on the mountain." These operations are illustrated as follows.

ILLUSTRATION **2.1**   Write symbolically the sentence "The clouds are hanging low and it looks like snow." Here we assign

> p: The clouds are hanging low.
> q: It looks like snow.

The sentence is then written "$p \wedge q$."

ILLUSTRATION **2.2**   Write in acceptable English the symbolic sentence $p \wedge q'$, where

> p: The clouds are hanging low.
> q: It looks like snow.

The symbol "$p \wedge q'$" may be translated

$p \wedge q'$:   The clouds are hanging low, but it does not look like snow.

ILLUSTRATION **2.3**   Write symbolically the sentence "The roof is leaking, or the water is running in the upstairs bath." Here we write

> p: The roof is leaking.
> q: The water is running in the upstairs bath.

The given sentence is written symbolically "$p \lor q$."

The concept of a Boolean function as defined in Definition 2.5 is carried over into the algebra of logical propositions. Such a function involves a finite number of arguments $p_i \in B$ and the operations $\lor$, $\land$, $'$, defined above. We shall speak of such functions as *compound propositions* and the arguments p_i as the *component propositions* or, simply, the *components of the function*.

It has been previously stated that each component proposition is mapped into 1 or 0 according as it is true or false. How, then, are we to determine the truth value of a compound proposition? Clearly, it is necessary first to postulate the truth values of the three basic compound propositions arising from the use of the connectives and negation, namely $p \lor q$, $p \land q$, and p' and then extend these to the more complex compound propositions. This is done in the following definitions, for which truth tables are given for convenience.

DEFINITION 2.6 The *inclusive disjunction*, $p \lor q$, of two logical propositions p and q is considered to be true when at least one of the components, p or q, is true; otherwise, the disjunction is false (see Table 2.10).

TABLE 2.10

Truth Table for (Inclusive) Disjunction, $p \lor q$

p	q	$p \lor q$
1	1	1
1	0	1
0	1	1
0	0	0

DEFINITION 2.7 The *conjunction*, $p \land q$, of two logical propositions p and q is considered to be true only when both component functions, p and q, are true; otherwise, the conjunction is false (see Table 2.11).

DEFINITION 2.8 The *negation*, p', of a logical proposition p is considered to be false when p is true and true when p is false (see Table 2.12).

Often a proposition is *conditioned* or *implied* by another. Although it is possible to reword conditional statements in such a way that they may be symbolically represented by the connectives already defined in the preceding discussion, it is more convenient to introduce another connective, which is called an *implication* and which is denoted by the symbol "$\rightarrow$."

DEFINITION **2.9** For arbitrary (but fixed) logical propositions p and q the symbol $p \to q$ denotes an *implication*, "if p, then q," defined by the following axioms (see Table 2.13):

(a) If the *antecedent p* is true and the *consequent q* is false, the implication $p \to q$ is false.

(b) In all other cases $p \to q$ is true.

TABLE 2.11

Truth Table for Conjunction, $p \wedge q$

p	q	$p \wedge q$
1	1	1
1	0	0
0	1	0
0	0	0

TABLE 2.12

Truth Table for Negation, p'

p	p'
1	0
0	1

TABLE 2.13

Truth Table for the Implication $p \to q$

p	q	$p \to q$
1	1	1
1	0	0
0	1	1
0	0	1

The conditional "if..., then..." is used frequently in mathematical theorems. Generally the antecedent is called the *hypothesis* and the consequent the *conclusion*. For example, "If a and b are both odd integers, then the sum $a + b$ is an even integer."

The converse, $q \rightarrow p$, does not always follow from $p \rightarrow q$. Thus, in the preceding example it is not necessarily true that "if the sum $a + b$ is an even integer, then a and b are odd." In this illustration the condition "a and b are both odd integers" is said to be *sufficient* to insure that $a + b$ be an even integer but not *necessary* to do so.

On the other hand, consider the conditional proposition "If the three sides of a triangle are equal, then the three angles are equal," which has the converse "If the three angles of a triangle are equal, then the three sides are equal." Both of these conditional propositions being valid, the hypothesis and the conclusion can be interchanged, for whenever the one is true the other is true, and whenever the one is false the other is false. That is to say, it is impossible for either the antecedent or the consequent to be false when the other is true. In this case the condition "Three sides of a triangle are equal" is both *necessary* and *sufficient* to insure the conclusion "Three angles of a triangle are equal." These considerations and others of similar nature lead to the following definition.

DEFINITION **2.10**   For arbitrary (but fixed) logical propositions p and q the symbol "$p \leftrightarrow q$," which is read "p, if and only if q," denotes a *biconditional*, or *equivalence*. It is defined by the following axioms (see Table 2.14):

(a) If the left and right sides, p and q respectively, are both true or both false, the equivalence is true.

(b) If one side is true and the other is false, the equivalence is false.

TABLE 2.14

Truth Table for the Equivalence $p \leftrightarrow q$

p	q	$p \leftrightarrow q$
1	1	1
1	0	0
0	1	0
0	0	1

Besides its frequent use in mathematical theorems, the phrase "if and only if" occurs quite often in mathematical definitions. For example, in the definition of *set equality* we find "Two sets are *equal* if and only if every element of each set is an element of the other." From this statement it may be inferred that, whenever two sets are said to be equal, they have exactly the same elements and, conversely, when it is demonstrated that two sets have exactly the same elements, it may be concluded that the sets are equal.

It is important to note that the equivalence $p \leftrightarrow q$ does not assert that the propositions p and q are identical or that they have the same meaning. All that can be inferred from equivalent propositions is that they have the same truth values.

Although it is true that the truth value of a compound proposition usually depends upon the truth values of its components, it sometimes happens that because of the logical structure of a compound proposition it will have a constant truth value of 1 or 0 for all possible choices of truth values of its components.

DEFINITION **2.11**   A proposition whose truth value is always true is a *tautology* and a proposition whose truth value is always false is an *absurdity*. Such propositions are denoted by **1** and **0**, respectively.

Tautologies and absurdities play the same roles in the algebra of logical propositions as do the special elements 1 and 0, respectively, in abstract Boolean algebra.

THEOREM **2.24**   *For an arbitrary proposition p in B, $p \vee 0 \leftrightarrow p$ and $p \wedge 1 \leftrightarrow p$.*

Proof.   These results are established by the construction of truth tables for all possible cases (see Table 2.15).

TABLE 2.15

$p \vee 0 \leftrightarrow p$ and $p \wedge 1 \leftrightarrow p$

p	**0**	$p \vee 0$	**1**	$p \wedge 1$
1	0	1	1	1
0	0	0	1	0

As was pointed out earlier, the disjunction and conjunction connectives in the algebra of logical propositions are analogous to the binary operations of union and multiplication in abstract Boolean algebra. The results determined in the next two theorems show that these connectives also possess the properties of commutativity and associativity.

THEOREM **2.25**   *For arbitrary (but fixed) propositions p and q in B, $(p \vee q) \leftrightarrow (q \vee p)$ and $(p \wedge q) \leftrightarrow (q \wedge p)$.*

Proof. We establish these results by constructing truth tables for all $2^2 = 4$ possible ordered pairs of the symbols $\{0, 1\}$ (see Table 2.16).

TABLE 2.16

$(p \lor q) \leftrightarrow (q \lor p), (p \land q) \leftrightarrow (q \land p)$

p	q	$p \lor q$	$q \lor p$	$(p \lor q) \leftrightarrow (q \lor p)$	$p \land q$	$q \land p$	$(p \land q) \leftrightarrow (q \land p)$
1	1	1	1	1	1	1	1
1	0	1	1	1	0	0	1
0	1	1	1	1	0	0	1
0	0	0	0	1	0	0	1

THEOREM **2.26** *For arbitrary (but fixed) propositions p, q, and r in B,* $p \lor (q \lor r) \leftrightarrow (p \lor q) \lor r$ *and* $p \land (q \land r) \leftrightarrow (p \land q) \land r.$

Proof. The first of these results is verified by constructing a truth table for all $2^3 = 8$ possible ordered triples of the symbols $\{0, 1\}$ (see Table 2.17). The reader is requested to provide a similar proof of the second result (Problem 6(a), this section).

TABLE 2.17

$(p \lor q) \lor r \leftrightarrow p \lor (q \lor r)$

p	q	r	$p \lor q$	$q \lor r$	$(p \lor q) \lor r \leftrightarrow p \lor (q \lor r)$		
1	1	1	1	1	1	1	1
1	1	0	1	1	1	1	1
1	0	1	1	1	1	1	1
1	0	0	1	0	1	1	1
0	1	1	1	1	1	1	1
0	1	0	1	1	1	1	1
0	0	1	0	1	1	1	1
0	0	0	0	0	0	1	0

When the implication, $\rightarrow$, was introduced in Definition 2.9, it was pointed out that it could be expressed in terms of the basic connectives disjunction and negation. This relationship is established in the following theorem.

THEOREM **2.27** *For arbitrary (but fixed) propositions p and q in B,* $(p \rightarrow q) \leftrightarrow (p' \lor q).$

Proof. The theorem is established by the construction of a truth table for all possible ordered pairs of the symbols {0, 1}; see Table 2.18.

TABLE 2.18

$$(p \to q) \leftrightarrow (p' \lor q)$$

p	p'	q	$(p \to q)$	$\leftrightarrow$	$(p' \lor q)$
1	0	1	1	1	1
1	0	0	0	1	0
0	1	1	1	1	1
0	1	0	1	1	1

We conclude this section with a brief comparison of abstract Boolean algebra, set algebra, and propositional algebra.

TABLE 2.19

Comparison of Algebras

	Boolean Algebra	Set Algebra	Propositional Algebra
Operations Binary	∨ union · multiplication	∪ union ∩ intersection	∨ disjunction ∧ conjunction
Unary	′ complementation	′ complement	′ negation
Special elements	1 one 0 zero	U universal set ∅ empty set	**1** tautology **0** absurdity

PROBLEMS

1. Express each of the following sentences symbolically.
   (a) A prime number is either the integer 2 or it is an odd integer.
   (b) If n is an even integer, then $(n + 1)$ is an odd integer.
   (c) This is either an isosceles triangle or it is a right triangle.
   (d) A triangle is equilateral if and only if it is equiangular.
   (e) Either I shall toss a "head" or I shall toss a "tail," if the coin is fair.

(f) If $4x = 3$, then $x = 0.75$.

(g) The course is not difficult and the grades are not low.

(h) It was a cool afternoon and a find day for golf.

(i) It is not true that this course is difficult.

(j) Early to bed and early to rise makes Jack alert in his classes.

2. Let p be "The course is difficult" and q be "The grades are low." Write symbolically each of the following sentences.

   (a) If the course is difficult, the grades are low.

   (b) The course is not difficult, nor are the grades low.

   (c) The grades are not low, and the course is not difficult.

   (d) The course is not difficult, but the grades are low.

   (e) The grades are low, only if the course is difficult.

3. Construct a truth table for each of the statements in Problem 2.

4. Construct a truth table for each of the following.

   (a) $p' \vee (p \wedge q)$.   (f) $(p \vee q) \rightarrow p$.

   (b) $p' \wedge (p \vee q)$.   (g) $p' \vee p$.

   (c) $p \vee (p' \wedge q)$.   (h) $p \wedge p'$.

   (d) $(p \vee q) \wedge q'$.   (i) $p \wedge (p \rightarrow q)$.

   (e) $p' \rightarrow q$.

5. Construct truth tables for each of the following statements compounded from three propositions.

   (a) $(p \vee q) \wedge (p \vee r)$.   (d) $(p' \vee q') \wedge r$.

   (b) $(p' \vee q) \rightarrow r$.   (e) $p \rightarrow (q \vee r)$.

   (c) $p' \vee (q \wedge r)$.   (f) $p \wedge (q \rightarrow r)$.

6. Prove the following.

   (a) $p \wedge (q \wedge r) \leftrightarrow (p \wedge q) \wedge r$.

   (b) $p \vee (q \wedge r) \leftrightarrow (p \vee q) \wedge (p \vee r)$.

   (c) $p \wedge (q \vee r) \rightarrow (p \wedge q) \vee (p \wedge r)$.

   (d) $p \wedge p' \leftrightarrow \mathbf{0}$.

   (e) $p' \vee p \leftrightarrow \mathbf{1}$.

   (f) $p \wedge (p \vee q) \leftrightarrow p$.

   (g) $p \vee (p \wedge q) \leftrightarrow p$.

   (h) $(p \rightarrow q)' \leftrightarrow p \wedge q'$.

   (i) $(p')' \leftrightarrow p$.

   (j) $(p \vee q)' \leftrightarrow p' \wedge q'$.

   (k) $(p \wedge q)' \leftrightarrow p' \vee q'$.

   (l) $(p \rightarrow q) \leftrightarrow (q' \rightarrow p')$.

   (m) $\{[(p \rightarrow q) \wedge (q \rightarrow r)] \rightarrow (p \rightarrow r)\} \leftrightarrow \mathbf{1}$.

2.6 VALID ARGUMENTS

Mathematics is a deductive science and makes no assertions of absolute truth. Rather, a *body* of mathematics or a *mathematical system* consists of the following.

1. A set of *undefined elements*.

2. Certain *unproved propositions*, or *axioms* (not truths), that pertain to these elements and establish relationships among them.

3. A set of further *propositions*, or *theorems*, logically deduced from the axioms as premises.

4. A *mathematical argument*, or *proof*, that is the deductive process by which the conclusions are reached from the given premises.

In the discussion that follows we shall point out certain aspects of the problem of determining what constitutes a valid mathematical argument and demonstrate the use of symbolic logic in testing its validity. To this end we first state and prove certain rules or laws which lead to valid arguments.

THE LAW OF DETACHMENT. If a proposition p implies a proposition q and it is established that p is true, then it may be concluded that q is true.

On examination of Table 2.20 it is found that only in the first row of this table are both p and $p \rightarrow q$ true, and in this row q also is true.

TABLE 2.20

Truth Table for Implication $p \rightarrow q$

p	q	$p \rightarrow q$
1	1	1
1	0	0
0	1	1
0	0	1

THE LAW OF SUBSTITUTION. In a mathematical argument any proposition can be substituted for an equivalent one.

This follows immediately, since the validity of a mathematical argument depends on the truth values of the component propositions and not on the propositions themselves. Since equivalent propositions have identical truth values the validity of the argument will be unaffected by their interchange.

THE LAW OF THE EXCLUDED MIDDLE. If p is a logical proposition, then $(p \wedge p')$ is an absurdity.

This law states that a logical proposition cannot be true and false simultaneously (see Problem 6(d), Section 2.5).

THE LAW OF SYLLOGISM.   If p, q, and r are logical propositions, then $[(p \to q) \land (q \to r)] \to (p \to r)$ is a tautology.

This law is perhaps the one most often resorted to in deductive reasoning. It states that if a proposition p implies a proposition q and if, in turn, q implies a proposition r, then p implies r. Thus, this law is essentially a statement that *implication is transitive* (see Problem 6 (m), Section 2.5).

In every mathematical argument an implication $p \to q$ plays an essential role. If the components p and q of the conditional proposition are interchanged or negated in various ways, we obtain *derived implications* which may or may not be equivalent to the given proposition. The following occur most often and merit specific names. For the given implication $p \to q$:

(a) $q \to p$ is the *converse*.
(b) $p' \to q'$ is the *inverse*.
(c) $q' \to p'$ is the *contrapositive*.

A comparison of the truth values of the derived implications with those of the original (Table 2.21) shows that *only the contrapositive, $q' \to p'$, is equivalent to the given implication, $p \to q$.*

TABLE 2.21
Comparison of Derived Implications

p	q	$p \to q$	$q' \to p'$	$q \to p$	$p' \to q'$
1	1	1	1	1	1
1	0	0	0	1	1
0	1	1	1	0	0
0	0	1	1	1	1

The most common type of proof is the *direct* one, in which a chain of implications is constructed: $p_1 \to p_2$, $p_2 \to p_3, \ldots, p_{n-1} \to p_n$, $p_n \to r$. If the chain is unbroken and if the initial premise is true, then by repeated application of the laws of syllogism and of detachment the conclusion r is true.

ILLUSTRATION **2.4**

Given: (a) p is true.
       (b) $p \to q$ is true.
       (c) $r' \to q'$ is true.

Prove: r is true.

By the law of substitution we may replace the third premise by the
contrapositive, $(q')' \to (r')'$. Using the result of Problem 6 (i), Section 2.5,
we may write the latter implication as $q \to r$. The argument now becomes
$p \to q$, $q \to r$ and, because p is true, by the law of syllogism the conclusion r
is true. Hence, the argument is valid.

ILLUSTRATION **2.5**

> Given: (a) p is true.
> (b) $q \to p$ is true.
> (c) $q \to r$ is true.
>
> Prove: r is true.

To establish a chain of implications starting with the first premise and
ending with the conclusion, it is necessary to substitute $p \to q$ for the second
implication. However, $p \to q$ is the converse of $q \to p$ and *it has been
established* in Table 2.21 *that these implications are not equivalent.* Hence,
the argument is not valid and *r is not true.*

ILLUSTRATION **2.6**   Is the following a valid argument?

Premise 1: If girls are pretty, they are popular with the boys.
Premise 2: Intellectual girls are unpopular with the boys.
Conclusion: Pretty girls are not intellectual.

To determine whether or not the argument is valid, we set

> p: Girls are pretty.
> q: Girls are popular with the boys.
> r: Girls are intellectual.

The problem now becomes

> Given: (a) $p \to q$ assumed true.
> (b) $r \to q'$
> Prove: $p \to r'$

By the law of substitution we may replace Premise 2 by the contrapositive,
$q \to r'$, and by the law of syllogism we may conclude from $p \to q$, $q \to r'$ that
the argument is valid. We hasten to point out, however, that the conclusion
is *true* only if the premises are true.

ILLUSTRATION **2.7**   Determine whether or not the following is a valid
argument.

Premise 1: If Jones is registered to vote, he is at least 21 years old.
Premise 2: Jones is not registered.
Conclusion: Jones is not yet 21 years old.

We shall show that the conclusion *is not valid, based on the given premises.* We write

p: Jones is registered to vote.

q: Jones is at least 21 years old.

Given: (a) $p \rightarrow q$ is true.

(b) p' is true.

Prove: q' is true.

To introduce p' and q' into the argument, it is necessary to substitute the inverse, $p' \rightarrow q'$, for Premise 1. However, the argument and the conclusion are not valid, because $p' \rightarrow q'$ and $p \rightarrow q$ are not equivalent (see Table 2.21).

It sometimes happens that we cannot find a direct proof of a certain result. In such case we may be able to make use of an *indirect proof*, which has as its basis the fact that, when a logical propsition r' is false, the proposition r is true.

In an indirect proof of an argument that has the initial premise "p is true" and the conclusion "r is true," we begin by making the assumption that "r is false" or, equivalently, "r' is true." Then if an unbroken chain of implications leads to the result "p' is true," contradicting the initial assumption that "p is true," we may presume that "r is true."

ILLUSTRATION 2.8

Given: (a) p is true.

(b) $q \rightarrow p'$

(c) $r' \rightarrow q$

Prove: r is true.

A solution by indirect proof is as follows. Assume r' is true. Then,

from (c): $r' \rightarrow q$,

and from (b): $q \rightarrow p'$.

Therefore, p' is true, and p is false. This contradicts the initial assumption that p is true. Therefore, the assumption that r' is true is not correct, and hence r must be true.

Other methods of establishing the validity of an argument involve the use of truth tables or, if desired, direct application of the axioms and theorems of Boolean algebra. For, if q is a valid conclusion logically deducible from a set of premises p_k, where $k = 1, 2, \ldots, n$, then the logical function

$$f = p_1 \wedge p_2 \wedge \cdots \wedge p_n \rightarrow q$$

must be true for all possible truth values of the premises p_k and the conclusion q. That is to say, if the argument is valid, then f must be logically true and therefore a tautology.

For example, in Illustration 2.6 we were given premises $p \rightarrow q$ and $r \rightarrow q'$ and conclusion $p \rightarrow r'$. The validity of this argument was quite easily established by the law of syllogism, but the argument will serve as an adequate demonstration of the method described in the preceding paragraph. The truth table for the function $f = (p \rightarrow q) \wedge (r \rightarrow q') \rightarrow (p \rightarrow r')$ is determined for the equivalent form of f, namely

$$f = [(p \wedge q') \vee (r \wedge q)] \vee [p' \vee r'].$$

It should be noted that the fact that f is a tautology is established in column 10 of Table 2.22.

TABLE 2.22

$f = [(p \wedge q') \vee (r \wedge q)] \vee [(p' \vee r')] \leftrightarrow 1$

p	q	r	p'	q'	r'	$[(p \wedge q')$	$\vee$	$(r \wedge q)]$	$\vee$	$[p' \vee r']$
1	1	1	0	0	0	0	1	1	1	0
1	1	0	0	0	1	0	0	0	1	1
1	0	1	0	1	0	1	1	0	1	0
1	0	0	0	1	1	1	1	0	1	1
0	1	1	1	0	0	0	1	1	1	1
0	1	0	1	0	1	0	0	0	1	1
0	0	1	1	1	0	0	0	0	1	1
0	0	0	1	1	1	0	0	0	1	1

(1)	(2)	(3)	(4)	(5)	(6)	(7)	(8)	(9)	(10)	(11)

In the foregoing discussion the formal algebra of logical propositions and the concept of the validity of logical arguments have been introduced. The elements $p, q, r, \ldots$ of the set B of such an algebra were undefined simple statements or were compound propositions involving simple statements and the connectives $\vee$, $\wedge$, $\rightarrow$, etc.

Up to this point nothing has been said of what constitutes a simple statement, except that it is a declarative sentence free from ambiguity whose truth or falsity can be determined. Indeed, any detailed discussion of the construction of logical propositions is beyond the scope of this text. However, there is one small segment of this subject that is of particular interest, if we are to apply symbolic logic to mathematical arguments. This is the subject of *quantifiers*, those words or phrases in a proposition which tell "how many" of a certain set of things are to be considered.

We begin by noting the distinction that is made in mathematical arguments between an *equation of condition*, such as $3x - 2 = 4$, and an *identity*,
such as $(x - 2)^2 = x^2 - 4x + 4$. The former is a valid statement for only
the restricted set of values $x = 2$, whereas the latter is valid for all values of
the number x, both real and complex. In trigonometry, too, may be found
equations of the type which are valid for restricted sets of the argument,
for example, $\sin \theta = 1/2$. Specifically, the given equation is true for
$\theta = \pi/6 + 2n\pi$ and $\theta = 5\pi/6 + 2n\pi$, where n is any integer, and false
for all other values of θ. On the other hand, there are identities such as
$\sin^2 \theta + \cos^2 \theta = 1$, which are true for all values of θ.

In the one case the statement should read "There *exist* real numbers θ
such that $\sin \theta = 1/2$," meaning thereby that the proposition $\sin \theta = 1/2$ is
valid for a restricted set of values of θ. In the other case the statement should
read "For *all* real values of θ, $\sin^2 \theta + \cos^2 \theta = 1$."

The phrase "There exist ... such that" is called an *existential quantifier*.
The phrase "For all ... such that" is an example of a *universal quantifier*.
In many cases the quantifier is implicitly understood as existential or universal,
but in every case it is an essential part of a mathematical expression involving
variables.

Mathematical statements employing variables that are not specified are
classified as *propositional functions*. We cannot properly ask whether such
propositions are true or false, when they are not completely specified. Only
when x (or θ) is replaced by a specific number can the truth or falsity of a
propositional function be determined. A propositional function has but one
truth set, regardless of the variables used. In a real sense the variables
entering a propositional function play a role of place-holder and are a
convenience rather than a necessity.

Assuming that p is a propositional function which involves the argument
x, then the symbol $\exists_x p$ represents the *existential quantifier*. It is usually
read "There exists an x such that p" or "For some x, p" or, more precisely,
"For at least one x, p."

The *universal quantifier* is denoted by the symbol $\forall_x p$ and is usually
read, "For all x, p," or "For every x, p."

For example, if x and y represent real numbers, then:

$\exists_x (x \leqslant 5)$ is read "For some real number x not greater than 5."

$(\forall_x)(\forall_y)[(x + y)^2 = x^2 + 2xy + y^2]$ is read "For every pair of real
numbers x and y, $(x + y)^2 = x^2 + 2xy + y^2$."

$(\forall_x)(\exists_y)(x + 2y = 10)$ is read "For every x there exists a y such that
$x + 2y = 10$."

If $\exists_x p$ is translated "For some x, p," what meaning should be given to
the negation, $(\exists_x p)'$, of this quantified propositional function? Recalling
that the negation of a logical proposition is false when the proposition is

true and is true when the proposition is false, we must define $(\exists_x p)' \leftrightarrow \forall_x p'$.

For example, let x be a real number, and assume "p: The square of x is negative." Then we may write:

$\exists_x p$:   There exists a real number x whose square is negative,

$(\exists_x p)'$:   There exists no real number whose square is negative.

This last proposition is equivalent to the statement

$\forall_x p'$:   For all real numbers x, the square is positive, or, more smoothly,

$\forall_x p'$:   The square of every real number is positive.

Similarly, we define $(\forall_x p)' \leftrightarrow \exists_x p'$. This is easier to understand when it is looked at from the point of view of what is required to disprove a statement p which is supposed to be universally true, namely a *single* counterexample.

For example, let x be an odd integer and p be the propositional function "x is a prime number." Then, in order to disprove the quantified statement "$\forall_x p$: All odd integers are prime numbers," we need only to establish the existence of a single odd integer that is not a prime. That is to say, the statement "$(\forall_x p)'$: Not all odd integers are prime numbers" is equivalent to "$\exists_x p'$: There exists an odd integer that is not a prime number."

PROBLEMS

1. Examine the validity of the argument:
   (a) If the rod is spared, the child is spoiled.
   (b) The child is spoiled.
   Conclusion: The rod has been spared.

2. Examine the validity of the argument:
   (a) If the rod is spared, the child is spoiled.
   (b) The child is unspoiled.
   Conclusion: The rod has not been spared.

3. Given the following argument:
   (a) If the market is up, it is time to sell stocks.
   (b) If it is time to sell stocks, taxes are high.
   What logical conclusion is valid if we are given the additional premise that "taxes have been cut"? If we are given the premise that "the market is down"? What is the contrapositive of (a) and of (b)?

4. Is the conclusion valid for the following argument?
   (a) If beans are planted by the light of the moon, the crop will be heavy.
   (b) If there is a light crop of beans, the price of corn is high.
   Conclusion: If beans are planted by the light of the moon, the price of corn is low.

5. What are valid conclusions for the following three arguments?
   (a) When it snows, I get chilled.
   (b) Only when I get chilled will I get sick.
   (c_1) I got sick; (c_2) It snowed; (c_3) I did not get sick.

6. Given the premise "When a man marries, his troubles begin," what logical conclusions may be reached if we are given the further premises (b_1) "John Smith has no troubles" and (b_2) "John Smith is not married"?

7. Is the conclusion valid in the following argument:
   (a) If a set of points lies in one plane, the points are coplanar.
   (b) Two intersecting lines determine a plane.
   (c) A line is a set of points.
   Conclusion: The points of intersecting lines are coplanar.

8. What valid conclusion can be reached from the given statements?
   (a) A set of points is convex, if for every two points P and Q of S, the entire segment PQ lies in S.
   (b) The interior and boundary points of a circle form a convex set.
   (c) The radius of a circle is a line segment which joins the center of the circle to a boundary point.

9. Write in symbolic notation the following statements.
   (a) For every pair of nonzero real numbers a and b there exists a number y such that $ay = b$.
   (b) There exists a number x such that either $p(x)$ or $q(x)$.
   (c) There exists a number x such that either $p(x)$ for the number x or $q(y)$ for a number y.

10. Assume x, y, and z are nonzero real numbers. Translate each of the following symbolic statements into acceptable English.
    (a) $\forall_x[xx^{-1} = 1]$.
    (b) $\exists_y[yz = 1]$.
    (c) $\forall_y\forall_x[(xy = x) \rightarrow (y = 1)]$.
    (d) $\forall_x\forall_y\forall_z[(xy = 1) \wedge (xz = 1) \rightarrow (y = z)]$.

11. Form the negation of each of the following statements.
    (a) Every man's home is his castle.
    (b) There exists a number less than δ.
    (c) All real numbers are either even or odd.
    (d) There is at least one number whose absolute value is negative.
    (e) No man can live unto himself.

12. Prove that the following statement is false by giving a counterexample: "For n an integer and π a prime, $\forall_n[(n^2 - n + 41) \rightarrow \pi]$."

13. Determine the validity of the following argument.
    (a) If n is an arbitrary odd integer, then n can be written $2k + 1$, where k is an integer.
    (b) If two integers are equal, their squares are equal.
    (c) $n^2 = 4k^2 + 4k + 1$.
    Conclusion: The square of every odd integer is an odd integer.

14. Prove: If n^2 is an even integer, then n is an even integer. Use an indirect proof by assuming n is odd, and use the result of Problem 13 to obtain a contradiction.

2.7   BOOLEAN ALGEBRA AND ITS APPLICATION TO SWITCHING CIRCUITS

While it is not the objective of this section to explain the physical properties of a switching circuit, it does seem reasonable that we should make as clear as possible the general nature of such a device in order to show that Boolean algebra is a reasonably good mathematical model. An electric switch and an electromagnetic contact or relay are examples of what are referred to as *bistable* or *two-state devices*, that is, devices which are capable of being in either one of two *states*, "on" or "off," "opened" or "closed," "good" or "bad," and so on. Such devices are found in data-processing and communications systems, among others.

A switching circuit usually consists of conductors and switches connecting an *input* terminal, T_i, and an *output* terminal, T_o. From the point of view of *transmission* of current, if the *state* of a switch is "open," the circuit is broken and the flow of current is prevented. On the other hand, if the switch is in a "closed" state, current flows through the circuit.

For this discussion only two-terminal circuits with switches connected either in parallel or in series will be considered. More complex circuits, which might include cross-connecting paths between parallel paths of series elements, are known as bridge-type networks. Such networks can be analyzed by tracing all possible paths between the input and output terminals and can be transformed into a series-parallel system.

In Section 2.3 we discussed a very simple model of Boolean algebra consisting of just two elements, 0, and 1, subject to two binary operations, union ($\vee$) and multiplication ($\cdot$), defined by the tables

$\vee$	0	1
0	0	1
1	1	1

$\cdot$	0	1
0	0	0
1	0	1

In Sections 2.5 and 2.6 the application of Boolean algebra to two-valued logical propositions was developed. In this section we shall find a blending of these ideas, which yields a mathematical model of a switching circuit.

We consider a set $B = \{x, y, z, \ldots\}$ of undefined states of the switches or relays in an electric circuit. These $x, y, z, \ldots$, or circuit variables, as they are sometimes called, are each assigned the value 0 according as the switches X, Y, Z, $\ldots$, respectively, are open, and the value 1 when they are closed.

The simplest circuit is that consisting of two terminals, T_i and T_o, a conductor, and a single relay or switch, X (see Figure 2.1). In Table 2.23 we have an analysis of the figure.

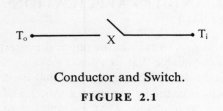

Conductor and Switch.

FIGURE 2.1

TABLE 2.23

Truth Table for x of Figure 2.1

x	Circuit
1	closed
0	open

There are four possible combinations of states of two switches X and Y. These are "X closed and Y open," "X open and Y closed," "both closed," and "both open." If the switches are connected in series (see Figure 2.2), then current will flow in the circuit only when both X and Y are closed. Upon examination of Table 2.24 it will be seen that this switching circuit has a truth table identical with that of the conjunction $x \cdot y$ of two Boolean elements x and y.

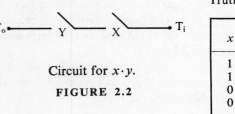

Circuit for $x \cdot y$.

FIGURE 2.2

TABLE 2.24

Truth Table for $x \cdot y$ of Figure 2.2

x	y	$x \cdot y$	Circuit
1	1	1	closed
1	0	0	open
0	1	0	open
0	0	0	open

Similarly, when two switches, X and Y, are connected in parallel (see Figure 2.3), there are four possible combinations of states of the switches.

Current flows when either switch, X or Y, is closed. This yields a truth table identical with that of the disjunction of states x and y, $x \lor y$ (see Table 2.25).

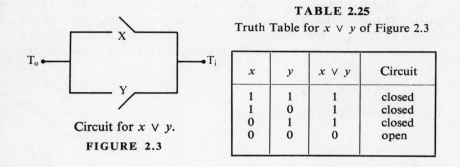

Circuit for $x \lor y$.

FIGURE 2.3

TABLE 2.25

Truth Table for $x \lor y$ of Figure 2.3

x	y	$x \lor y$	Circuit
1	1	1	closed
1	0	1	closed
0	1	1	closed
0	0	0	open

The unary operation of complementation in Boolean algebra (or negation in propositional algebra) is useful in electric circuits. Circuits can be so designed that the closing of one switch opens (or closes) one or more other switches. When the closing of switch X causes another switch to open, the second switch is denoted by $\overline{X}$. Then the statement "Switch X is in state x" implies the statement "Switch $\overline{X}$ is in state $\bar{x}$," where $\bar{x}$ is the complement of x (see Table 2.26).

TABLE 2.26

Complementation in Switching Circuit

x	$\bar{x}$	X	$\overline{X}$
1	0	closed	open
0	1	open	closed

An isomorphism can be established between the binary Boolean algebra, $\mathscr{B} = \{\{0, 1\}, \cdot, \lor\}$, and switching circuits thus:

Switches		Boolean Algebra
Open	$\leftrightarrow$	0
Closed	$\leftrightarrow$	1
In series	$\leftrightarrow$	$\cdot$
In parallel	$\leftrightarrow$	$\lor$

This means that the two systems, electric switching circuits on the one hand and Boolean algebra on the other, are abstractly identical.

ILLUSTRATION **2.9**   Show that the circuits (a) and (b) in Figure 2.4 are equivalent: that is, that they are open or closed for identical states of the switches X, Y, and Z. The circuit in (a) is a realization of the Boolean function $(x \vee y) \cdot z$. The circuit in (b) is a realization of $(x \cdot z) \vee (y \cdot z)$. By the distributive law we have

$$(x \vee y) \cdot z = (x \cdot z) \vee (y \cdot z).$$

Hence, the two circuits are equivalent.

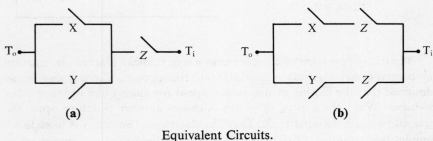

Equivalent Circuits.

FIGURE 2.4

ILLUSTRATION **2.10**   Show that the circuits in Figure 2.5, (a) and (b), are equivalent.

It should be clear that the circuit in (a) is closed or open whenever switch X is closed or open, respectively. That is, switch Y apparently is

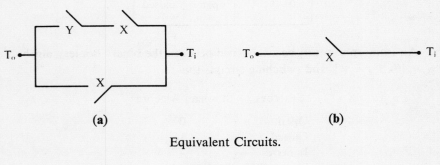

Equivalent Circuits.

FIGURE 2.5

superfluous. Hence, the circuit in (b), consisting of the single switch X, should be equivalent to the more complicated circuit in (a). Another way of showing that the circuits are equivalent is to establish the equality of their corresponding Boolean functions: that is, $(x \cdot y) \vee x = x$. This is easily verified by constructing the truth table (see Table 2.27).

TABLE 2.27

Truth Table for $(x \cdot y) \vee x = x$ of Figure 2.5

x	y	$(x \cdot y)$	$\vee$	x
1	1	1	1	1
1	0	0	1	1
0	1	0	0	0
0	0	0	0	0

ILLUSTRATION **2.11**   In a Boolean algebra there are two special elements, 0 and 1, characterized by certain axioms. What switching circuits correspond to the following Boolean equations: (a) $x \vee \bar{x} = 1$, (b) $x \cdot \bar{x} = 0$, (c) $0 \vee x = x$, (d) $1 \cdot x = x$?

(a) Essentially, the equation $x \vee \bar{x} = 1$ states that current is flowing at all times, since one of two switches in parallel is closed; see Figure 2.6 (a).

(b) The circuit corresponding to the equation $x \cdot \bar{x} = 0$ is always open and no current can flow, since one of the switches in series is always open; see Figure 2.6 (b).

(c) Because 0 indicates an open circuit, the equation $0 \vee x = x$ states that when a switch and an open circuit are placed in parallel, the resulting circuit is open or closed whenever the switch X is in that state; see Figure 2.6 (c).

(d) Here 1 designates a closed circuit, and the equation $1 \cdot x = x$ states that current flows or does not flow through the circuit as switch X is closed or open; see Figure 2.6 (d).

ILLUSTRATION **2.12**   Analyze the switching circuit in Figure 2.7.

As a first step in the analysis of the given circuit, we write the corresponding Boolean function of the states of the switches in the circuit:

$$f = [(x \cdot \bar{y}) \vee (\bar{x} \cdot y)] \cdot z.$$

The function indicates that z is in conjunction with a certain function of x and y. Because the conjunction has truth value 1 if and only if both components have truth value 1, the circuit is closed only when both $z = 1$ and

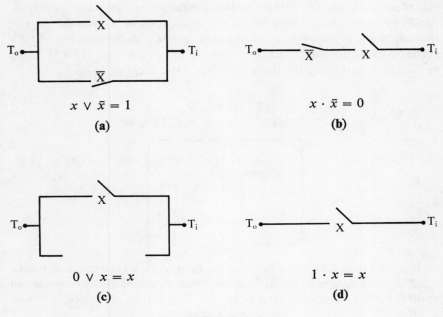

$$x \vee \bar{x} = 1$$

(a)

$$x \cdot \bar{x} = 0$$

(b)

$$0 \vee x = x$$

(c)

$$1 \cdot x = x$$

(d)

FIGURE 2.6

$(x \cdot \bar{y}) \vee (\bar{x} \cdot y) = 1$. Further investigation shows that in only two cases can current flow. They are given in Table 2.28.

Up to this point it has been demonstrated that a switching circuit may be represented by a Boolean function. The converse problem, that of designing a switching circuit with prescribed on-off characteristics, also can be solved by means of Boolean algebra.

Since every Boolean function has realization in a switching circuit, a

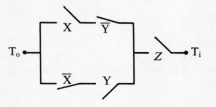

$$f = [(x \cdot \bar{y}) \vee (\bar{x} \cdot y)] \cdot z.$$

FIGURE 2.7

TABLE 2.28
Truth Table for Figure 2.7

x	y	z	$(x \cdot \bar{y})$	$\vee$	$(\bar{x} \cdot y)$	f
1	0	1	1	1	0	1
0	1	1	0	1	1	1

circuit is basically designed when a Boolean function can be constructed that has the value 1 when the circuit is closed and the value 0 when the circuit is open. Essentially, then, the mathematical problem reduces to that of constructing a Boolean function of a specified number of variables which has a given truth table.

A systematic procedure for the formulation of such a function is based on the truth values of the connectives, conjunction and disjunction:

(a) The conjunction has truth value 1 if and only if *every one* of its components has truth value 1.

(b) The disjunction has truth value 1 if *any one* of its components has truth value 1.

For the two states x and y the *basic conjunctions* are

$$x \cdot y, \qquad x \cdot \bar{y}, \qquad \bar{x} \cdot y, \qquad \bar{x} \cdot \bar{y}.$$

The importance of these conjunctions rests on the fact that each maps exactly one and only one of the ordered pairs $(1, 1)$, $(1, 0)$, $(0, 1)$, $(0, 0)$ into 1 and the remaining into 0 (see Table 2.29).

TABLE 2.29
Basic Conjunctions for Two States, x and y

x	y	$x \cdot y$	$x \cdot \bar{y}$	$\bar{x} \cdot y$	$\bar{x} \cdot \bar{y}$
1	1	1	0	0	0
1	0	0	1	0	0
0	1	0	0	1	0
0	0	0	0	0	1

If we form the disjunction of any number of these basic conjunctions, we get a Boolean function that has the value 1 only when one of the basic conjunctions has the value 1 and that has the value 0 otherwise.

For example, the function $f_1 = x \cdot y \vee \bar{x} \cdot \bar{y}$ has the value 1 for the states $(x, y) = (1, 1)$ and $(x, y) = (0, 0)$ and is 0 for all other possible states.

Accordingly, the corresponding circuit is closed if and only if *both* switches, X and Y, are closed or both are open; see Figure 2.8 (a).

On the other hand, if we wish to design a circuit with two switches, X and Y, that will be closed only when one switch is open and the other closed, the corresponding Boolean function is $f_2 = x \cdot \bar{y} \vee \bar{x} \cdot y$; see Figure 2.8 (b).

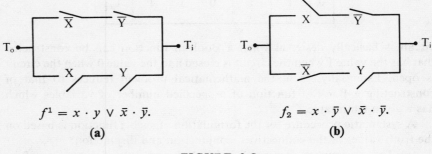

$$f^1 = x \cdot y \vee \bar{x} \cdot \bar{y}. \qquad\qquad f_2 = x \cdot \bar{y} \vee \bar{x} \cdot \bar{y}.$$

(a)   **(b)**

FIGURE 2.8

The following are basic conjunctions involving three states x, y, z. In each case only the ordered triple (x, y, z) that is mapped into 1 is given, since in each case the remaining seven ordered triples are all mapped into 0:

$x \cdot y \cdot z$ maps $(1, 1, 1)$ into 1 and all other possible states into 0

$x \cdot y \cdot \bar{z}$,, $(1, 1, 0)$,,   1   ,,   ,,   ,,   ,,   ,,   ,,   0

$x \cdot \bar{y} \cdot z$,, $(1, 0, 1)$,,   1   ,,   ,,   ,,   ,,   ,,   ,,   0

$x \cdot \bar{y} \cdot \bar{z}$,, $(1, 0, 0)$,,   1   ,,   ,,   ,,   ,,   ,,   ,,   0

$\bar{x} \cdot y \cdot z$,, $(0, 1, 1)$,,   1   ,,   ,,   ,,   ,,   ,,   ,,   0

$\bar{x} \cdot y \cdot \bar{z}$,, $(0, 1, 0)$,,   1   ,,   ,,   ,,   ,,   ,,   ,,   0

$\bar{x} \cdot \bar{y} \cdot z$,, $(0, 0, 1)$,,   1   ,,   ,,   ,,   ,,   ,,   ,,   0

$\bar{x} \cdot \bar{y} \cdot \bar{z}$,, $(0, 0, 0)$,,   1   ,,   ,,   ,,   ,,   ,,   ,,   0.

By forming the disjunction of any number of these basic conjunctions one can design a circuit that involves three switches, X, Y, and Z, and that will be closed for any specified combination of states x, y, and z. Although we have limited this discussion to the design of circuits involving either two or three switches, the method is general and can be extended to any finite number.

ILLUSTRATION **2.13** Design a switching circuit that will be closed when any two of three switches are closed.

We need to construct a Boolean function $f(x, y, z)$ that will map $(1, 1, 0)$, $(1, 0, 1)$, $(0, 1, 1)$ into 1 and all other states into 0. One such function is

$$f(x, y, z) = x \cdot y \cdot \bar{z} \vee x \cdot \bar{y} \cdot z \vee \bar{x} \cdot y \cdot z.$$

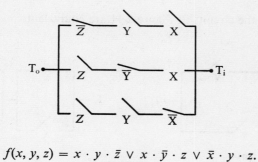

$$f(x, y, z) = x \cdot y \cdot \bar{z} \vee x \cdot \bar{y} \cdot z \vee \bar{x} \cdot y \cdot z.$$

FIGURE 2.9

The corresponding switching circuit is given in Figure 2.9.

PROBLEMS

1. Determine a Boolean function for each of the circuits given in Figure 2.10. Construct a truth table for each function, and state whether the circuit is open or closed for each possible combination of states of the switches.

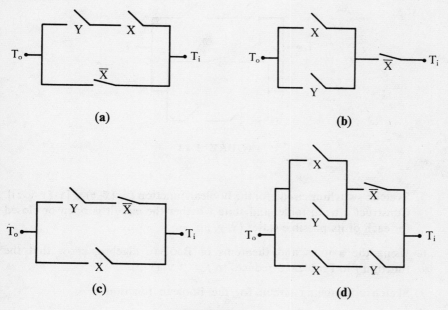

FIGURE 2.10

2. Show that the circuits in Figure 2.11 are equivalent.

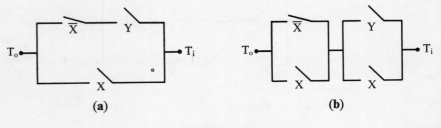

(a)   (b)

FIGURE 2.11

3. Recalling that $(p \to q) \leftrightarrow (p' \vee q)$, design a switching circuit for the conditional $p \to q$.

4. Determine a Boolean function for the circuit in Figure 2.12. Construct the corresponding truth table, and state whether the circuit is open or closed for each possible combination of states (x, y, z).

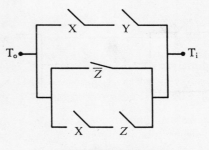

FIGURE 2.12

5. Sketch a switching circuit for the Boolean function $f = (\bar{x} \cdot y) \vee [x \cdot (y \vee z)]$. Construct a truth table, and state whether the circuit is open or closed for each of its possible states (x, y, z).

6. Using the axioms and theorems of Boolean algebra, show that the function f in Problem 5 reduces to $f = y \vee (x \cdot z)$.

7. Sketch a switching circuit for the Boolean function

$$f = x \vee (y \cdot z) \vee x \vee (\bar{x} \cdot y).$$

Construct its truth table, and state whether the circuit is open or closed for each of the possible combination of states (x, y, z).

8. Using the axioms and theorems of Boolean algebra, show that the function f in Problem 7 reduces to $f = x \lor y$. Sketch the equivalent circuit.

9. Construct two Boolean functions involving three states, x, y, and z, the first function to have the truth values listed in column (a) of Table 2.30, and the second to have truth values listed in column (b). Sketch the corresponding switching circuits.

TABLE 2.30

x	y	z	(a)	(b)
1	1	1	1	0
1	1	0	0	1
1	0	1	0	1
1	0	0	1	0
0	1	1	1	0
0	1	0	0	0
0	0	1	0	1
0	0	0	0	1

10. Show that the function $f = (x \cdot y \cdot z) \lor (x \cdot \bar{y} \cdot \bar{z}) \lor (\bar{x} \cdot y \cdot z)$ reduces to $f = (y \cdot z) \lor (x \cdot \bar{y} \cdot \bar{z})$. Sketch both circuits. Show that the circuits are closed for $(1, 1, 1)$, $(1, 0, 0)$, $(0, 1, 1)$ and for no other states of the switches.

11. Sketch a circuit connecting two switches, X and Y, with a light, L, in such a way that either switch controls the light independently of the other. Show that the truth table of such a circuit is that of Table 2.31. Write the corresponding Boolean function, and draw the circuit.

TABLE 2.31

x	y	L
1	1	1
1	0	0
0	1	0
0	0	1

Supplementary Reading

ALLENDOERFER, C. B., and C. O. OAKLEY, *Principles of Mathematics*, 2nd ed., McGraw-Hill, New York, 1965.

BIRKHOFF, G., and S. MAC LANE, *A Survey of Modern Algebra*, 3rd ed., Macmillan, New York, 1965.

HOHN, F. E., *Applied Boolean Algebra*, Macmillan, New York, 1960.

STOLL, R. R., *Sets, Logic, and Axiomatic Theories*, Freeman, San Francisco, 1961.

WHITSETT, J. E., *Boolean Algebra and Its Applications*, Addison-Wesley, Reading, Mass., 1961.

3

PROBABILITY

3.1 INTRODUCTION

Probability means many things to many people. Perhaps the most common definition evolves from a situation such as the following. Let us suppose that an experiment is conducted in the field or laboratory under controlled or standardized conditions. As the experiment progresses over a long period of time or is repeated under the same conditions many times, a certain phenomenon takes place. The person conducting the experiment is aware that there are certain *outcomes* that may occur, but because of the experience and information that have been accumulated he finds himself enabled to predict or calculate that some outcomes will be more likely to occur than others.

If, for example, a single coin is tossed five times in succession, no one can predict with certainty whether it will fall "heads up" or "tails up" on any particular toss. On the other hand, one feels intuitively that it is highly unlikely that it will fall heads up in all five tosses or even in four of the five tosses. Indeed, we are tempted to say that the *chance* of such an *event* occurring is very small. However, if a coin is tossed a thousand times or if a thousand coins are tossed at one time, we should not be surprised to find about five hundred heads and five hundred tails. That is, when a "fair" coin is tossed a great many times the laws of chance dictate that heads and tails should occur with about the same *frequency*. The mathematical aspects of the laws of chance are studied in the theory of probability.

The founders of the mathematical theory of probability were two French mathematicians of the seventeenth century, Pierre Fermat (1601–1665) and Blaise Pascal (1623–1662). Both these men are rated high in the mathematical fraternity for the great originality of their works. Fermat is also famous for his discoveries in the theory of numbers, and Pascal was a brilliant geometer who, before he was sixteen years old, had discovered and proved one of the most beautiful theorems in the whole range of geometry. (If a hexagon is inscribed in a conic, the points of intersection of opposite sides are collinear.)

Historically, the initial problem out of which the vast theory of probability grew was a gambling problem proposed to Pascal by a gambler, the Chevalier de Méré. The problem, in brief, was basically a question of how the stakes should be divided between two players in a game of chance if they decided to stop the game before it was finished. In the course of solving this rather simple problem, other challenging questions in probability and the laws of chance occurred to Pascal. Unable to solve some of them, he turned to his friend Fermat, and a very profitable correspondence arose which in time, resulted in some of the basic concepts of the theory of probability.

The theory that originated in a game of chance has become of great importance in the modern world. It is the mathematical foundation of all kinds of financial insurance and mathematical statistics. It finds application in many aspects of the biological and social sciences and in physics and engineering.

In the discussion that follows it will be found convenient to choose illustrations that use dice, cards, or coins. These are objects which with most of us are familiar and, besides, their probabilistic aspects are often reasonable to compute. Moreover, they provide good illustrations of the basic principles of the theory.

3.2 RELATIVE FREQUENCY

Suppose that a certain experiment consisted of throwing a die 1000 times in succession. Each time the die was thrown a record was made of the number of points that showed; 165 times the die showed 1 point, 172 times the die showed 2 points, and so on. Table 3.1 shows the results of this experiment, listing the ordered pairs (x, y), where $x \in \{1, 2, 3, 4, 5, 6\}$ and y is the recorded number of times the point x occurred in the experiment.

We shall call the elements x the *possible outcomes* of the experiment, and the second component y in the ordered pair (x, y) is called the *frequency* of the outcome. Had it been desirable, a record could have been made of the

TABLE 3.1

Frequency Table of Outcome x

x	1	2	3	4	5	6
y	165	172	167	171	167	158

frequency of the outcome occurring in the set $E_1 = \{2, 3, 4\}$, the set $E_2 = \{1, 3, 5\}$ (see Table 3.2), or any of the members of the power set of $U = \{1, 2, 3, 4, 5, 6\}$. In this way, the experiment determines a mapping called the *frequency mapping* on the power set of the universal set U. The range of this mapping is the set of positive and zero integers.

TABLE 3.2

Frequency Mapping of Events

E	E_1	E_2	$E_1 \cup E_2$	$\varnothing$	U
$f(E)$	510	499	842	0	1000

In probability theory we shall find it convenient to speak of the universal set—in this case the set of all possible outcomes of an experiment—as the *sample space* of the experiment. In the general theory of probability sample spaces that are infinite as well as those that are finite are considered. In this book *we shall limit the discussion to finite sample spaces*.

Returning to the experiment of throwing a die, we find the sample space in this case to be the set of points on the six faces of the die; that is, $U = \{1, 2, 3, 4, 5, 6\}$. The sample space associated with the experiment of drawing a card from a standard deck of playing cards is the set

$$U = \{A_c, K_c, \ldots, 2_c, A_d, K_d, \ldots, 2_d, A_h, K_h, \ldots, 2_h, A_s, K_s, \ldots, 2_s\}$$

of 52 elements corresponding to the 52 possible outcomes.

Each element in the sample space corresponds to a possible outcome of the experiment. The subsets of the sample space are called *events*, and we say that the *event E occurs* if the outcome of the experiment corresponds to an element in E. For example, if the experiment is to throw an *even* point with a die, the possible outcomes for a *success* belong to the event $E_1 = \{2, 4, 6\}$

while the possible outcomes for a *failure* belong to the event $E_2 = \{1, 3, 5\}$. Hence, if an even point is thrown, we say that E_1 occurs.

If the experiment is that of drawing an ace from a standard deck of playing cards, then the event $E_1 = \{A_c, A_d, A_h, A_s\}$, whose elements correspond to the four aces in the deck, occurs if the experiment is a success. Similarly, if the experiment is to draw a spade, the event $E_2 = \{A_s, K_s, \ldots, 2_s\}$, with elements corresponding to the 13 spades in the deck, occurs if a spade is drawn. On the other hand, if the experiment is to draw the ace of spades from the deck, the favorable event containing this outcome is the singleton $\{A_s\}$, consisting of the single element A_s which corresponds to the ace of spades. Clearly, the event $\{A_s\}$ is the intersection of events E_1 and E_2, and we write $\{A_s\} = E_1 \cap E_2$.

It sometimes happens that two events, say E_i and E_j, do not have a possible outcome in common; that is, $E_i \cap E_j = \varnothing$. For this reason, it seems appropriate to define *the image of the empty set $\varnothing$ in the frequency mapping as zero* (see Table 3.2).

In the problem shown in Table 3.2 the frequency of the event $E_1 = \{2, 3, 4\}$ is 510 and that of $E_2 = \{1, 3, 5\}$ is 499. The frequency of $E_1 \cup E_2 = \{1, 2, 3, 4, 5\}$ is 842. Clearly, this frequency is *not* equal to the sum of the frequencies of E_1 and E_2, which is $510 + 499 = 1009$. In this case, we can say with certainty that the set mapping that we have defined as the frequency mapping is *not additive*. The discrepancy is caused by the fact that the two events in question have an outcome in common, the point 3 occurring in both E_1 and E_2. Hence, when the frequencies of these two events are added, the frequency of their intersection, $E_1 \cap E_2 = \{3\}$, is counted twice. The correct result can be obtained by subtracting this frequency, which is 167, from the sum of the frequencies. Thus,

$$f[E_1 \cup E_2] = f(E_1) + f(E_2) - f(E_1 \cap E_2)$$
$$= 510 + 499 - 167$$
$$= 842.$$

The *relative frequency of an event E* is defined as

$$\frac{f(E)}{f(U)} = \frac{\text{frequency of the event}}{\text{frequency of the sample space}}.$$

In the problem of 1000 throws of a die, $f(E_1) = 510$ and $f(U) = 1000$. That is, the frequency of the event $E_1 = \{2, 3, 4\}$, in which the point 2 or the point 3 or the point 4 occurs, is 510, and the frequency of $U = \{1, 2, 3, 4, 5, 6\}$ is 1000, the latter event occurring each time the die is thrown. Therefore, $f(E_1)/f(U) = 510/1000 = 0.510$. Similarly, $f(E_2)/f(U) = 499/1000 = 0.499$.

If the experiment of throwing a die were repeated with the same total number of throws, the frequency mappings of the various events would probably differ from the first experiment. Nevertheless, experience shows that if a sequence of similar experiments is continued over a long period, the relative frequency corresponding to any given event E tends to become stable. This empirical result, the relative frequency of an event, finds a counterpart in the mathematical theory of probability. It is called the *probability measure* or, simply, the *probability of an event*. In the next section we begin a study of this mathematical model.

PROBLEMS

1. What is the relative frequency of $\varnothing$? Of U?

2. Show that in the die experiment

$$\frac{f(\{1\}) + f(\{2\}) + f(\{3\}) + f(\{4\}) + f(\{5\}) + f(\{6\})}{f(U)} = 1.$$

3. Show that, if $E_1 = \{1, 2\}$ and $E_2 = \{5, 6\}$ in the die experiment, then $f(E_1) + f(E_2) = f(E_1 \cup E_2)$.

4. Let $E = \{1, 3, 5\}$. What is $\bar{E}$? Show that the relative frequency of $\bar{E}$ is equal to 1 minus the relative frequency of E.

5. If a pair of coins were tossed a thousand times, would you expect the event {head, tail} to have the same relative frequency or a larger relative frequency than the event {head, head}? Give a reason for your answer. If a large number of tosses were made, which figure—25%, 30%, 40%, 50%—would come closest to your estimation of the relative frequency?

6. In an experiment consisting of drawing from a deck of cards, determine the following events:
   (a) The card to be drawn is either a king or a queen.
   (b) The card to be drawn is a diamond.
   (c) The card to be drawn is either the king or the queen of diamonds.
   (d) The card to be drawn is the king of diamonds.

7. Each of twenty-six cards, all appearing identical in size and color, has printed on one side one of the letters of the English alphabet. Assume that there are no duplicates and that the cards are drawn at random, and determine the following events:
   (a) The sample space of the experiment.
   (b) The card to be drawn is a vowel.
   (c) The card to be drawn is a consonant.
   (d) The card to be drawn is the letter Z.

8. Of 100 shots fired at a target, a marksman scores:

> 35 hits in region 1
> 28 hits in region 2
> 12 hits in region 3
> 10 hits in region 4
> 8 hits in region 5
> 7 hits in region 6

Determine the relative frequencies of each event.

9. According to Mendelian inheritance, offspring of a certain crossing should be colored roan, black, or white in the ratios $9:3:4$. By actual experiment, 72, 33, and 39 offspring fell in the respective categories. How do the relative frequencies compare with the theoretical values?

3.3 PROBABILITY MEASURE

In the preceding sections we have outlined how chance enters into certain experiments. Certain outcomes occur with *frequencies* that seem to indicate that there are laws of chance that may be arrived at inductively. The mathematical theory of probability is the mathematician's attempt to create a model of this phenomenon that will allow him to arrive at other conclusions by logical deduction.

This theory begins with the universal set, or *sample space*, U, which is the mathematical counterpart of the experiment and consists of the totality of all possible outcomes of the experiment.

For example, if the experiment consists of drawing a card from a standard deck of playing cards, then $U = \{x_1, x_2, \ldots, x_{52}\}$, where x_i represents one and only one of the 52 cards in the deck. If the experiment consists of tossing a coin, then $U = \{h, t\}$, where "h" and "t" stand for heads and tails, respectively. On the other hand, if the experiment consists of tossing two coins and the one is to be distinguished from the other the sample space is written

$$U = \{(H, h), (H, t), (T, h), (T, t)\}.$$

Similarly, if a pair of dice, one red and the other green, is thrown, the sample space consists of 36 outcomes,

$$U = \begin{Bmatrix} (1,1), (1,2), (1,3), (1,4), (1,5), (1,6) \\ (2,1), (2,2), (2,3), (2,4), (2,5), (2,6) \\ (3,1), (3,2), (3,3), (3,4), (3,5), (3,6) \\ (4,1), (4,2), (4,3), (4,4), (4,5), (4,6) \\ (5,1), (5,2), (5,3), (5,4), (5,5), (5,6) \\ (6,1), (6,2), (6,3), (6,4), (6,5), (6,6) \end{Bmatrix},$$

where in each ordered pair (i, j) the point i was made on the red die and the point j on the green.

If an experiment in genetics involves a certain set $\{a_1, a_2, \ldots, a_n\}$ of alleles, and if we are interested in the number m of genotypes at a given locus of the individuals of the parent generation, the sample space is written

$$U = \{\{a_{i_1}, a_{j_1}\}, \{a_{i_2}, a_{j_2}\}, \ldots, \{a_{i_m}, a_{j_m}\}\},$$

where the braces around each a_i, a_j indicate that only the *particular pair of alleles is important, not their order.*

Any subset of the sample space is an *event*. Since subsets range from the empty set $\varnothing$ through the universal set U, it is clear that we may speak of an event $\varnothing$ that is vacuous and define it as *an event that has no possible outcomes.* The sample space U is a *certain event* since every possible outcome occurs in this event. By a *simple event*, a *singleton*, we shall mean a subset $\{x_i\}$ of U containing only one possible outcome.

For example, if the experiment is that of throwing a die, the sample space is $U = \{1, 2, 3, 4, 5, 6\}$, in which the possible outcomes are the points on the top face of the die. The simple events are $\{1\}, \{2\}, \ldots, \{6\}$. The event $E_1 = \{2, 4, 6\}$ is not a simple event but is the union of the three simple events: $\{2\} \cup \{4\} \cup \{6\}$. If the event is "throw an even point," then $E_1 = \{2, 4, 6\}$ is the event. If the event is "throw a point less than or equal to 4," then $E_2 = \{1, 2, 3, 4\}$ is the event. If the event is "throw an even point less than or equal to 4," then we write $E_1 \cap E_2 = \{2, 4\}$.

Probability measure is the mathematical model of relative frequency. It is defined as follows:

DEFINITION **3.1** (Probability Measure)   Let $U = \{x_1, x_2, \ldots, x_n\}$ be a finite sample space. To each simple event $\{x_i\}$ we assign a number $p(\{x_i\})$, called the *probability of the simple event* $\{x_i\}$. These numbers, or probabilities, are arbitrary, subject to the conditions

(a) $p(\{x_i\}) \geqslant 0$,
(b) $p(\{x_1\}) + p(\{x_2\}) + \cdots + p(\{x_n\}) = 1$.

Having defined the probability of a *simple* event, we make the natural extension of this concept to that of the union of several simple events, $\{x_i\}$.

DEFINITION **3.2** (Probability of Event)   Let $E = \{x_1, x_2, \ldots, x_k\}$ be an event with possible outcomes $x_1, x_2, \ldots, x_k$; then the *probability of the event* E is:

(a) $p(E) = p(\{x_1\}) + p(\{x_2\}) + \cdots + p(\{x_k\})$
(b) $p(\varnothing) = 0$.

ILLUSTRATION **3.1**   Let $U = \{(H, h), (H, t), (T, h), (T, t)\}$ be the set of all possible outcomes of tossing two coins. The outcomes x_i of Definition 3.1

are the ordered pairs (H, h), (H, t), and so on. The probabilities that we assign are based on the assumption that the coins are "fair," that there is no bias favoring either side of either of them. Since there are 4 "equally likely" outcomes, we have $p(x_i) = \frac{1}{4}$. The event of getting at least one head is $E_1 = \{(H, h), (H, t), (T, h)\}$, and the probability of getting at least one head, on the assumption that the coins are fair, is $p(E_1) = \frac{1}{4} + \frac{1}{4} + \frac{1}{4} = \frac{3}{4}$. The probability of getting a head on the "first" coin is

$$p(E_2) = p\{(H, h), (H, t)\} = \frac{1}{4} + \frac{1}{4} = \frac{1}{2}.$$

The probability of getting no heads is

$$p(\bar{E}_1) = p(U - E_1) = p\{(T, t)\} = \frac{1}{4}.$$

ILLUSTRATION **3.2** If 2 coins are tossed and we do not distinguish between the coins, so that the order is not taken into consideration, we then write as the sample space, $U = \{\{h, h\}, \{h, t\}, \{t, t\}\}$. Thus, the outcomes x_i are no longer ordered pairs but are sets $\{h, h\}, \{h, t\}, \{t, t\}$. In an actual experiment of tossing a pair of coins the frequency table would be constructed by "lumping" together the head-tail cases. In all likelihood we should find the frequency of this outcome about twice that of the head-head and tail-tail cases. Hence, we assign the probabilities $p(\{h, h\}) = \frac{1}{4}$, $p(\{h, t\}) = \frac{1}{2}$, and $p(\{t, t\}) = \frac{1}{4}$.

We shall define the *probability space* of an experiment as the combination of the sample space and the probabilities assigned to the simple events of the sample space.

Suppose in the experiment of Illustration 3.2 the observer concludes from the frequency table that the three cases $\{h, h\}, \{h, t\}, \{t, t\}$, are equally likely. Then the probabilities of the single event involving at least one head would be chosen $p(\{h, t\}) = \frac{1}{3} = p(\{h, h\})$ and, as a consequence, the probability of the event "at least one coin falling head up when two are tossed" is $p(\{h, t\}) + p(\{h, h\}) = \frac{1}{3} + \frac{1}{3} = \frac{2}{3}$, whereas the probability of the same event is $\frac{3}{4}$, according to the computation in Illustration 3.1. This simple example demonstrates the necessity for stating *exactly what* probability space is being used for the computation of the probability of a given event. Although the probability of a particular event will be the same for all observers using the same probability space, it is important to keep in mind that the assignment of probabilities to single events is in theory quite arbitrary and subject to just two conditions:

(a) The probabilities must be nonnegative.

(b) The sum of the probabilities must be 1.

A list of some expressions common in probability theory and the corresponding set theory notation are given in Table 3.3.

TABLE 3.3

A Glossary of Probability Expressions and Set Notation

Probability Theory	Set Theory
All possible outcomes	$\{x \mid x \in U\}$
x is a possible outcome	$x \in U$
E is an event	$E \subseteq U$
E is an event that must occur	$E = U$
E is an impossible event	$E = \varnothing$
Outcome x occurs in event E	$x \in E$
Outcome x occurs in event A or B	$x \in A \cup B$
Outcome x occurs in events A and B	$x \in A \cap B$
Events A and B are incompatible or mutually exclusive	$A \cap B = \varnothing$
The event that occurs when E does not	$\bar{E}$
If event B occurs, then event A occurs	$B \subseteq A$

The following theorems are logically deduced from the basic definitions and axioms of probability theory and of set theory.

THEOREM **3.1**   *The probability of the sample space is* 1.

Proof.   By definition, the sample space $U = \{x_1, x_2, \ldots, x_n\}$ contains all of the possible outcomes, x_i. By Definition 3.2,

$$p(U) = p(\{x_1\}) + p(\{x_2\}) + \cdots + p(\{x_n\}).$$

The right side of this equation is equal to 1, by Definition 3.1. Therefore, the theorem is proved.

THEOREM **3.2**   *If A and B are incompatible events, then*

$$p(A \cup B) = p(A) + p(B).$$

Proof.   Since A and B are incompatible, $A \cap B = \varnothing$. Set $A = \{x_1, \ldots, x_r\}$ and $B = \{y_1, \ldots, y_s\}$, where $x_i \neq y_j$ for all $i = 1, \ldots, r$ and $j = 1, \ldots, s$. Then

$$p(A) = p(\{x_1\}) + \cdots + p(\{x_r\})$$
$$p(B) = p(\{y_1\}) + \cdots + p(\{y_s\})$$

$$A \cup B = \{x_1, \ldots, x_r, y_1, \ldots, y_s\}.$$

$$\therefore \; p(A \cup B) = p(\{x_1\}) + \cdots + p(\{x_r\}) + p(\{y_1\}) + \cdots + p(\{y_s\})$$
$$= p(A) + p(B).$$

Theorem 3.2 can be extended to the case of r events that are incompatible in pairs, Theorem 3.3. The reader is requested to give a proof of this theorem.

THEOREM **3.3** *If $E_1, E_2, \ldots, E_r$ are events that are incompatible in pairs, then*
$$p(E_1 \cup E_2 \cup \cdots \cup E_r) = p(E_1) + p(E_2) + \cdots + p(E_r).$$

THEOREM **3.4** *If A and B are not incompatible events, then*
$$p(A \cup B) = p(A) + p(B) - p(A \cap B).$$

Proof.   Write $A = A_1 \cup (A \cap B)$ and $B = B_1 \cup (A \cap B)$; then
$$A \cup B = A_1 \cup (A \cap B) \cup B_1.$$
By Theorem 3.3,
$$p(A \cup B) = p(A_1) + p(A \cap B) + p(B_1)$$
$$p(A) = p(A_1) + p(A \cap B)$$
$$p(B) = p(B_1) + p(A \cap B)$$
$$p(A) + p(B) = p(A_1) + p(B_1) + 2p(A \cap B)$$
$$\therefore \ p(A \cup B) = p(A) + p(B) - p(A \cap B).$$

THEOREM **3.5** *The probability of a given event not occurring is 1 minus the probability that it will occur.*

Proof.   Let E be the event; then $\bar{E}$ is the event that occurs when E does not occur. From the theory of sets, $\bar{E} \cup E = U$. Since $\bar{E} \cap E = \varnothing$, we have by Theorem 3.2
$$p(\bar{E} \cup E) = p(\bar{E}) + p(E) = p(U)$$
$$\therefore \ p(\bar{E}) + p(E) = 1$$
$$p(\bar{E}) = 1 - p(E).$$

PROBLEMS

1. Express each of the following in set theory notation.
    (a) Both events A and B occur.
    (b) Event A occurs, but B does not.
    (c) If A occurs, then B occurs.
    (d) If A occurs, then B does not occur.
    (e) None of the events A, B, C occurs.
    (f) Only A occurs among the events A, B, C.
    (g) Exactly one of the events A, B, C, occurs.

2. Six plots of ground, plots A to F, are available, of which three are to be selected at *random*; that is, we shall agree to assign equal probabilities to each simple event {A}, {B}, ..., {F}, the selection of one of the plots.
    (a) Write out the sample space.

(b) How many outcomes in which one of the plots is plot A does the event have?

(c) What is the probability that one of the plots selected will be A?

(d) What is the probability that plots A and B will be selected?

(e) What is the probability that plots A, B, and C will be selected?

3. A letter of the English alphabet is selected at random. Find the probability that the letter selected
   (a) is a consonant.
   (b) is a vowel.
   (c) precedes "h" in the alphabet.
   (d) precedes "h" and is a vowel.

4. Suppose a red die and a green die are thrown. Find the probability of the following events, assuming that the simple events have equal probabilities.
   (a) The sum of the points is 5.
   (b) The sum of the points is not 5.
   (c) The sum of the points is less than 5.
   (d) One die is 6 and the other is less than 4.

5. If three coins are tossed, what is the probability of getting the following events, assuming equal probabilities for all the simple events?
   (a) Exactly one head.
   (b) At least one head.
   (c) Exactly two heads.
   (d) No more than two heads.
   (e) At least two heads.
   (f) No tails.

6. (a) An urn contains four marbles uniform in size and colored red, green, blue, and yellow, respectively. A sample of three marbles is drawn from the urn. Determine the sample space and the probability of a simple event.

   (b) The three marbles are drawn from the urn in succession and without replacement. Determine the sample space and the probability that the red marble will be drawn first.

   (c) Same experiment as (b). Find the probability that the marbles will be drawn red first and green second.

7. A box contains four plastic discs, identical in size and shape and printed with the numbers 1, 5, 10, and 25, respectively. A pair of discs is drawn from the box.

   (a) Determine the sample space and the probability of each simple event.

(b) Determine the probability that the sum of the numbers on the two discs drawn is less than 20.

(c) Determine the probability that the sum of the numbers on the two discs is divisible by 15.

(d) Determine the probability that the sum of the numbers on the discs is divisible by 5.

(e) Determine the probability that the sum of the numbers on the two discs is even.

8. In an experiment a coin is tossed twice, and the probability of the event $E = \{(h, h)\ (h, t),\ (t, h)\}$ is determined as $p(E) = p\{(h, h)\} + p\{(h, t)\} + p\{(t, h)\} = 1 + 0 + 0 = 1$. Is this a "correct" solution to the problem? If so, what reason could be given for choosing these probabilities?

9. In an experiment consisting of throwing a single die which is not uniform, it is known that the probability that a given face will come up is proportional to the number of points on the face.
(a) Find the probability of each simple event in the sample space.
(b) Find the probability that a single throw will be even.
(c) Find the probability that a single throw will be odd.
(d) Find the probability that a single throw will not be 1 or 3.

10. A meteorologist predicts four types of weather for a given week end: fair, cloudy, rain, and sleet. If cloudy, rainy, and sleety weather are equally likely, but cloudy is twice as likely as fair, what is the probability of each simple event?

3.4 CONDITIONAL PROBABILITY

It has been mentioned that the probability space of a given experiment may differ from observer to observer. Actually, for the probability of an event to be discussed intelligently the conditions of the problem must be defined very precisely. Thus, in a real sense the probability is conditional on the probability space under consideration. It is not realistic to speak of unconditional probabilities. However, there is another way in which the probability of an event A might be interpreted as conditional. This exists when the sample space of event A is altered because of the occurrence of event B. The probability is said to be *conditional probability* in this case.

To illustrate this idea, let us consider again the experiment of drawing a single card from a deck of 52 playing cards. We are interested in the event $A = \{A_s\}$ consisting of the single outcome, the ace of spades. Since we may assume that there are 52 equally likely possible outcomes, we have $p(A) = 1/52$.

Suppose a card is drawn, and we are informed by an observer that it is a spade. How does this information alter the probability of event A? Clearly, since event $B = \{A_s, K_s, \ldots, 2_s\}$ has occurred, the outcomes in the event $\bar{B} = U - B$ are no longer possible. Hence, the sample space has changed from 52 playing cards to 13 spades. Therefore, we *must compute the probability of event A relative to the new sample space*, B, and we write $p(A \mid B) = 1/13$.

In the general situation we consider an experiment with a given sample space U together with a set of probabilities consistent with the requirements of Definition 3.1. Assuming that A is the particular event we are interested in, we compute the probability $p(A)$ by adding the probabilities of the simple events whose union is A. Since $p(U) = 1$ and $A \cap U = A$, we may write

$$p(A) = \frac{p(A \cap U)}{p(U)}.$$

That is, the *probability of event A is the ratio of the part of A that is included in U to the probability of U.*

If we are told that event B has occurred, then outcomes corresponding to $\bar{B} = U - B$ are no longer possible. Thus, the additional information regarding the possible outcomes of the experiment dictates that event B, which now contains *all* the possible outcomes, replaces U as the sample space and that the probability of event A must be revised to accord with this new sample space B. If we denote the revised probability by $p(A \mid B)$, we have $p(A \mid B) = p(A \cap B)/p(B)$ provided $p(B) > 0$. Thus we are led to the following definition.

DEFINITION 3.3 (Conditional Probability)   If A and B are events and if $p(B) > 0$, then the *conditional probability of the occurrence of A given the occurrence of B* is

$$p(A \mid B) = \frac{p(A \cap B)}{p(B)}.$$

ILLUSTRATION 3.3   Suppose two plants manufacture radios sold under the trade name of a certain chain store. Plant A manufactures 60% of these radios and Plant B manufactures 40% of them. At plant A, 85 out of every 100 are rated standard or better, but at plant B only 70 out of every 100 are given this rating. We are interested in the following questions:

(a) What is the probability of a consumer's obtaining a standard-quality radio from the chain store?

(b) What is the corresponding probability if it is learned that at the time of purchase all came from plant A? That all came from plant B?

(c) What is the probability that the radio purchased came from plant A?

What is the probability that it came from plant A if it has been established that the radio is of standard quality?

The problems are solved as follows.

(a) Out of every 100 radios purchased by the chain store

$$0.60 \times 85 = 51 \text{ come from plant A and are standard,}$$
$$0.40 \times 70 = 28 \text{ come from plant B and are standard,}$$
$$\overline{}$$
$$79 \text{ out of 100 are standard.}$$

Let S be the event "The radio purchased at the store is standard." Let S_A be the event "The radio is standard and came from plant A." Let S_B be the event "The radio is standard and came from plant B." Then we have the following probabilities:

$$p(S_A) = 51/100, \qquad p(S_B) = 28/100,$$
$$p(S) = p(S_A \cup S_B) = p(S_A) + p(S_B)$$
$$= 51/100 + 28/100 = 79/100.$$

(b) If all the radios at the time of purchase came from plant A, then, since 85 out of 100 radios manufactured at plant A are standard, we have

$$p(S) = p(S_A) = 85/100.$$

(c) Let E be the event "The radio purchased came from plant A." Let S be the event "The radio purchased at the store is standard." Then we have the following probabilities:

$$p(E) = 60/100 = 0.6,$$
$$p(E \mid S) = \frac{p(E \cap S)}{p(S)} = \frac{51/100}{79/100} = 51/79 = 0.65.$$

ILLUSTRATION **3.4**   On a certain floor of a dormitory it is found that

40 students take		mathematics,
35	,,	,, English,
30	,,	,, biology,
10	,,	,, mathematics and biology,
20	,,	,, mathematics and English,
15	,,	,, biology and English,
5	,,	,, mathematics, English, and biology.

(a) What is the probability that a student picked at random is taking mathematics only?

(b) What is the probability that a student is taking either biology or mathematics?

(c) What is the probability that a student picked at random is taking mathematics if it is known that he is taking biology?

(d) What is the probability that a student picked at random is taking mathematics if it is known that he is taking English?

The easiest way to sort out the students is to construct a Venn diagram consisting of three circles, as shown in Figure 3.1. Circle M corresponds to the event "students taking mathematics," circle E corresponds to the event "students taking English," and circle B corresponds to the event "students taking biology." Working from the given data, we find, in the order indicated,

$M \cap B \cap E$ (students taking all subjects)		5
$M \cap B \cap E'$ (math–biology but not English)	$10 - 5$	$= 5$
$M \cap B' \cap E$ (math–English but not biology)	$20 - 5$	$= 15$
$M' \cap B \cap E$ (biology–English but not math)	$15 - 5$	$= 10$
$M' \cap B' \cap E$ (only English)	$35 - 30$	$= 5$
$M \cap B' \cap E'$ (only mathematics)	$40 - 25$	$= 15$
$M' \cap B \cap E'$ (only biology)	$30 - 20$	$= 10$

Sample space (total number of students)   65

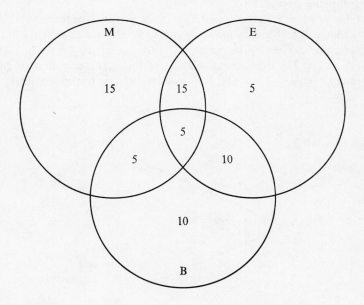

Students Taking Mathematics, Biology, and English.

FIGURE 3.1

(a) $p(M \cap B' \cap E') = 15/65 = 3/13$.

(b) $p(M \cap B) = 1 - p(M' \cap B' \cap E)$
$= 1 - 5/65 = 60/65 = 12/13$.

(c) $p(M \cap B' \cap E' \mid B) = \dfrac{p(M \cap B)}{p(B)} = \dfrac{10/65}{30/65} = 1/3$.

(d) $p(M \cap B' \cap E' \mid E) = \dfrac{p(M \cap E)}{p(E)} = \dfrac{20/65}{35/65} = 4/7$.

The equation in Definition 3.3, conditional probability, yields a formula for computing the probability of the intersection of two events, A and B:

$$p(A \cap B) = p(A) \cdot p(B \mid A) = p(B) \cdot p(A \mid B). \tag{3.1}$$

Often problems involving conditional probabilities are most conveniently solved by considering the compound situation as another event. Probabilities that arise at various stages of a complex experiment may be conveniently summarized by means of a device called a *tree diagram*, which is discussed in the following paragraphs.

Let us assume an experiment involving possible outcomes which, for reasons that will be obvious as we proceed, we classify as *primary outcomes*, x_1 and x_2, and *secondary outcomes*, x_{1j} and x_{2k}, where $j = 1, 2, \ldots, m$ and $k = 1, 2, \ldots, n$. The experiment consists of the occurrence first of either of the primary events $\{x_1\}$ and $\{x_2\}$ followed by any one of the secondary events

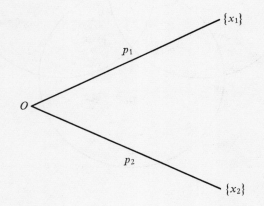

Primary Branches of Tree Diagram.

FIGURE 3.2

$\{x_{1j}\}$ and $\{x_{2k}\}$, where $\{x_{1j}\}$ is a conditional event dependent upon the occurrence of $\{x_1\}$ and $\{x_{2k}\}$ is a conditional event dependent upon the occurrence of $\{x_2\}$. By Equation 3.1, the probability that both events $\{x_1\}$ and $\{x_{1j}\}$ occur is

$$p(\{x_1\} \cap \{x_{1j}\}) = p\{x_1\} \cdot p(\{x_{1j}\} \mid \{x_1\}).$$

But this is exactly the condition that must prevail if $\{x_{1j}\}$ occurs;

$$\therefore\ p\{x_{1j}\} = p\{x_1\} \cdot p(\{x_{1j}\} \mid \{x_1\}).$$

Similarly,

$$p\{x_{2k}\} = p\{x_2\} \cdot p(\{x_{2k}\} \mid \{x_2\}).$$

The construction of the tree diagram may be outlined as follows.

1. Starting at a point, which we shall call the origin, we draw the primary branches of the tree, which terminate at the nodes corresponding to the primary events, $\{x_1\}$ and $\{x_2\}$, respectively. On these branches we indicate the probabilities, $p\{x_1\} = p_1$ and $p\{x_2\} = p_2$ (see Figure 3.2).

2. At each of the nodes corresponding to $\{x_1\}$ and $\{x_2\}$ we draw branches to nodes corresponding to the events $\{x_{1j}\}$ and $\{x_{2k}\}$, and on these lines we place the probabilities of the secondary events relative to the sample spaces $\{x_1\}$ and $\{x_2\}$, respectively (see Figure 3.3).

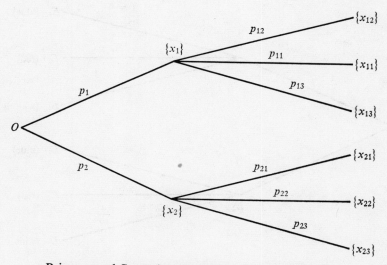

Primary and Secondary Branches of Tree Diagram.

FIGURE 3.3

3. If there are ternary events whose occurrence depends on the occurrence of secondary events, then we draw branches to each of them from the corresponding nodes, $\{x_{1j}\}$ and $\{x_{2k}\}$, respectively, and place the probabilities of these events on the branches leading to them.

4. We continue in this manner until the tree is completed. It is then possible to compute the probability of any event by multiplying the probabilities on the branches leading from the origin to the node of the event in question.

ILLUSTRATION 3.5 Two urns containing colored marbles are placed before an observer. He is to choose either urn and then pick a marble without looking in the urn. If

(a) urn A has 3 red, 2 white, and 4 blue marbles,
(b) urn B has 3 red, 4 white, and 3 blue marbles,

what is the probability that a blue marble is selected?

The probability of selecting at random urn A or urn B is 1/2, and we indicate this probability on each branch of the tree leading from the origin to the nodes, which correspond to the events $E_1 = \{$urn A$\}$ and $E_2 = \{$urn B$\}$ of the first trial. From each of these nodes we draw branches to nodes corresponding to the events of the second trial and indicate the conditional

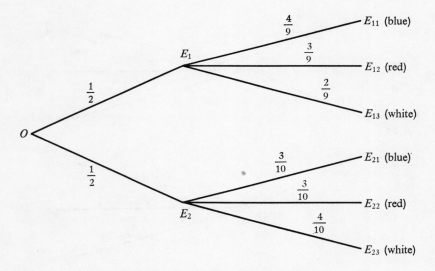

Tree Diagram for Urn Problem.

FIGURE 3.4

probabilities on each of these lines. Because the problem is to determine the probability of selecting a blue marble, we are concerned with two *exclusive events* (see Figure 3.4):

$F = E_1 \cap E_{11} =$ choose urn A, and select from it one of 4 blue marbles among 9.

$G = E_2 \cap E_{21} =$ choose urn B, and select from it one of 3 blue marbles among 10.

F and G being mutually exclusive events, it follows that the event $E =$ "A blue marble is selected" may be expressed as $F \cup G$, and we have

$$p(E) = p(F) + p(G)$$
$$= p(E_1 \cap E_{11}) + p(E_2 \cap E_{21}). \tag{3.2}$$

From Figure 3.4 we have

$$p(F) = p(E_1) \cdot p(E_{11} \mid E_1) = \tfrac{1}{2} \times \tfrac{4}{9} = \tfrac{2}{9}, \tag{3.3}$$

$$p(G) = p(E_2) \cdot p(E_{21} \mid E_2) = \tfrac{1}{2} \times \tfrac{3}{10} = \tfrac{3}{20}. \tag{3.4}$$

Finally, substituting from Equations 3.3 and 3.4 into Equation 3.2, we have

$$p(E) = \tfrac{2}{9} + \tfrac{3}{20} = \tfrac{67}{180},$$

as the required probability.

PROBLEMS

1. Among students taking both mathematics and biology during a certain term 6% failed mathematics, 10% failed biology, and 3% failed both mathematics and biology.
   (a) What percentage passed mathematics and failed biology?
   (b) Among those who failed mathematics, what percentage also failed biology?

2. Two dice are thrown:
   (a) What is the probability of throwing a "7"?
   (b) If one die thrown shows a "3," what is the probability of throwing a "7"?
   (c) If one die shows a "3," what is the probability of throwing at least a "7"?

3. Three identical bags contain red, white, and blue marbles as follows: B_1, (3, 2, 3); B_2, (1, 3, 4); B_3, (3, 0, 5). If a bag is chosen at random and a marble is drawn from it, what are the probabilities of (a) picking a white marble and (b) not picking a white marble?

4. Three men, Brown, White, and Jones, are nominated for offices in a club. The man with the largest number of votes is to be named president and the next highest is to be named vice-president. What is the probability that Brown will be elected president and White vice-president?
   (a) Work by constructing a tree diagram.
   (b) Work by constructing a sample space and assigning equal probabilities to the simple events.

5. A survey is made of the reading habits of a group of students. It is found that 35% of the group reads magazine A, 42% reads magazine B, and 20% reads both A and B.
   (a) What percentage reads magazine A and does not read magazine B?
   (b) Of those who read B, what percentage also reads A?

6. A box contains 2 defective flashlight batteries and 3 good ones. They are tested by pairs in a flashlight that operates only when two good batteries are placed in it. Find the probability that the flashlight will operate with the first pair used, assuming that they are picked at random.
   (a) Solve by means of a sample space.
   (b) Solve by constructing a tree diagram.

7. Derive the following results by using the definition of conditional probability:
   (a) $p(A \mid A) = 1$.
   (b) $p(A \mid U) = p(A)$.
   (c) $p(\varnothing \mid A) = 0$.

8. Two identical coolers contain bottled drinks. In cooler 1 are 5 Pepsis, 3 Sprites, and 2 Cokes. In cooler 2 are 3 Pepsis, 2 Sprites, and 4 Cokes. Assuming that one does not attempt to identify the drink by the shape of the bottle, what is the probability of picking a Coke?

9. In an election five men are running for an office. A pre-election survey shows the following probabilities for election: $p(A) = 0.2$, $p(B) = 0.3$, $p(C) = 0.1$, $p(D) = 0.3$, $p(E) = 0.1$. Just before the election candidates C and E withdraw from the race. Determine the new probabilities for the remaining candidates.

10. A survey of the members of a fraternity shows that 18 are taking mathematics, 22 are taking English, 14 are taking history, 8 are taking history and mathematics, 7 are taking English and history, 10 are taking mathematics and English, and 5 are taking all three subjects.
    (a) What is the probability that a person picked at random is taking mathematics only? English only? History only?

(b) What is the probability that a person chosen at random is taking mathematics *and* English? Mathematics *or* English?
(c) A person is picked at random, and it is determined that he is taking English. What is the probability that he is also taking mathematics? Mathematics and history?

11. Two identical boxes, each containing 10 plastic buttons with numbers printed on them, are placed before an observer. He is to choose either box and draw a button. If box A has 3 even-numbered buttons, 5 odd-numbered, and 2 blanks and box B has 4 evens, 3 odds, and 3 blanks, what is the probability that the observer draws a blank?

3.5 INDEPENDENT EVENTS AND INDEPENDENT TRIALS

In probability theory the term *independent events* does not mean that the events so described are mutually exclusive or incompatible, even though we may intuitively think that this might be the case. The term *stochastically independent events* is sometimes used instead. Because both terms refer to an independence arising out of probabilistic considerations, perhaps the latter is preferable to the unmodified "independent events."

What is meant by independent events A and B is that *the conditional probability $p(A \mid B)$ of an event A when event B has occurred is the same as the probability $p(A)$*; that is, $p(A \mid B) = p(A)$. Similarly, we require that $p(B \mid A) = p(B)$. In view of these conditions, we obtain from the equations $p(A \mid B) = p(A \cap B)/p(B)$ and $p(B \mid A) = p(A \cap B)/p(A)$ the following criterion.

DEFINITION **3.4** (Independent Events)   Two events A and B are said to be *independent* if and only if $p(A \cap B) = p(A) \times p(B)$.

To illustrate, suppose a red die and a green die are thrown. Let event A be "Throw a 5 with the red die" and event B be "Throw a 6 with the green die." In this experiment $A \cap B = \{(5, 6)\}$ is one of 36 simple events in the sample space, and so we have

$$p(A \cap B) = \tfrac{1}{36} = p(A) \cdot p(B) = \tfrac{1}{6} \cdot \tfrac{1}{6}$$

and, by Definition 3.4, events A and B are independent.

Now consider the experiment of tossing two coins. Let A be the event "Toss two heads" and B be "Toss two tails"; that is, $A = \{\{h, h\}\}$, $B = \{\{t, t\}\}$. Clearly, $A \cap B = \varnothing$ and, hence, $p(A \cap B) = p(\varnothing) = 0$. But $p(A) = \tfrac{1}{4}$ and $p(B) = \tfrac{1}{4}$, so that a *misapplication* of the formula, $p(A \cap B) = p(A) \times p(B)$, would give $0 = \tfrac{1}{4} \times \tfrac{1}{4} = \tfrac{1}{16}$, which is definitely wrong. Thus, mutually exclusive events are *not* independent.

As a final illustration, suppose that radios are assembled by a sequence of operations on an assembly line. Assume that one out of a hundred is defective. If the outcomes for successive radios are independent, what is the probability that two successive radios on the line are defective? Let E_1 be "First radio is defective" and E_2 be "Second radio is defective." Then

$$p(E_1 \cap E_2) = p(E_1) \cdot p(E_2)$$
$$= (0.01) \cdot (0.01)$$
$$= 0.0001.$$

We now turn to an important concept in probability theory, that of *independent trials*. Let $U_1 = \{x_1, x_2, \ldots, x_n\}$ be the sample space of a given experiment. If this experiment is repeated and a new experiment is designed with the sample space $U_2 = U_1 \times U_1$, we shall say that the second experiment is *made up of two trials of the first experiment*.

We recall from Chapter 1 that, if $U_1 = \{x_1, x_2, \ldots, x_n\}$, then the sample space after two trials is

$$U_2 = U_1 \times U_1$$
$$= \{(x_1, x_1), (x_1, x_2), \ldots, (x_i, x_j), \ldots, (x_n, x_n)\},$$

where the n^2 possible outcomes (x_i, x_j) are all of the distinct ordered pairs formed from the n elements x_i of U_1.

Having determined the sample space, we are ready to decide on the probabilities to be assigned to the simple events, $\{(x_i, x_j)\}$. Although it is true that any set of nonnegative numbers, $p\{(x_i, x_j)\}$, could be assigned to these simple events provided that

$$\sum^{n^2} p\{(x_i, x_j)\} = 1,$$

we shall require the two trials to be *independent trials*, and so choose the probabilities as to satisfy the additional condition of Definition 3.4, namely that $p\{(x_i, x_j)\} = p\{x_i\} \cdot p\{x_j\}$ for all values of i and j, where $i = 1, 2, \ldots, n$ and $j = 1, 2, \ldots, n$.

For example, if $U_1 = \{1, 2, 3, 4, 5, 6\}$ is the sample space of the experiment of throwing a die, then the assignment of probabilities made on the basis of "equally likely" and a "fair" die is 1/6 for each simple event. If U_1 is repeated, then after two trials the sample space is

$$U_2 = U_1 \times U_1 = \left\{ \begin{array}{l} (1, 1), (1, 2), \ldots, (1, 6) \\ (2, 1), (2, 2), \ldots, (2, 6) \\ \vdots \qquad \vdots \qquad \quad \vdots \\ (6, 1), (6, 2), \ldots, (6, 6) \end{array} \right\},$$

and accordingly we designate the probability of the simple event $\{(m, n)\}$ as

$$p\{(m, n)\} = p\{m\} \cdot p\{n\} = \tfrac{1}{6} \cdot \tfrac{1}{6} = \tfrac{1}{36}.$$

In the general case of an experiment consisting of two independent trials with sample space equal to the product set, $U_1 \times U_1$, to assign $p\{(x_i, x_j)\} = p\{x_i\} \cdot p\{x_j\}$ the probability of the event $\{(x_i, x_j)\}$ was determined by the definition of independent events. Having chosen the probability measures, we must now prove that our selections satisfy the two conditions required by the definition of probability measure, namely, that the probabilities be nonnegative and that their sum be 1.

Because $p\{x_i\}$ and $p\{x_j\}$ are nonnegative numbers, $p\{(x_i, x_j)\} = p\{x_i\} \cdot p\{x_j\}$ is certainly nonnegative. In order to find the sum of all of the probabilities $p\{(x_i, x_j)\}$, we shall find it convenient to write them in rows and columns as follows:

$$p\{(x_1, x_1)\}, p\{(x_1, x_2)\}, \ldots, p\{(x_1, x_n)\}$$
$$p\{(x_2, x_1)\}, p\{(x_2, x_2)\}, \ldots, p\{(x_2, x_n)\}$$
$$\vdots \qquad \vdots \qquad \vdots$$
$$p\{(x_n, x_1)\}, p\{(x_n, x_2)\}, \ldots, p\{(x_n, x_n)\}.$$

The sum of all of the probabilities in the first column is

$$\sum_{i=1}^{n} p\{(x_i, x_1)\} = \sum_{i=1}^{n} p\{x_i\} \cdot p\{x_1\} = p\{x_1\} \sum_{i=1}^{n} p\{x_i\} = p\{x_1\} \cdot 1 = p\{x_1\}.$$

Similarly, the sum of all the probabilities in the second column is $p\{x_2\}$, and the sum in the kth column is $p\{x_k\}$, where $k = 1, 2, \ldots, n$. Now that we have the column totals for the n columns, we can find the sum of all the probabilities by summing the n column totals, and we obtain

$$\sum_{k=1}^{n} p\{x_k\} = 1,$$

which indicates that the choice of probability measures satisfies all conditions required by the definition.

The preceding discussion leads to the following definition.

DEFINITION 3.5   Let $U = \{x_1, x_2, \ldots, x_n\}$ be a sample space of a given experiment with probability measures $p\{x_i\}$, where $i = 1, 2, \ldots, n$. An experiment is said to be *two independent trials* of the given experiment if and only if its sample space is the product set $U \times U$ and the probability measures of the simple events $\{(x_i, x_j)\}$ are $p\{(x_i, x_j)\} = p\{x_i\} \cdot p\{x_j\}$ for all i and j, where $i = 1, 2, \ldots, n$ and $j = 1, 2, \ldots, n$.

A natural generalization can be made to any finite number of repetitions of the same experiment or to different experiments.

DEFINITION 3.6   Let $U_k = \{x_{k1}, x_{k2}, \ldots, x_{kn_k}\}$, where $k = 1, 2, \ldots, N$, be the respective sample spaces of N experiments. By the experiment consisting of N *independent trials, the first corresponding to* U_1, *the second to* $U_2, \ldots$, and *the* N^{th} *to* U_N, we shall mean an experiment with sample space $U_1 \times U_2 \times \cdots \times U_N$ whose elements are the $n_1 \times n_2 \times \cdots \times n_N$ ordered N-tuples $(x_{1j_1}, x_{2j_2}, \ldots, x_{Nj_N})$ with probability measures defined by

$$p\{(x_{1j_1}, x_{2j_2}, \ldots, x_{Nj_N})\} = p\{x_{1j_1}\} \times p\{x_{2j_2}\} \times \cdots \times p\{x_{Nj_N}\}.$$

ILLUSTRATION 3.6   Suppose a random selection of three committee members is made, the first member being chosen from a list of 7 Democrats, the second from a list of 5 Republicans, and the third from a list of 3 Socialists. If we denote the three sample spaces (lists) D, R, and S, respectively, what is a typical element in the sample space of the committees? What is the probability of a simple event in this space, if the experiment is treated as three independent trials?

Clearly, the experiment has a sample space, $D \times R \times S$, whose elements are the $7 \times 5 \times 3 = 105$ distinct ordered triples (d_i, r_j, s_k), with $i = 1, 2, \ldots,$ 7, $j = 1, 2, \ldots, 5$, and $k = 1, 2, 3$. The probability measure of a simple event is

$$p\{(d_i, r_j, s_k)\} = \tfrac{1}{7} \cdot \tfrac{1}{5} \cdot \tfrac{1}{3} = \tfrac{1}{105}.$$

ILLUSTRATION 3.7   A certain quiz consists of five multiple-choice questions, each having four choices of which only one is right. A student selects answers to each question at random. Assuming his successive answers are independent, what is the probability that he will guess more right answers than wrong.

There are five sets of answers, one for each question. Each set is of the type $Q_k = \{r_k, w_{k1}, w_{k2}, w_{k3}\}$, where r_k is the right answer for the kth question, Q_k, and w_{k1}, w_{k2}, w_{k3} are the three wrong answers. The sample space is $Q_1 \times Q_2 \times Q_3 \times Q_4 \times Q_5$, whose elements are $4^5 = 1024$ ordered 5-tuples, whose first element is either r or w from Q_1, whose second element is either r or w from Q_2, and so on.

The event we are interested in is the union of three mutually exclusive events:

$$E_1 = \{(r, r, r, r, r)\},$$
$$E_2 = \{5 \text{ elements of the type } (r, r, r, r, w)\},$$
$$E_3 = \{10 \text{ elements of the type } (r, r, r, w, w)\}.$$

The probabilities of the simple events are computed first:

$$p\{(r, r, r, r, r)\} = \left(\frac{1}{4}\right)^5 = \frac{1}{1024}$$

$$p\{(r, r, r, r, w)\} = \left(\frac{1}{4}\right)^4 \cdot \frac{3}{4} = \frac{3}{1024}$$

$$p\{(r, r, r, w, w)\} = \left(\frac{1}{4}\right)^3 \cdot \left(\frac{3}{4}\right)^2 = \frac{9}{1024}$$

$$\therefore\ p(E_1) = \frac{1}{1024}$$

$$p(E_2) = 5 \cdot \frac{3}{1024} = \frac{15}{1024}$$

$$p(E_3) = 10 \cdot \frac{9}{1024} = \frac{90}{1024}$$

$$p(E_1 \cup E_2 \cup E_3) = \frac{1 + 15 + 90}{1024} = \frac{106}{1024}$$

PROBLEMS

1. Compute the probability of obtaining exactly two heads in four independent tosses of a fair coin.

2. Compute the probability of obtaining exactly two heads in four independent tosses of a biassed coin with probability 0.6 that heads will show and 0.4 that tails will show.

3. A baseball player has probability 0.25 for getting a hit. Assuming that his hits form an independent trials process, what is the probability of getting at least three hits out of four times at bat?

4. In a certain class there are 5 girls and 12 boys. A random sample of 3 with replacements is taken.
   (a) Describe the sample space.
   (b) Assign the probabilities to the simple events.
   (c) Find the probability that there will be at most one girl in the sample.

5. A multiple-choice quiz consists of 6 questions with 3 choices of answers (1 correct, 2 wrong) for each question. A student guesses independently on each question.
   (a) What is the probability that he will guess exactly 5 correct answers?
   (b) What is the probability that he will guess at least 5 correct answers?

6. At a certain intersection there is a probability of 0.01 of a traffic accident occurring. A certain person drives through this intersection twice a day for a period of 60 days. What is the probability that he will not be involved in an accident at this intersection during this time?

7. A football team is rated as having a probability of 0.5 of winning each of its next three games, a probability of 0.3 of tying, and a probability of 0.2 of losing. Find the probability of the team winning more games than losing or tying.

8. A baseball player has a probability of 0.3 of getting a hit, 0.2 of getting a base on balls, and 0.5 of being struck out. Assuming that the four times the player is up to bat constitute four independent trials, compute the probability that the batter will:
(a) Get two hits and two outs.
(b) Get two hits, a walk, and an out.

Supplementary Reading

GOLDBERG, S., *Probability, An Introduction*, Prentice-Hall, Englewood Cliffs, N.J., 1962.
KEMENY, J. G., J. L. SNELL, and G. L. THOMPSON, *Introduction to Finite Mathematics*, Prentice-Hall, Englewood Cliffs, N.J., 1957.

VECTOR SPACES

4.1 INTRODUCTION

The concept of a binary operation on a set was introduced formally in Definition 2.1 in connection with Boolean algebra and its applications. It will be recalled that such an operation is a rule or a function that associates with each ordered pair (a, b) of elements a and b of the given set a unique image c of the set. That is, a binary operation ρ on a set A is a function of the product set $A \times A$ into A, $\rho: A \times A \to A$. Since ρ maps a pair of elements of A into an element of A, the set is closed with respect to the operation.

Binary operations on the set of real numbers, for example, are ordinary addition and multiplication. In set algebra, in which the elements are subsets of a universal set, these operations are union and intersection of sets. In the application of Boolean algebra to logical propositions, they are disjunction and conjunction.

Each binary operation has certain properties that must be postulated. Some of the more common of these are defined here for future reference.

For a given set $A = \{a, b, c, \ldots\}$ of undefined elements with binary operation denoted by the symbol $\oplus$, the following laws are postulated:

ASSOCIATIVITY $a \oplus (b \oplus c) = (a \oplus b) \oplus c$ for all a, b, c.

COMMUTATIVITY $a \oplus b = b \oplus a$ for all a and b.

IDENTITY For each element a in A there exists a unique element z in A, such that $a \oplus z = z \oplus a = a$.

INVERSES For each element a in A there exists a unique element $(-a)$ in A, such that $a \oplus (-a) = (-a) \oplus a = z$.

In the case of two binary operations, $\oplus$ and $\otimes$, defined on a set, such as addition and multiplication in the algebra of real numbers, we may require that the distributive laws hold; for example:

DISTRIBUTIVITY
(a) $a \otimes (b \oplus c) = (a \otimes b) \oplus (a \otimes c)$,
(b) $(b \oplus c) \otimes a = (b \otimes a) \oplus (c \otimes a)$.

ILLUSTRATION **4.1** The set $\{1, -1, i, -i\}$ is closed with respect to a binary operation, called multiplication, which is defined by the table:

$\otimes$	1	-1	i	$-i$
1	1	-1	i	$-i$
-1	-1	1	$-i$	i
i	i	$-i$	-1	1
$-i$	$-i$	i	1	-1

It can be verified that all five properties given apply in this case. It should be pointed out, however, that the identity in this illustration is denoted by 1. It has the property $a \otimes 1 = 1 \otimes a = a$, which is required of a *multiplicative* identity.

ILLUSTRATION **4.2** The set of positive integers is closed with respect to two binary operations, ordinary addition and multiplication. The associative and commutative laws are valid, and the distributive law holds for "multiplication across addition." It should be recalled that in this system the distributive law "addition across multiplication" does not hold. This system also has a multiplicative identity, 1, but it does not have an additive identity, since zero is not included in the set.

ILLUSTRATION **4.3** It may be verified that the set $\{1, \omega, \omega^2\}$ with the binary operation defined by the following table,

$\otimes$	1	ω	ω^2
1	1	ω	ω^2
ω	ω	ω^2	1
ω^2	ω^2	1	ω

has the five properties listed. (See Problem 1, this section.)

ILLUSTRATION **4.4**   The set {0, 1} together with the binary operations $\oplus$ and $\otimes$ defined by the tables

$\oplus$	0	1		$\otimes$	0	1
0	0	1		0	0	0
1	1	0		1	0	1

can be shown to have the five properties. In this system 0 is the additive identity and each element is its own inverse. The multiplicative identity is 1, and although 1 is its own multiplicative inverse, 0 does not have an inverse with respect to multiplication.

4.2   ALGEBRAIC SYSTEMS

A set and binary operation(s), together with whatever properties that may be postulated, constitute an *algebraic system*. Certain algebraic systems are of particular importance and are named as follows.

The simplest consists of a set and a binary operation; it is called a *groupoid*.

A *semigroup* is an associative groupoid, which is a set and a binary operation that is associative.

A *monoid* is a semigroup with an identity element; that is, it consists of a set, an associative binary operation, and a unique identity.

A *group* is a monoid in which each element has a unique inverse. Thus, a group consists of a set, a binary operation that is associative, a unique identity element, and a unique inverse for each element.

These algebraic systems are summarized in Table 4.1.

ILLUSTRATION **4.5**   The system consisting of the set {0, 1} and the binary operation $\vee$ defined by the following table is a *groupoid*:

$\vee$	0	1
0	0	1
1	1	1

ILLUSTRATION **4.6**   The set of positive integers and the binary operation of ordinary addition form a *semigroup*.

ILLUSTRATION **4.7**   The set of positive integers and the binary operation of ordinary multiplication have associativity and an identity element and form, therefore, a *monoid*.

TABLE 4.1

Properties of Algebraic Systems

	Binary Operation	Associativity	Identity	Inverses
Groupoid	yes			
Semigroup	yes	yes		
Monoid	yes	yes	yes	
Group	yes	yes	yes	yes

ILLUSTRATION **4.8**   The set $\{0, 1, 2\}$ and the binary operation defined in the following table form a *group*:

$\oplus$	0	1	2
0	0	1	2
1	1	2	0
2	2	0	1

All of these examples are commutative systems. The next one is a non-commutative monoid.

ILLUSTRATION **4.9**   Let $S = \{a_1, a_2, \ldots, a_n\}$ be a nonempty set of undefined elements. Denote by W the set of "words" formed by placing the a_i in juxtaposition without restriction as to their number or type. For $w_i = a_{i_1}a_{i_2}\cdots a_{i_k}$ and $w_j = a_{j_1}a_{j_2}\cdots a_{j_m}$, we define the binary operation $w_i \otimes w_j$ as

$$w_i \otimes w_j = a_{i_1}a_{i_2}\cdots a_{i_k}a_{j_1}a_{j_2}\cdots a_{j_m}.$$

The system $\{W, \otimes\}$ is closed and associative but *not commutative*, since two "words" are *not identical* even when they have the same letters (as "decimal" and "medical"), unless the letters have the same arrangements. For the system to be a monoid, we must exhibit an element e such that $w_i \otimes e = e \otimes w_i = w_i$ for each "word" w_i. To this end we define e as the *empty word*, that is, the word with no elements of S in it. Then, $w_i \otimes e = e \otimes w_i = w_i$, and e is an identity element in W. Therefore, the algebraic system $\{W, \otimes\}$ is a noncommutative monoid.

ILLUSTRATION **4.10**   Let $S = \{a_1, a_2, a_3\}$ be a set of undefined elements called "letters." By the symbol

$$\pi = \begin{pmatrix} 1 & 2 & 3 \\ 2 & 3 & 1 \end{pmatrix}$$

we mean the operation of replacing a_1 by a_2, a_2 by a_3, and a_3 by a_1. An operation such as π is called a *permutation on the set S*. In particular, there are $3! = 6$ permutations on a set of 3 letters, $4! = 24$ permutations on 4 letters, and, in general, $n!$ permutations on n letters. The 6 permutations on 3 elements are the following:

$$\pi_1 = \begin{pmatrix} 1 & 2 & 3 \\ 1 & 2 & 3 \end{pmatrix}, \quad \pi_2 = \begin{pmatrix} 1 & 2 & 3 \\ 2 & 1 & 3 \end{pmatrix}, \quad \pi_3 = \begin{pmatrix} 1 & 2 & 3 \\ 3 & 2 & 1 \end{pmatrix},$$

$$\pi_4 = \begin{pmatrix} 1 & 2 & 3 \\ 1 & 3 & 2 \end{pmatrix}, \quad \pi_5 = \begin{pmatrix} 1 & 2 & 3 \\ 2 & 3 & 1 \end{pmatrix}, \quad \pi_6 = \begin{pmatrix} 1 & 2 & 3 \\ 3 & 1 & 2 \end{pmatrix}.$$

If we apply two permutations in succession to the elements of S, the result is again a permutation. For example,

$$\pi_2\pi_3 = \begin{pmatrix} 1 & 2 & 3 \\ 2 & 1 & 3 \end{pmatrix}\begin{pmatrix} 1 & 2 & 3 \\ 3 & 2 & 1 \end{pmatrix} = \begin{pmatrix} 1 & 2 & 3 \\ 2 & 3 & 1 \end{pmatrix} = \pi_5,$$

and

$$\pi_3\pi_5 = \begin{pmatrix} 1 & 2 & 3 \\ 3 & 2 & 1 \end{pmatrix}\begin{pmatrix} 1 & 2 & 3 \\ 2 & 3 & 1 \end{pmatrix} = \begin{pmatrix} 1 & 2 & 3 \\ 1 & 3 & 2 \end{pmatrix} = \pi_4.$$

The resultant permutation is called the "product" of the pair of permutations on the left. Since the product $\pi_i\pi_j$ of each ordered pair (π_i, π_j) of permutations corresponds to a unique element of the set this defines a binary operation on the set $\{\pi_1, \pi_2, \ldots, \pi_6\}$. Since

$$\pi_5\pi_3 = \begin{pmatrix} 1 & 2 & 3 \\ 2 & 3 & 1 \end{pmatrix}\begin{pmatrix} 1 & 2 & 3 \\ 3 & 2 & 1 \end{pmatrix} = \begin{pmatrix} 1 & 2 & 3 \\ 2 & 1 & 3 \end{pmatrix} = \pi_2$$

and $\pi_3\pi_5 = \pi_4$, it is clear that the system is *not commutative*.

The element

$$\pi_1 = \begin{pmatrix} 1 & 2 & 3 \\ 1 & 2 & 3 \end{pmatrix}$$

behaves as the *identity element* in the system, because $\pi_1\pi_k = \pi_k\pi_1 = \pi_k$ for all k, where $k = 1, 2, \ldots, 6$.

The following products are easily verified:

$$\pi_1\pi_1 = \pi_1, \quad \pi_2\pi_2 = \pi_1, \quad \pi_3\pi_3 = \pi_1,$$
$$\pi_4\pi_4 = \pi_1, \quad \pi_5\pi_6 = \pi_1, \quad \pi_6\pi_5 = \pi_1.$$

Therefore, the *inverse* of each element is uniquely defined as follows:

$$\pi_1^{-1} = \pi_1, \quad \pi_2^{-1} = \pi_2, \quad \pi_3^{-1} = \pi_3,$$
$$\pi_4^{-1} = \pi_4, \quad \pi_5^{-1} = \pi_6, \quad \pi_6^{-1} = \pi_5.$$

To show that this system is *associative*, let us assume that the indicated permutations perform substitutions on typical elements of S in the following manner.

$$\pi_r = \begin{pmatrix} \cdots w \cdots \\ \cdots x \cdots \end{pmatrix}, \qquad \pi_s = \begin{pmatrix} \cdots x \cdots \\ \cdots y \cdots \end{pmatrix}, \qquad \pi_t = \begin{pmatrix} \cdots y \cdots \\ \cdots z \cdots \end{pmatrix}.$$

We wish to show that $\pi_r(\pi_s\pi_t) = (\pi_r\pi_s)\pi_t$; then

$$(\pi_s\pi_t) = \begin{pmatrix} \cdots x \cdots \\ \cdots z \cdots \end{pmatrix} \qquad \text{and} \qquad \pi_r(\pi_s\pi_t) = \begin{pmatrix} \cdots w \cdots \\ \cdots z \cdots \end{pmatrix}.$$

On the other hand,

$$(\pi_r\pi_s) = \begin{pmatrix} \cdots w \cdots \\ \cdots y \cdots \end{pmatrix} \qquad \text{and} \qquad (\pi_r\pi_s)\pi_t = \begin{pmatrix} \cdots w \cdots \\ \cdots z \cdots \end{pmatrix}.$$

Therefore, $\pi_r(\pi_s\pi_t) = (\pi_r\pi_s)\pi_t$. The system is a group and belongs to an important classification called *permutation* groups.

We now discuss briefly algebraic systems with two binary operations. The first of these is a *ring*, which is defined formally as follows.

DEFINITION **4.1** A *ring* $\mathscr{R}$ is a set R and two binary operations denoted by $\oplus$ and $\otimes$, which are called, for convenience, addition and multiplication, respectively. The system $\mathscr{R} = \{R, \oplus, \otimes\}$ satisfies the following postulates.

(a) With respect to addition, the system $\mathscr{R}$ is a commutative group. That is, for all elements, $a, b, c \in R$:

    (i) $a \oplus b \in R$ (*closure*),

    (ii) $a \oplus b = b \oplus a$ (*commutativity*),

    (iii) $a \oplus (b \oplus c) = (a \oplus b) \oplus c$ (*associativity*),

    (iv)   there exists a unique element, $z \in R$, such that $a \oplus z = a$ (*additive identity*),

    (v)   for each $a \in R$, there exists a unique element, $(-a) \in R$, such that $a \oplus (-a) = z$ (*additive inverses*).

(b) With respect to multiplication, the system $\mathscr{R}$ is a semigroup. That is, for all elements, $a, b, c \in R$:

    (i) $a \otimes b \in R$ (*closure*),

    (ii) $a \otimes (b \otimes c) = (a \otimes b) \otimes c$ (*associativity*).

(c) The system is distributive, "multiplication across addition." That is, for all elements $a, b, c \in R$.

    (i) $a \otimes (b \oplus c) = (a \otimes b) \oplus (a \otimes c)$,

    (ii) $(b \oplus c) \otimes a = (b \otimes a) \oplus (c \otimes a)$.

ILLUSTRATION **4.11** The set I of integers and the binary operations of ordinary addition and multiplication form a ring.

(a) The system is closed with respect to both operations, since the sum and the product of integers are integers.

(b) The system is commutative with respect to both addition and multiplication.

(c) The system is associative with respect to both addition and multiplication.

(d) The number zero, 0, behaves as the additive identity.

(e) Each integer n has a unique additive inverse, $(-n)$, in the set.

(f) The system is distributive, "multiplication across addition."

ILLUSTRATION **4.12** The set $\{0, 1, 2\}$ and addition and multiplication, modulo 3, form a ring (see Section 1.7 for the definition of congruence). The addition and multiplication tables are of the form.

$\oplus$	0	1	2
0	0	1	2
1	1	2	0
2	2	0	1

$\otimes$	0	1	2
0	0	0	0
1	0	1	2
2	0	2	1

(a) Since the only elements appearing in the tables are members of the set, it is clear that the system is closed with respect to the operations.

(b) The system is commutative with respect to both operations, as may be seen by the symmetry of the tables.

(c) It can be verified that the associative and distributive laws are satisfied. However, the verification requires $3^3 = 27$ computations for each law.

(d) The additive identity is 0.

(e) The additive inverses are $(-0) = 0$, $(-1) = 2$, $(-2) = 1$.

The second of these systems to be considered is a *field*, which is defined as follows.

DEFINITION **4.2** A *field* $\mathscr{F}$ consists of a set, F, containing at least two elements, and two binary operations denoted by $\oplus$ and $\otimes$ and called addition and multiplication, respectively. The system satisfies the following postulates.

(a) With respect to addition, the system $\mathscr{F} = \{F, \oplus, \otimes\}$ is a commutative group. That is, for all elements, $a, b, c \in F$:

(i) $a \oplus b \in F$ (*closure*),

(ii) $a \oplus b = b \oplus a$ (*commutativity*),

(iii) $a \oplus (b \oplus c) = (a \oplus b) \oplus c$ (*associativity*),

(iv)   there exists a unique element, $z \in F$, such that $a \oplus z = a$ (*additive identity*),

(v)   for each $a \in F$ there exists a unique element, $(-a) \in F$, such that $a \oplus (-a) = z$ (*additive inverse*).

(b)   Except for the additive identity, the system $\mathscr{F}$ is a commutative group with respect to multiplication. That is for all elements $a, b, c \in F$:

(i) $a \otimes b \in F$ (*closure*),

(ii) $a \otimes b = b \otimes a$ (*commutativity*),

(iii) $a \otimes (b \otimes c) = (a \otimes b) \otimes c$ (*associativity*),

(iv)   there exists a unique element, $e \in F$, such that $a \otimes e = a$ (*multiplicative identity*),

(v)   for every element $a \neq z$ there exists a unique *multiplicative inverse*, $a^{-1} \in F$, such that $a \otimes a^{-1} = e$.

(c)   The system is distributive, "multiplication across addition": $a \otimes (b \oplus c) = (a \otimes b) \oplus (a \otimes c)$.

ILLUSTRATION **4.13**   The set of all rational numbers together with the binary operations of addition and multiplication form a field. The system is closed, since the sum and product of two rational numbers is rational. The system is associative, commutative, and distributive. The additive identity is 0, and the additive inverse of the rational number p/q is $-p/q$. The multiplicative identity is 1, and the multiplicative inverse of p/q is q/p, where $p \neq 0$ and $q \neq 0$.

ILLUSTRATION **4.14**   The set of all real numbers together with the binary operations of addition and multiplication form a field $\mathscr{R}$. Indeed, the field of rational numbers is a special case of this system, and is called a *subfield* of the field of real numbers.

ILLUSTRATION **4.15**   The set of all complex numbers, $a + bi$, where a and b are real numbers and $i^2 = -1$, forms a field, $\mathscr{C}$, with addition and multiplication, which are defined by the rules,

$$(a + bi) + (c + di) = (a + c) + (b + d)i,$$
$$(a + bi)(c + di) = (ac - bd) + (ad + bc)i.$$

The additive identity is $0 + 0i$, and the additive inverse of $a + bi$ is $-a - bi$. The multiplicative identity is $1 + 0i$ and, if a and b are not both 0, the multiplicative inverse of $a + bi$ is $(a - bi)/(a^2 + b^2)$.

Each of the systems in Illustrations 4.13 and 4.14 are subfields of the system in this illustration.

In the discussion of the topics in the rest of this chapter we shall refer to the elements of the given algebraic system as *scalars*. When we "add" or "multiply" within these systems, we shall use the standard symbols to indicate these operations. Except in a very few cases, the additive identity will be indicated by 0 and the multiplicative identity by 1.

PROBLEMS

1. Show that the set $\{1, \omega, \omega^2\}$ is a group with respect to the operation $\otimes$ indicated in the table:

$\otimes$	1	ω	ω^2
1	1	ω	ω^2
ω	ω	ω^2	1
ω^2	ω^2	1	ω

   (a) What is the identity element?
   (b) What is the inverse of ω? Of ω^2?
   (c) Is this a commutative group?
   (d) Show that, if $\omega = -1/2 + \sqrt{3}\,i/2$, then $\omega^2 = -1/2 - \sqrt{3}\,i/2$ and $\omega^3 = 1$.

2. Assume a radius vector is rotated about its origin in a plane. Let each rotation be a multiple of 120°, and define two rotations as equal if the corresponding positions of the radius vector are identical. Then rotations $k \cdot 120° \pm n \cdot 360°$ are equal for an arbitrary (but fixed) integer k and for each integer n. Thus, if R_0, R_{120}, R_{240} represent rotations of 0°, 120°, and 240°, respectively, and we make the statement $R_\alpha \oplus R_\beta = R_{\alpha+\beta}$, where $\alpha + \beta$ is addition, modulo 360°, we obtain an algebraic system.

   (a) Construct a multiplication table, and show that this system is abstractly identical with that of Problem 1 and the system in Illustration 4.8.
   (b) What is the identity element in this system?
   (c) What is the inverse of R_α? What is the geometric interpretation of the inverse of R_α?

3. Consider the set $\{0, 3, 6, 9\}$, together with operations $\oplus$ and $\otimes$ defined by the tables:

$\oplus$	0	3	6	9
0	0	3	6	9
3	3	6	9	0
6	6	9	0	3
9	9	0	3	6

$\otimes$	0	3	6	9
0	0	0	0	0
3	0	9	6	3
6	0	6	0	6
9	0	3	6	9

(a) What is the additive identity?
(b) What is the additive inverse of 3? Of 6? Of 9?
(c) Is the system commutative with respect to addition? Multiplication?
(d) Does the system have a multiplicative identity?
(e) Does 6 have a multiplicative inverse?
(f) Is the system a field? A ring?

4. Discuss the following system consisting of a set $\{a, b, c, d\}$ with addition and multiplication defined by the tables:

$\oplus$	a	b	c	d
a	a	b	c	d
b	b	a	d	c
c	c	d	a	b
d	d	c	b	a

$\otimes$	a	b	c	d
a	a	a	a	a
b	a	b	c	d
c	a	a	a	a
d	a	b	c	d

(a) Is it a ring? (Assume the associative and distributive laws.)
(b) What is the additive identity?
(c) List the additive inverses.
(d) Is the system commutative with respect to $\otimes$?
(e) Is there a multiplicative identity? Are there two?
(f) Does c have a multiplicative inverse?

5. Show that the system consisting of the set $\{0, 1\}$ and the binary operations of addition, $\oplus$, and multiplication, $\otimes$, defined by the tables is a field:

$\oplus$	0	1
0	0	1
1	1	0

$\otimes$	0	1
0	0	0
1	0	1

6. Show that the system consisting of all numbers of the form $x + y\sqrt{2}$, where x and y are rational numbers, is closed with respect to addition and multiplication. Prove that, if x and y are not both zero, then the

number $x + y\sqrt{2}$ always has a multiplicative inverse. (You may assume that $\sqrt{2}$ is an irrational number.)

7. Show that the set $\{0, 1, 2\}$ with the indicated operations forms a field.

$\oplus$	0	1	2		$\otimes$	0	1	2
0	0	1	2		0	0	0	0
1	1	2	0		1	0	1	2
2	2	0	1		2	0	2	1

Verify the associative and distributive laws for several cases.

4.3 VECTORS AND THEIR GEOMETRICAL INTERPRETATION

In the biological and physical sciences many entities arise that have both magnitude and direction such as displacement, velocity, force, acceleration, and diffusion. These entities are called vectors.

It is convenient to represent a given vector geometrically by an arrow whose length, drawn to some convenient scale, is proportional to the magnitude of the vector, and whose direction relative to a fixed reference line corresponds to the direction of the vector.

In contrast to the concept of vector is that of *scalar* which is a quantity that has magnitude but does not have direction. Examples of scalars are the real numbers, length, and mass.

Our interest in vectors will be restricted for the most part to an algebraic abstraction of their physical properties and those of the corresponding geometrical models. For example, two vectors are considered *equal* if they have the same magnitude and direction. Geometrically two vectors (arrows) are said to be equal if they have the same length and the same direction. Hence our choice of an equals relation in the algebraic representation of vectors should be consistent with these physical and geometrical conditions for equality if the algebraic system is to be a faithful model of the physical.

In order to orient our thinking we shall first consider the arithmetic of plane vectors. Using these considerations as a spring board, we shall develop the algebraic system which is called a *vector space*. In what follows we shall use Latin letters to denote scalars and Greek letters to designate vectors.

The *scalar multiple* of a vector α by a positive real number k is a vector, $k\alpha$, whose magnitude is k times the magnitude of α and whose direction is the same as that of α. When k is negative, $k\alpha$ is a vector whose magnitude is $|k|$ times the magnitude of α and whose direction is the reverse of that of α.

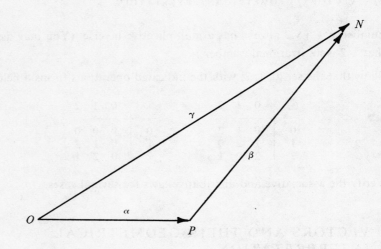

Construction of $\gamma = \alpha + \beta$.

FIGURE 4.1

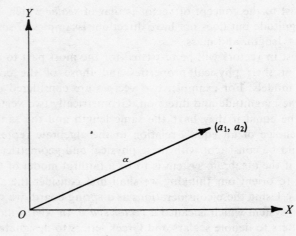

The Plane Vector $\alpha = (a_1, a_2)$.

FIGURE 4.2

The *sum* of the vectors α and β is denoted by $\alpha + \beta$ and is constructed by means of the *parallelogram law*. Thus, to obtain $\gamma = \alpha + \beta$ we draw α and construct the vector β at its terminus P. The sum $\alpha + \beta$ is the directed line γ drawn from the origin O of α to the terminus N of β (see Figure 4.1).

In what follows the only vectors we shall consider are those that emanate from the origin of a Cartesian reference frame. Recalling that in the Cartesian plane a point is uniquely designated by an ordered pair of real numbers (a_1, a_2), which locates it relative to the reference frame, a vector α with initial point at the origin O and terminus at the point (a_1, a_2) *is likewise uniquely designated by this ordered pair*. The vector α is said to have *components a_1 and a_2 relative to the given reference frame*, and we write $\alpha = (a_1, a_2)$ (see Figure 4.2).

For plane vectors, the concepts of vector equality, vector sum, and scalar multiplication may be expressed in terms of the components of the vectors involved as follows.

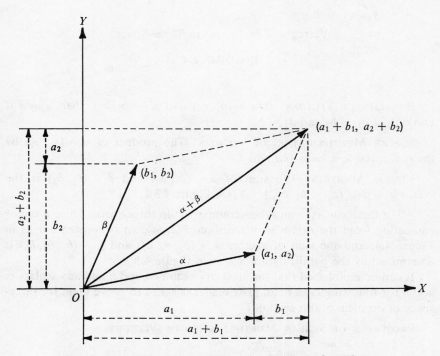

The Sum $\alpha + \beta$ of Two Vectors in the Cartesian Plane.

FIGURE 4.3

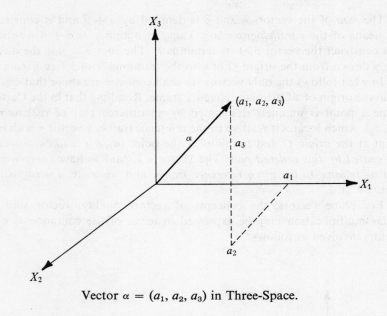

Vector $\alpha = (a_1, a_2, a_3)$ in Three-Space.

FIGURE 4.4

EQUALITY OF VECTORS   If $\alpha = (a_1, a_2)$ and $\beta = (b_1, b_2)$, then $\alpha = \beta$ if and only if $a_1 = b_1$ and $a_2 = b_2$.

SCALAR MULTIPLICATION OF VECTORS   The product of $\alpha = (a_1, a_2)$ by the real scalar k is $k\alpha = (ka_1, ka_2)$.

VECTOR ADDITION   The sum of $\alpha = (a_1, a_2)$ and $\beta = (b_1, b_2)$ is the vector $\alpha + \beta = (a_1 + b_1, a_2 + b_2)$ (see Figure 4.3).

All of these concepts find their counterpart in three-space. Thus, a vector emanating from the origin with terminus $P(a_1, a_2, a_3)$ is constructed as in Figure 4.4, and the sum of vectors $\alpha = (a_1, a_2, a_3)$ and $\beta = (b_1, b_2, b_3)$ is determined by the parallelogram law as in Figure 4.5.

It can be established that for arbitrary vectors α and β and any scalars m and n the following laws hold. (The reader is asked to prove them for three-space in Problem 5, this section.)

PROPERTIES OF SCALAR MULTIPLICATION OF VECTORS

    (a) $m\alpha = \alpha m$.
    (b) $m(n\alpha) = (mn)\alpha$.
    (c) $(m + n)\alpha = m\alpha + n\alpha$.
    (d) $m(\alpha + \beta) = m\alpha + m\beta$.

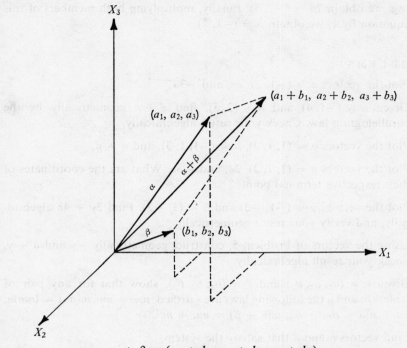

$$\alpha + \beta = (a_1 + b_1, a_2 + b_2, a_3 + b_3).$$

FIGURE 4.5

ILLUSTRATION **4.16**   Find vectors α and β that satisfy the system of vectors

$$\alpha - 3\beta = (2, -1)$$
$$2\alpha + \beta = (-3, 1).$$

Using property (d) multiply both members of the second equation by 3 to obtain

$$\alpha - 3\beta = (2, -1)$$
$$6\alpha + 3\beta = (-9, 3).$$

Using property (c) we eliminate β, obtaining

$$7\alpha = (-7, 2).$$

Next, using property (b) we multiply by $\frac{1}{7}$ to obtain $\alpha = (-1, \frac{2}{7})$. Similarly, we eliminate α by first writing the given equations in the form

$$-2\alpha + 6\beta = (-4, 2)$$
$$2\alpha + \ \beta = (-3, 1)$$

Adding, we obtain $7\beta = (-7, 3)$. Finally, multiplying both members of this last equation by $\frac{1}{7}$, we obtain $\beta = (-1, \frac{3}{7})$.

PROBLEMS

1. Plot the vectors $\alpha = (-1, 2)$, 2α, and -3α.

2. Given $\alpha = (-1, 4)$ and $\beta = (2, 3)$, find $\alpha + \beta$ geometrically by the parallelogram law. Check your result algebraically.

3. Plot the vectors $\alpha = (1, 1, 2)$, $\beta = (-1, 1, 3)$, and $\alpha + \beta$.

4. Plot the vectors $\alpha = (1, 1, 2)$, 2α, and -3α. What are the coordinates of their respective terminal points?

5. Plot the vectors $\gamma = (-1, -3)$ and $\delta = (2, -2)$. Find $2\gamma + 4\delta$ algebraically, and verify your result geometrically.

6. Using the vectors of Problem 5, construct geometrically $-\gamma$ and $\delta - \gamma$. Check your result algebraically.

7. Given $\alpha = (a_1, a_2, a_3)$ and $\beta = (b_1, b_2, b_3)$, show that for any pair of scalars m and n the following laws are satisfied: $m\alpha = \alpha m, m(n\alpha) = (mn)\alpha$, $(m + n)\alpha = m\alpha + n\alpha$, $m(\alpha + \beta) = m\alpha + m\beta$.

8. Find vectors α and β that satisfy the system,

$$2\alpha + \beta = (-2, 3, -2)$$
$$\alpha - 2\beta = (-1, -1, -6).$$

9. Given the following vector equations, solve for α and β,

$$2\alpha + 3\beta = (-1, 2, 3)$$
$$\alpha - 2\beta = (0, -3, 1).$$

10. Determine vectors α, β, γ, that satisfy the system

$$\alpha - \beta + 2\gamma = (2, 2, 3)$$
$$2\alpha - \gamma = (2, 1, 3)$$
$$\alpha + 2\beta = (-1, 3, 4).$$

4.4   VECTORS AND VECTOR SPACES

We now generalize the concept of a vector in two ways. First, instead of limiting our discussion to vectors with two or three components, we shall discuss vectors with n components, where n is a positive integer. Second, we shall generalize by selecting the components from any scalar field $\mathscr{F}$. In most instances the components will be rational numbers. However, they may be any real numbers, complex numbers, or elements of a finite field.

DEFINITION **4.3**   An *n-dimensional vector over a field* $\mathscr{F}$ is an ordered *n*-tuple, $\alpha = (a_1, a_2, \ldots, a_n)$, where *n* is a positive integer and $a_i \in \mathscr{F}$, where $i = 1, 2, \ldots, n$.

DEFINITION **4.4**   Two *n*-dimensional vectors, $\alpha = (a_1, a_2, \ldots, a_n)$ and $\beta = (b_1, b_2, \ldots, b_n)$, are *equal* if and only if $a_i = b_i$ for all *i*, where $i = 1, 2, \ldots, n$.

DEFINITION **4.5**   A *vector space*, $V_n(\mathscr{F})$, is an algebraic system consisting of the set of all *n*-dimensional vectors, $\{\alpha, \beta, \ldots\}$, over a field $\mathscr{F}$ together with the following operations:

(a)   *Vector addition*, for all vectors $\alpha, \beta, \ldots$ in the set,

$$\alpha + \beta = (a_1 + b_1, a_2 + b_2, \ldots, a_n + b_n);$$

(b)   *Scalar multiplication*, for any vector α in the set and all scalars k in $\mathscr{F}$,

$$k\alpha = (ka_1, ka_2, \ldots, ka_n).$$

ILLUSTRATION **4.17**   Let $\mathscr{F}$ be the finite field consisting of the set $\{0, 1, 2\}$ together with addition and multiplication as defined in Problem 7, Section 4.2. Find $2\alpha + \beta$, where $\alpha = (1, 1, 2)$ and $\beta = (2, 0, 1)$.

The solution is:

$$2\alpha = (2, 2, 1)$$
$$\beta = (2, 0, 1)$$
$$\overline{\qquad 2\alpha + \beta = (1, 2, 2) \qquad}$$

The results obtained in the following theorems are useful in extending the algebra of vector spaces.

THEOREM **4.1**   *Vector addition is commutative.*

Proof.   Let $\alpha = (a_1, a_2, \ldots, a_n)$ and $\beta = (b_1, b_2, \ldots, b_n)$ belong to $V_n(\mathscr{F})$; then

$$
\begin{aligned}
\alpha + \beta &= (a_1 + b_1, a_2 + b_2, \ldots, a_n + b_n) \\
&= (b_1 + a_1, b_2 + a_2, \ldots, b_n + a_n) \quad \text{(since $\mathscr{F}$ is a field)} \\
&= \beta + \alpha.
\end{aligned}
$$

THEOREM **4.2**   *Vector addition is associative.*

Proof. Let $\alpha = (a_1, a_2, \ldots, a_n)$, $\beta = (b_1, b_2, \ldots, b_n)$, $\gamma = (c_1, c_2, \ldots, c_n)$ belong to $V_n(\mathscr{F})$; then

$$
\begin{aligned}
\alpha + (\beta + \gamma) &= (a_1, a_2, \ldots, a_n) + (b_1 + c_1, b_2 + c_2, \ldots, b_n + c_n) \\
&= [a_1 + (b_1 + c_1), a_2 + (b_2 + c_2), \ldots, a_n + (b_n + c_n)] \\
&= [(a_1 + b_1) + c_1, (a_2 + b_2) + c_2, \ldots, (a_n + b_n) + c_n] \\
&= (\alpha + \beta) + \gamma.
\end{aligned}
$$

The associative law holds for vector addition, so we shall omit the parentheses and write $\alpha + \beta + \gamma$.

ILLUSTRATION **4.18** Given that $\mathscr{F}$ is the field of complex numbers and that $\alpha = (1, 1 - i, 2i)$, $\beta = (i, 1 + i, -2)$, and $\gamma = (1 + i, 2, -2 + 2i)$, show that $(1 - i)\alpha + 2\beta - \gamma = (0, 0, 0)$.

The solution is:

$$
\begin{aligned}
(1 - i)\alpha &= (1 - i, -2i, 2 + 2i) \\
2\beta &= (2i, 2 + 2i, -4) \\
-\gamma &= (-1 - i, -2, 2 - 2i) \\
\hline
(1 - i)\alpha + 2\beta - \gamma &= (0, 0, 0)
\end{aligned}
$$

In the preceding illustration the vector $(0, 0, 0)$ is used; this is called the *zero vector* in $V_3(\mathscr{F})$. $\mathscr{F}$ is the complex field. The general case follows.

DEFINITION **4.6** The *zero vector* in $V_n(\mathscr{F})$ is the vector $\theta = (0, 0, \ldots, 0)$, each of whose n components is the additive identity in the scalar field $\mathscr{F}$.

DEFINITION **4.7** If $\alpha = (a_1, a_2, \ldots, a_n)$ is in $V_n(\mathscr{F})$, and if the additive inverse of a_i is denoted by $-a_i$, then the vector $(-\alpha) = (-a_1, -a_2, \ldots, -a_n)$ is defined as the *inverse* of α. *Note*: $\alpha + (-\alpha) = (a_1 - a_1, a_2 - a_2, \ldots, a_n - a_n) = (0, \ldots, 0) = \theta$.

PROBLEMS

1. Given $\alpha = (2, -1, 3, 2)$, $\beta = (-1, -1, 2, 3)$, and $\gamma = (1, -1, -2, 0)$, find $2\alpha - 3\beta + \gamma$, $3\alpha - \beta + 2\gamma$, and $2\alpha + 3\beta + 3\gamma$.

2. Given $\alpha = (1, 2, 1, 0)$, $\beta = (3, -1, 2, 2)$, and $\gamma = (-1, 5, 0, -2)$, show that $2\alpha - \beta - \gamma = \theta$.

3. Given $2\alpha - 3\beta = (1, -1, 2)$ and $3\alpha + \beta = (2, 2, -3)$, find α and β.

4. Given $F = \{0, 1, 2\}$, with addition and multiplication defined as in Problem 7, Section 4.2, do the following.
   (a) Show that the inverse of $\alpha = (1, 2, 1)$ is $(-\alpha) = (2, 1, 2)$.
   (b) Solve $2\beta + \gamma = (1, 1, 2)$ and $\beta + \gamma = (2, 1, 0)$ for β and γ.

5. Given the vectors $\alpha = (1 - i, 2i, 2 + i)$, $\beta = (i, 1, 1 + i)$, and $\gamma = (2i, -1 + i, -1 + 4i)$, show that $i\alpha + (1 + i)\beta - \gamma = \theta$.

6. Given that the scalars and components of the vectors in the following set of equations belong to the algebraic system described in Problem 7, Section 4.2, solve for the vectors α, β, γ:

$$\begin{aligned} \alpha + 2\beta + \gamma &= (2, 1, 2) \\ 2\alpha \quad\quad + \gamma &= (1, 1, 1) \\ \alpha \quad\quad + \gamma &= (2, 1, 0) \end{aligned}$$

7. Given the same as in Problem 6, solve for the vectors α, β, γ:

$$\begin{aligned} 2\alpha + 2\beta + \gamma &= (0, 2, 1) \\ \alpha \quad \beta \quad\quad &= (1, 0, 2) \\ 2\alpha + \beta + 2\gamma &= (2, 2, 2) \end{aligned}$$

8. Solve for α and β given that the components of the vectors and the coefficients in the following equations are complex numbers.

$$\begin{aligned} i\alpha + 2\beta &= (2 + 5i, -1 + 9i, 5 + 2i) \\ 3\alpha + 2i\beta &= (-1 + 2i, -5 + 3i, -2 + i). \end{aligned}$$

9. Same as Problem 8, for the system

$$\begin{aligned} i\alpha - 2\beta &= (1 - i, 1 - 4i, -2 - 4i) \\ 3\alpha + 2i\beta &= (1 - 3i, i, -8 + 2i). \end{aligned}$$

4.5 LINEAR DEPENDENCE AND INDEPENDENCE

Let $\alpha = (a_1, a_2, a_3)$ and $\beta = (b_1, b_2, b_3)$ be *equal* vectors in $V_3(\mathscr{F})$. Then by definition of equality, it is necessary and sufficient that $a_1 = b_1$, $a_2 = b_2$, $a_3 = b_3$.

The vectors γ and δ are said to be *proportional* if there exist scalars r and s (not both zero) such that $r\gamma = s\delta$ or, equivalently, $r\gamma - s\delta = \theta$.

For example, if $\gamma = (1, -2, -1)$ and $3\gamma - 2\delta = \theta$, then $\delta = (\frac{3}{2}, -3, -\frac{3}{2})$.

We now generalize these notions by considering a finite set, $\{\alpha_1, \alpha_2, \ldots, \alpha_r\}$, of n-dimensional vectors whose components belong to a field $\mathscr{F}$:

$$\begin{aligned} \alpha_1 &= (a_{11}, a_{12}, \ldots, a_{1n}) \\ \alpha_2 &= (a_{21}, a_{22}, \ldots, a_{2n}) \\ &\vdots \quad\quad \vdots \quad\quad \vdots \quad\quad \vdots \\ \alpha_r &= (a_{r1}, a_{r2}, \ldots, a_{rn}). \end{aligned} \qquad (4.1)$$

DEFINITION **4.8** A vector β in $V_n(\mathscr{F})$ is a *linear combination* of the vectors (4.1) if and only if

$$\beta = k_1\alpha_1 + k_2\alpha_2 + \cdots + k_r\alpha_r,$$

where $k_1, k_2, \ldots, k_r$ are scalars in the field $\mathscr{F}$.

ILLUSTRATION **4.19** Let $\alpha_1 = (1, -1, -2)$, $\alpha_2 = (0, 2, 1)$, and $\alpha_3 = (-3, 2, 2)$; then the vector,

$$\begin{aligned}
\beta &= 2\alpha_1 - \alpha_2 + \alpha_3 \\
&= (2, -2, -4) + (0, -2, -1) + (-3, 2, 2) \\
&= (-1, -2, -3),
\end{aligned}$$

is a linear combination of the vectors α_1, α_2, α_3.

A natural generalization of a pair of proportional vectors is the concept of a *linearly dependent* set of r vectors formally defined and discussed below.

DEFINITION **4.9** The set of vectors (4.1) is said to be *linearly dependent* if and only if there exist scalars $h_1, h_2, \ldots, h_r$ in the field $\mathscr{F}$, not all zero, such that

$$h_1\alpha_1 + h_2\alpha_2 + \cdots + h_r\alpha_r = \theta,$$

where $\theta = (0, 0, \ldots, 0)$ is the zero vector in $V_n(\mathscr{F})$.

ILLUSTRATION **4.20** If $\alpha_1 = (1, -1, 1)$, $\alpha_2 = (2, 0, -1)$, and $\alpha_3 = (0, -2, 3)$, then, since

$$\begin{aligned}
2\alpha_1 - \alpha_2 - \alpha_3 &= (2, -2, 2) + (-2, 0, 1) + (0, 2, -3) \\
&= (0, 0, 0) \\
&= \theta,
\end{aligned}$$

the set $\{\alpha_1, \alpha_2, \alpha_3\}$ is linearly dependent in the vector space $V_3(\mathscr{R})$, where $\mathscr{R}$ is the real field.

In contrast to the notion of linear dependence is the following concept.

DEFINITION **4.10** A set $\{\beta_1, \beta_2, \ldots, \beta_s\}$ of vectors in $V_n(\mathscr{F})$ is *linearly independent* if and only if the linear combination $k_1\beta_1 + k_2\beta_2 + \cdots + k_s\beta_s = \theta$ implies that $k_1 = k_2 = \cdots = k_s = 0$.

A set of linearly independent vectors corresponds to a pair of vectors that are *not* proportional.

ILLUSTRATION **4.21** Let us show that a set of vectors, $\{\beta_1, \beta_2, \beta_3\}$, where $\beta_1 = (1, -1, 1)$, $\beta_2 = (2, 2, 0)$, and $\beta_3 = (1, 3, 2)$, is linearly independent.

Assume scalars k_1, k_2, k_3 such that $k_1\beta_1 + k_2\beta_2 + k_3\beta_3 = \theta$. Performing the indicated operations, we obtain

$$
\begin{aligned}
k_1\beta_1 + k_2\beta_2 + k_3\beta_3 &= (k_1, -k_1, k_1) + (2k_2, 2k_2, 0) + (k_3, 3k_3, 2k_3) \\
&= (k_1 + 2k_2 + k_3, -k_1 + 2k_2 + 3k_3, k_1 + 2k_3) \\
&= (0, 0, 0).
\end{aligned}
$$

By the definition of equality of vectors, we have, on equating components, the following system of equations.

$$
\begin{aligned}
k_1 + 2k_2 + k_3 &= 0 \\
-k_1 + 2k_2 + 3k_3 &= 0 \\
k_1 + 2k_3 &= 0.
\end{aligned}
$$

From the third equation we have $k_1 = -2k_3$. Substituting $-2k_3$ for k_1 in the first and second equations, we obtain

$$
\begin{aligned}
2k_2 - k_3 &= 0 \\
2k_2 + 5k_3 &= 0.
\end{aligned}
$$

Subtracting gives $6k_3 = 0$. Thus, $k_1 = k_2 = k_3 = 0$. By Definition 4.10 the given vectors are independent.

An important set of n linearly independent vectors is the set of *unit* vectors,

$$
\begin{aligned}
\varepsilon_1 &= (1, 0, \ldots, 0) \\
\varepsilon_2 &= (0, 1, \ldots, 0) \\
&\vdots \\
\varepsilon_n &= (0, 0, \ldots, 1),
\end{aligned}
\tag{4.2}
$$

where the typical vector ε_i has 1 for its ith component and each of the remaining $n - 1$ components is zero. It is easy to see that these vectors are linearly independent for, if the linear combination $k_1\varepsilon_1 + k_2\varepsilon_2 + \cdots + k_n\varepsilon_n$ is formed, we have

$$(k_1, 0, \ldots, 0) + (0, k_2, \ldots, 0) + \cdots + (0, 0, \ldots, k_n) = (k_1, k_2, \ldots, k_n).$$

However, if the vector $(k_1, k_2, \ldots, k_n)$ is the zero vector, then $k_1 = k_2 = \cdots = k_n = 0$. Hence, by Definition 4.10 the set of unit vectors (4.2) is linearly independent.

There are many interesting theorems in the theory of linear dependence. However, we limit ourselves to two theorems that are important to our immediate needs.

THEOREM **4.3**   *If a set $V = \{\alpha_1, \alpha_2, \ldots, \alpha_s\}$ of vectors in $V_n(\mathscr{F})$ contains a subset of r linearly dependent vectors, where $0 < r \leqslant s$, then the entire set V is linearly dependent.*

Proof. We lose no generality in assuming that the r dependent vectors are the first r vectors in the set V, since they can be rearranged and re-numbered, if necessary. By Definition 4.9 there exist r scalars, $h_1, h_2, \ldots, h_r$, *not all zero*, such that $h_1\alpha_1 + h_2\alpha_2 + \cdots + h_r\alpha_r = \theta$; therefore, choosing $h_{r+1} = h_{r+2} = \cdots = h_s = 0$, we have

$$h_1\alpha_1 + h_2\alpha_2 + \cdots + h_r\alpha_r + h_{r+1}\alpha_{r+1} + \cdots + h_s\alpha_s = \theta,$$

where not every $h_i = 0$, which establishes the theorem.

For example, the vectors $\alpha_1 = (1, -1)$, $\alpha_2 = (2, 0)$, $\alpha_3 = (-1, 3)$ $\alpha_4 = (1, 1)$ are dependent, since $-3\alpha_1 + \alpha_2 - \alpha_3 = \theta$.

Any set $\{\alpha_1, \alpha_2, \ldots, \alpha_m\}$ that contains the zero vector θ is dependent. We may choose any scalar $h \neq 0$ for the coefficient of θ and choose all the rest of the coefficients in the linear combination zero if necessary. In any case, $h\theta + h_1\alpha_1 + \cdots + h_m\alpha_m = \theta$, where at least one coefficient h is different from zero. Therefore, the set V is linearly dependent.

THEOREM **4.4** *If a set $V = \{\beta_1, \beta_2, \ldots, \beta_m\}$ of vectors in $V_n(\mathscr{F})$ is linearly independent, but the set $\{\beta_1, \beta_2, \ldots, \beta_m, \alpha\}$ is linearly dependent, then the vector α is a linear combination of the vectors in V.*

Proof. Since the set $\{\beta_1, \ldots, \beta_m, \alpha\}$ is linearly dependent there exist scalars, $k_1, \ldots, k_m, k_{m+1}$ (not all zero), such that $k_1\beta_1 + \cdots + k_m\beta_m + k_{m+1}\alpha = \theta$. Furthermore, $k_{m+1} \neq 0$, for otherwise we should have $k_1\beta_1 + \cdots + k_m\beta_m = \theta$, where not all the coefficients k_i are zero. This contradicts the assumption that the set V is independent. Hence, $k_{m+1} \neq 0$, and its inverse, k_{m+1}^{-1}, exists. Therefore,

$$\alpha = -k_{m+1}^{-1}(k_1\beta_1 + \cdots + k_m\beta_m),$$

which states that α is a linear combination of the vectors in the set V.

For example, the vectors $\beta_1 = (1, -1, 1)$, $\beta_2 = (2, 2, 0)$, and $\beta_3 = (1, 3, 2)$ were shown to be linearly independent (see Illustration 4.21). However, the vectors β_1, β_2, β_3, and α, where $\alpha = (-1, 1, 0)$, are dependent. Indeed, $\alpha = -\frac{2}{3}\beta_1 - \frac{1}{3}\beta_2 + \frac{1}{3}\beta_3$.

PROBLEMS

1. Prove that the vectors $\alpha_1 = (1, 1, -1)$, $\alpha_2 = (2, 1, 1)$, and $\alpha_3 = (1, 0, 4)$ are independent.

2. Prove that $\alpha_1 = (1, 1, -1)$ and $\alpha_2 = (2, 1, 1)$ are independent but that the set $\{\alpha_1, \alpha_2, \beta\}$, where $\beta = (0, 1, -3)$, is dependent. Express β as a linear combination of α_1 and α_2.

3. Prove that the vectors $\alpha_1 = (1, -1, 0)$, $\alpha_2 = (2, 2, 1)$, and $\alpha_3 = (0, 4, 1)$ are dependent, and express α_3 as a linear combination of α_1 and α_2.

4. Prove that any two vectors in $V_n(\mathscr{F})$ are dependent if and only if their components are proportional.

5. Use the result proved in Problem 4 along with Theorem 4.3 to prove that the following vectors are dependent: $\alpha_1 = (1, -1, 2)$, $\alpha_2 = (3, 0, 4)$, and $\alpha_3 = (-2, 2, -4)$.

6. Write $\alpha_1 = (1, -1)$ and $\alpha_2 = (1, 3)$ as linear combinations of the unit vectors $\varepsilon_1 = (1, 0)$ and $\varepsilon_2 = (0, 1)$.

7. Solve the vector equation found in Problem 6 for ε_1 and ε_2 as linear combinations of α_1 and α_2.

8. Find the value of x which will make the following vectors linearly dependent: $\alpha_1 = (1, x - 1, -2)$, $\alpha_2 = (0, 2x, -4)$, and $\alpha_3 = (3, x - 1, 1)$.

9. Find the three vectors α, β, and γ belonging to $V_3(\mathscr{R})$, in which $\alpha - \beta = (-1, -1, 1)$, $\alpha + \gamma = (1, 0, 1)$, and $2\alpha + \beta + \gamma = (4, -1, 4)$.

10. Prove that a necessary and sufficient condition that the vectors $\alpha = (a_1, a_2)$ and $\beta = (b_1, b_2)$ be linearly independent is that $a_1 b_2 - a_2 b_1 \neq 0$.

11. Prove that a set $\{\alpha\}$ consisting of a single vector α is dependent if and only if $\alpha = \theta$.

4.6 VECTOR SUBSPACES

In order to introduce the basic ideas of this section let us consider first the set of all three-dimensional vectors whose components are scalars in the real field. As we have seen (Section 4.3), this space, $V_3(\mathscr{R})$, is represented geometrically by all the vectors emanating from the origin of a reference frame in three-dimensional Euclidean space. In particular, however, all the vectors that lie in a fixed plane through the origin constitute a vector space V' in its own right, which is a part of the whole space, $V_3(\mathscr{R})$. Then the linear combinations of the vectors in this plane will yield only vectors *that lie in the same plane.* What this means geometrically is that, if we construct vectors by the only two operations available, namely scalar multiplication and addition by the parallelogram law, it is impossible to construct a vector that does not lie in the given plane. Thus, the vector space V' is *closed* with respect to scalar multiplication and vector addition. This concept will be extended to $V_n(\mathscr{F})$ in Definition 4.11.

ILLUSTRATION **4.22** Consider two vectors, $\alpha_1 = (2, 1, 3)$ and $\alpha_2 = (4, 2, 3)$, in three-dimensional Euclidean space. Sketch the given vectors and an arbitrary vector in the subspace (plane) determined by them. What is the general equation of a vector in this subspace?

The expression for an arbitrary vector having the same direction as α_1 is $k_1\alpha_1 = (2k_1, k_1, 3k_1)$, where k_1 is any real number. Similarly, an arbitrary vector with the same direction as α_2 is $k_2\alpha_2 = (4k_2, 2k_2, 3k_2)$. The expression

$$k_1\alpha_1 + k_2\alpha_2 = (2k_1 + 4k_2, k_1 + 2k_2, 3k_1 + 3k_2)$$

is the vector equation of all vectors coplanar with α_1 and α_2. The scalars k_1 and k_2 are parameters and, as they are allowed to vary over the set of real numbers, the expression $k_1\alpha_1 + k_2\alpha_2$ determines each and every one of the vectors in the plane of α_1 and α_2. In particular, if k_2 is 0 and k_1 is allowed to vary, the expression $k_1\alpha_1 + k_2\alpha_2$ determines all of the vectors $k_1\alpha_1$ having the same direction as α_1 and, if $k_1 = 0$, all of the vectors $k_2\alpha_2$ along the line of direction of α_2 are obtained (see Figure 4.6).

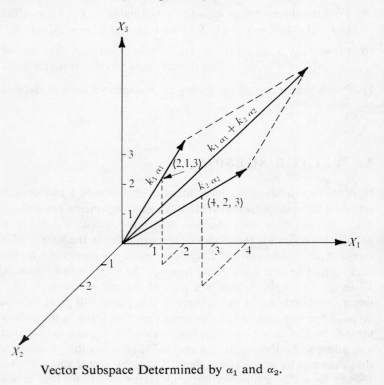

Vector Subspace Determined by α_1 and α_2.

FIGURE 4.6

DEFINITION **4.11**   A subset V of n-dimensional vectors, whose components are scalars belonging to a field $\mathscr{F}$, forms a *linear vector space* if and only if:

(a)   The sum of any two vectors in the set is also in the set.
(b)   All scalar multiples of any vector in the set are also in the set.

The set $\{\theta\}$ consisting of only the zero vector in $V_n(\mathscr{F})$ is an example of a linear vector space. An example which is not quite as trivial is the following.

ILLUSTRATION **4.23**   Show that all vectors of the type $(0, x_2, x_3)$, where 0 is the additive identity and x_2 and x_3 are arbitrary elements in $\mathscr{F}$, form a linear vector space.

Two arbitrary vectors in the set are $\alpha = (0, a_2, a_3)$ and $\beta = (0, b_2, b_3)$. Their sum is $\alpha + \beta = (0, a_2 + b_2, a_3 + b_3)$, which belongs to the set. If k also is an arbitrary element in $\mathscr{F}$, the scalar multiple $k\alpha = (0, ka_2, ka_3)$ is a vector in the set. Hence, by Definition 4.11, all vectors of the type $(0, x_2, x_3)$ constitute a linear vector space.

An example of *a set of vectors that does not constitute a linear vector space* is the following.

ILLUSTRATION **4.24**   The set S of vectors of the type $(1, x_2, x_3)$, where 1 is the multiplicative identity and x_2 and x_3 are arbitrary elements in a field $\mathscr{F}$, fails to satisfy requirement (b) of Definition 4.11. Let $\alpha = (1, a_2, a_3)$ be an arbitrary vector in S and $k \neq 1$ belong to $\mathscr{F}$. Since $k \times 1 = k$ for all $k \in \mathscr{F}$, it follows that $k\alpha = (k, ka_2, ka_3) \notin S$. Hence, the set S is not a linear vector space.

An important result that explains how *all* linear vector spaces are formed is given in the following theorem.

THEOREM **4.5**   *If S is a finite subset of vectors belonging to $V_n(\mathscr{F})$, then the set V of all linear combinations of the vectors in S is a linear vector space.*

Proof.   Let $S = \{\alpha_1, \alpha_2, \ldots, \alpha_r\}$ be a finite set of vectors in $V_n(\mathscr{F})$. Typical vectors in V may be written

$$\beta = b_1\alpha_1 + b_2\alpha_2 + \cdots + b_r\alpha_r,$$
$$\gamma = c_1\alpha_1 + c_2\alpha_2 + \cdots + c_r\alpha_r,$$

where the coefficients b_i and c_j are scalars in $\mathscr{F}$. Forming the sum,

$$\beta + \gamma = (b_1 + c_1)\alpha_1 + (b_2 + c_2)\alpha_2 + \cdots + (b_r + c_r)a_r,$$

and recalling that $b_k + c_k$ belongs to $\mathscr{F}$ whenever b_k and c_k belong to $\mathscr{F}$, we see that $\beta + \gamma$ belongs to V if β and γ belong to V.

Next, consider the scalar product of β and an arbitrary scalar k belonging to $\mathscr{F}$:

$$k\beta = (kb_1)\alpha_1 + (kb_2)\alpha_2 + \cdots + (kb_r)\alpha_r.$$

This also belongs to the set V, since the coefficients, kb_i, belong to $\mathscr{F}$. Hence, by Definition 4.11 the set V is a linear vector space.

ILLUSTRATION 4.25 If $\alpha = (1, -1, 2)$ and $\beta = (3, 0, -2)$, then

$$2\alpha - 3\beta = (2, -2, 4) + (-9, 0, 6) = (-7, -2, 10),$$
$$3\alpha + \beta = (3, -3, 6) + (3, 0, -2) = (6, -3, 4)$$

belong to the subspace of $V_3(\mathscr{R})$ formed by linearly combining vectors α and β.

DEFINITION 4.12 The linear vector space V obtained by forming all possible linear combinations of a finite subset $S = \{\alpha_1, \alpha_2, \ldots, \alpha_r\}$ of $V_n(\mathscr{F})$ is said to be the *subspace* of $V_n(\mathscr{F})$ *generated* by the vectors of S. These vectors in turn are said to *span* the space V.

Thus, in the above example, the vectors $\alpha = (1, -1, 2)$ and $\beta = (3, 0, -2)$ span the space whose general vector has the form

$$k_1\alpha + k_2\beta = (k_1 + 3k_2, -k_1, 2k_1 - 2k_2),$$

where k_1 and k_2 are arbitrary real scalars.

DEFINITION 4.13 A *basis* of a subspace V of $V_n(\mathscr{F})$ is a set of k linearly independent vectors in $V_n(\mathscr{F})$ that span V.

ILLUSTRATION 4.26 The unit vectors $\varepsilon_1 = (1, 0, \ldots, 0)$, $\varepsilon_2 = (0, 1, \ldots, 0)$, $\ldots, \varepsilon_n = (0, 0, \ldots, 1)$ of $V_n(\mathscr{F})$ are linearly independent (this was shown in Section 4.5). Furthermore, every vector in $V_n(\mathscr{F})$ is a linear combination of these vectors, for if $(k_1, k_2, \ldots, k_n)$ is an arbitrary vector in $V_n(\mathscr{F})$, then

$$(k_1, k_2, \ldots, k_n) = k_1\varepsilon_1 + k_2\varepsilon_2 + \cdots + k_n\varepsilon_n.$$

Hence the set $\{\varepsilon_1, \varepsilon_2, \ldots, \varepsilon_n\}$ is a basis of $V_n(\mathscr{F})$.

Thus, $V_n(\mathscr{F})$ may be considered to be a subspace of itself and, by Theorem 4.5, $V_n(\mathscr{F})$ is a linear vector space. Henceforth *we shall refer to $V_n(\mathscr{F})$ and its subspaces as vector spaces rather than as linear vector spaces.*

ILLUSTRATION 4.27 Show that the vectors $\alpha_1 = (1, -1, 0)$, $\alpha_2 = (1, 0, 1)$, and $\alpha_3 = (0, 1, -2)$ are independent and hence constitute a basis of a vector space. Write the general vector in the space spanned by the vectors of this basis.

In Problem 4, Section 4.5, we saw that two vectors are dependent only if their components are proportional. Since this is clearly not the case with vectors α_1 and α_2, they are independent.

To show that the three vectors α_1, α_2, and α_3 are linearly independent, we must show that the assumption that there exist scalars k_1, k_2, and k_3 such that $k_1\alpha_1 + k_2\alpha_2 + k_3\alpha_3 = \theta$ leads to the conclusion $k_1 = k_2 = k_3 = 0$. Forming the required linear combination, we have

$$k_1(1, -1, 0) + k_2(1, 0, 1) + k_3(0, 1, -2) = \theta$$

or, equivalently,

$$(k_1 + k_2, -k_1 + k_3, k_2 - 2k_3) = \theta.$$

Since two vectors are equal if and only if their corresponding components are equal, we have the following conditions involving the scalars k_i:

$$
\begin{aligned}
k_1 + k_2 &= 0, \\
-k_1 + k_3 &= 0, \\
k_2 - 2k_3 &= 0.
\end{aligned}
$$

From the last equation we have $k_2 = 2k_3$. Substituting from this equation into the first, we have, together with the second equation,

$$
\begin{aligned}
k_1 + 2k_3 &= 0, \\
-k_1 + k_3 &= 0.
\end{aligned}
$$

Solving these equations simultaneously, we obtain $k_1 = k_3 = 0$ and, hence, $k_2 = 2k_3 = 0$. Therefore, we may conclude that the set of vectors $\{\alpha_1, \alpha_2, \alpha_3\}$ is linearly independent and by Definition 4.13 is a basis of the vector space spanned by the set.

The general vector in the space with basis $\{\alpha_1, \alpha_2, \alpha_3\}$ is of the form

$$\xi = x_1\alpha_1 + x_2\alpha_2 + x_3\alpha_3 = (x_1 + x_2, -x_1 + x_3, x_2 - 2x_3).$$

The expression "a basis" in Definition 4.13 implies that there may be more than one basis of a vector space. This is quite true. However, as we shall prove, *all bases of a given vector space have the same number of vectors.* In the meantime it is important to know that each vector of a space can be expressed in one and only one way as a linear combination of the vectors of a particular basis.

THEOREM **4.6**   *Let $\{\alpha_1, \alpha_2, \ldots, \alpha_r\}$ be a basis of a vector space V. Then, every vector β in V is uniquely expressible as a linear combination of the α_i.*

Proof.   Let us assume that an arbitrary vector β in V is expressible in two ways as linear combinations of the vectors α_i:

$$\beta = \sum_{i=1}^{r} a_i\alpha_i = \sum_{i=1}^{r} b_i\alpha_i.$$

Upon transposing and collecting terms in this expression, we have

$$\sum_{i=1}^{r} (a_i - b_i)\alpha_i = \theta. \tag{4.3}$$

By assumption the vectors α_i are linearly independent, since they constitute a basis. Therefore, each coefficient in Equation 4.3 must vanish. Thus,

$$a_i - b_i = 0, \qquad i = 1, \ldots, r$$
$$a_i = b_i, \qquad i = 1, \ldots, r.$$

We see from Theorem 4.5 that *any* set of vectors in $V_n(\mathcal{F})$ generates a subspace. This does not imply, however, that this set of vectors constitutes a basis of the subspace, for *besides spanning the subspace the vectors must be linearly independent*. The following theorem throws some light on this point.

THEOREM **4.7** *Let a vector space V be spanned by a finite set* $\{\alpha_1, \alpha_2, \ldots, \alpha_s\}$ *of nonzero vectors. Then V has a basis which consists of m of these vectors, where* $1 \leqslant m \leqslant s$.

Proof If the set is linearly independent, then the theorem is true with $m = s$. If the set is dependent, rearrange its elements, if necessary, and assume that the subset $\{\alpha_1, \alpha_2, \ldots, \alpha_m\}$ is independent but that the subset

$$\{\alpha_1, \alpha_2, \ldots, \alpha_m, \alpha_k\}$$

is dependent for each k, $k = m + 1, m + 2, \ldots, s$. Then by Theorem 4.4 we know that each of the vectors $\alpha_{m+1}, \alpha_{m+2}, \ldots, \alpha_s$ is expressible as a linear combination of the vectors $\alpha_1, \alpha_2, \ldots, \alpha_m$. Thus we can eliminate these dependent vectors, obtaining thereby a set of m linearly independent vectors that spans the space V and, hence, is a basis of this space.

ILLUSTRATION **4.28** Determine a basis of the space V spanned by the vectors $\alpha_1 = (1, -1, 2)$, $\alpha_2 = (2, 0, 1)$, $\alpha_3 = (0, 2, -3)$, and $\alpha_4 = (1, 1, -1)$.

Referring to Problem 4, Section 4.5, we see that α_1 and α_2 are independent, since their components are not proportional. Hence we begin the construction of a basis by including α_1 and α_2. Next we examine $\{\alpha_1, \alpha_2, \alpha_3\}$ for independence. From the equation $k_1\alpha_1 + k_2\alpha_2 + k_3\alpha_3 = \theta$ we obtain

$$k_1 + 2k_2 \qquad = 0$$
$$-k_1 \qquad + 2k_3 = 0$$
$$2k_1 + k_2 - 3k_3 = 0.$$

Solving the first two equations for $k_2 = -\frac{1}{2}k_1$ and $k_3 = \frac{1}{2}k_1$, respectively, we substitute these expressions in the third equation and obtain $2k_1 - \frac{1}{2}k_1 - \frac{3}{2}k_1 = 0$. Because this is identically zero for all values of k_1 we may choose

$k_1 \neq 0$, say $k_1 = 2$. Then $k_2 = -\frac{1}{2}(2) = -1$ and $k_3 = \frac{1}{2}(2) = 1$. Thus, $2\alpha_1 - \alpha_2 + \alpha_3 = \theta$, and we may eliminate α_3 from all linear combinations involving this vector by using the equation $\alpha_3 = -2\alpha_1 + \alpha_2$.

In a similar manner the set $\{\alpha_1, \alpha_2, \alpha_4\}$ is examined for independence, and we find that α_4 can be eliminated, because $\alpha_1 - \alpha_2 + \alpha_4 = \theta$. Thus the set $\{\alpha_1, \alpha_2\}$ is independent and spans the space. It is therefore a basis of V.

THEOREM **4.8** *Every basis of a given vector space V has the same number of vectors.*

Proof. Assume V has two bases, $A = \{\alpha_1, \alpha_2, \ldots, \alpha_r\}$ and $B = \{\beta_1, \beta_2, \ldots, \beta_s\}$, where $r \neq s$. Let us assume first the case in which $r > s$.*

Since the set B is assumed to be a basis of V, and since α_1 is a vector in V, it follows that α_1 is expressible as a linear combination of the β's. Therefore, the following set of vectors is dependent: $\alpha_1, \beta_1, \beta_2, \ldots, \beta_{s-1}, \beta_s$. Furthermore, $\{\alpha_1\}$ is independent. If it were not, α_1 would be equal to θ (see Problem 11, Section 4.5) and the set A would be a dependent set, contrary to the assumption that A is a basis. It follows from Theorem 4.4 that some one of the β's is a linear combination of the vectors that precede it. By reordering and renumbering the β's, if necessary, we may assume that β_s is dependent on the vectors preceding it. Eliminating this vector, we find that the set $\{\alpha_1, \beta_1, \ldots, \beta_{s-1}\}$ spans the space V.

By a similar argument, since the vector α_2 is in the space V, the set $\{\alpha_2, \alpha_1, \beta_1, \ldots, \beta_{s-1}\}$ spans the space V and is dependent. Since α_1 and α_2 are members of a basis A, they are independent. Hence, some one of the β's is a linear combination of the vectors preceding it in this last set. Again, after rearranging and renumbering we may eliminate β_{s-1}. Thus the space V is spanned by the set $\{\alpha_2, \alpha_1, \beta_1, \ldots, \beta_{s-2}\}$.

Repeating the above argument s times, we are led to the conclusion that the set $\{\alpha_s, \alpha_{s-1}, \ldots, \alpha_2, \alpha_1\}$ spans the space V. Now, if $r > s$, the remaining vectors, $\alpha_{s+1}, \alpha_{s+2}, \ldots, \alpha_r$, are in V, and therefore each must be a linear combination of the set $\{\alpha_1, \alpha_2, \ldots, \alpha_s\}$. This is a contradiction, because by our initial assumption the set $A = \{\alpha_1, \alpha_2, \ldots, \alpha_r\}$ is a basis of V and is, therefore, independent. The same type of argument shows that the assumption that $s > r$ is false. Hence, we must conclude that $r = s$; that is to say, the two bases have the same number of vectors.

In Illustration 4.26 of this section we showed that the set of n unit vectors, $\{\varepsilon_1, \varepsilon_2, \ldots, \varepsilon_n\}$, is a basis of $V_n(\mathscr{F})$. Combining this result with Theorem 4.8 we have

---

* This is an example of the indirect method of proof. If all goes well, the logical argument will lead to a contradiction.

THEOREM **4.9** *Every basis of $V_n(\mathscr{F})$ has exactly n vectors.*

COROLLARY *An arbitrary set of $n + 1$ vectors of $V_n(\mathscr{F})$ is linearly dependent.*

DEFINITION **4.14** The *dimension* of a space V is the number of vectors in a basis of V.

DEFINITION **4.15** The *coordinates* of a vector β *relative to* a basis $A = \{\alpha_1, \alpha_2, \ldots, \alpha_s\}$ are the scalars $k_1, k_2, \ldots, k_s$ in the linear combination $\beta = k_1\alpha_1 + k_2\alpha_2 + \cdots + k_s\alpha_s$, which expresses β in terms of the given basis. We shall find it convenient to use the notation $\langle k_1, k_2, \ldots, k_s \rangle$ whenever the basis is a set of vectors other than the unit vectors.

ILLUSTRATION **4.29** Show that the vector $\beta = (-1, -3, 4)$ belongs to the space V spanned by $\alpha_1 = (1, -1, 2)$ and $\alpha_2 = (2, 0, 1)$ by finding the coordinates of β relative to the basis $\{\alpha_1, \alpha_2\}$.

Setting $k_1\alpha_1 + k_2\alpha_2 = \beta$, we obtain

$$\begin{aligned} k_1 + 2k_2 &= -1 \\ -k_1 \qquad &= -3 \\ 2k_1 + \ k_2 &= 4, \end{aligned}$$

which yields the solution $\langle 3, -2 \rangle$, the coordinates of β relative to $\{\alpha_1, \alpha_2\}$.

PROBLEMS

1. Find the dimension of the space spanned by the vectors $\alpha_1 = (1, -1, 2)$, $\alpha_2 = (-2, 2, -4)$, $\alpha_3 = (0, 1, 1)$, and $\alpha_4 = (1, 0, 3)$, and determine a basis of the space.

2. What are the coordinates of the vector $\beta = (1, 5, 1)$ relative to the basis consisting of the vectors $\alpha_1 = (2, 1, -1)$, $\alpha_2 = (1, -1, -1)$?

3. Prove that the vector $\beta = (1, -1, 3)$ does not belong to the space spanned by $\alpha_1 = (1, 1, -1)$ and $\alpha_2 = (2, 0, 1)$.

4. Prove that vectors of the form $(a_1, a_2, a_2 - a_1)$, where a_1 and a_2 are arbitrary elements in a field $\mathscr{F}$, constitute a subspace of $V_3(\mathscr{F})$.

5. Find the coordinates of $\beta = (3, 2, -5)$ relative to the basis $\{\alpha_1, \alpha_2, \alpha_3\}$, where $\alpha_1 = (1, 0, 2)$, $\alpha_2 = (0, 0, 1)$, and $\alpha_3 = (2, 1, -1)$ are vectors in $V_3(\mathscr{R})$.

6. Find the coordinates of $\beta = (-1, -i, 0)$ relative to the basis $\{\alpha_1, \alpha_2\}$, where $\alpha_1 = (1, -i, 1 + i)$ and $\alpha_2 = (1, 1, i)$ span a subspace V of

$V_3(\mathscr{C})$, that is, three-dimensional vectors over the field $\mathscr{C}$ of complex numbers.

7. Find a basis for the subspace of $V_3(\mathscr{R})$ spanned by the vectors $\alpha_1 = (1, -1, 1)$, $\alpha_2 = (-2, 1, 0)$, $\alpha_3 = (0, -1, 2)$, and $\alpha_4 = (1, 0, 1)$.

8. Show that the vectors $\alpha_1 = (1, i, 1 - i)$, $\alpha_2 = (i, -1, 2i)$, and $\alpha_3 = (1 + i, 0, 2)$ are independent and therefore constitute a basis of $V_3(\mathscr{C})$.

9. Determine the coordinates of $\varepsilon_1 = (1, 0, 0)$ relative to the basis in Problem 8. What does the result prove is true of ε_1?

10. Given the basis $\{\alpha_1, \alpha_2, \alpha_3\}$ of $V_3(\mathscr{R})$, where $\alpha_1 = (1, -1, 0)$, $\alpha_2 = (2, 0, 1)$ and $\alpha_3 = (1, 1, -1)$, write each vector α_i in terms of the unit vectors, ε_1, ε_2, and ε_3, of $V_3(\mathscr{R})$. Solve this set of equations for the vectors ε_i in terms of the α_i. From the last result determine the coordinates of the ε-basis relative to the α-basis.

11. Show that the vectors $\rho_1 = (1 + i, -2i, 3)$, $\rho_2 = (2 - i, 1 + i, 1 - i)$, and $\rho_3 = (-3 + 2i, 1 - i, 1 + 4i)$ are linearly dependent. Express ρ_3 as a linear combination of ρ_1 and ρ_2.

12. Find the dimension and a basis of the linear vector space spanned by the vectors $\gamma_1 = (-1, 2, 1)$, $\gamma_2 = (2, -4, -2)$, $\gamma_3 = (1, 0, 2)$, and $\gamma_4 = (0, 2, 3)$. Find the coordinates of $\delta = (-4, 4, -2)$ relative to the basis selected.

13. Show that all vectors of the type $\rho = (r_1, r_2, r_3, r_4)$, where $r_1 = r_2 - r_4$, $r_3 = r_2 + 2r_4$, and the r_i are elements of a field, constitute a linear vector space. Determine the dimension of this space and a basis.

14. Do vectors of the type $\rho = (r, s, r^2)$, where r and s are elements of a field, constitute a linear vector space?

15. A basis of a certain space consists of the vectors $\mu_1 = (1, -2, 2)$, $\mu_2 = (0, 1, -1)$. Show that $\rho = (3, -4, 4)$ is in this space, and find its coordinates relative to the basis $\{\mu_1, \mu_2\}$. What are the coordinates of μ_1 and μ_2 relative to the given basis?

16. Do vectors of the type $\rho = (r, s, r + 2)$, where r and s are real, constitute a linear vector space?

17. Prove that any set of vectors which contains the zero vector is linearly dependent.

18. Determine whether or not vectors of the type $(r_1, r_1 - r_3, r_3)$, r_i real, form a linear vector space. If so, obtain a basis.

4.7 THE INNER PRODUCT OF VECTORS

Until now the only binary operation that has been defined on a set of vectors is vector addition. As we have seen, this operation maps $V_n(\mathcal{F}) \times V_n(\mathcal{F})$ into $V_n(\mathcal{F})$; that is, the sum of two vectors of dimension n is a vector of dimension n. However, there are other binary operations on the set of vectors $V_n(\mathcal{F})$ that do not map $V_n(\mathcal{F})$ into itself. One such operation, which will prove of particular importance in the development of matrix theory in the succeeding chapters, is that of the *inner product*, or *dot product*, of two vectors of the same dimension.

DEFINITION **4.16** The *inner product* (or *dot product*) $\alpha \cdot \beta$ of two vectors $\alpha = (\alpha_1, a_2, \ldots, a_n)$ and $\beta = (b_1, b_2, \ldots, b_n)$ belonging to $V_n(\mathcal{F})$ is the scalar

$$\alpha \cdot \beta = a_1 \times b_1 + a_2 \times b_2 + \cdots + a_n \times b_n = \sum_{k=1}^{n} a_k \times b_k$$

formed by adding the products of corresponding elements of α and β.

ILLUSTRATION **4.30** If $\alpha = (1, 1, -2, 3)$ and $\beta = (2, 0, 1, -1)$, then their inner product is

$$\alpha \cdot \beta = 1 \times 2 + 1 \times 0 - 2 \times 1 + 3 \times (-1) = -3.$$

In particular, when two vectors α and β of $V_n(\mathcal{F})$ are such that their inner product, $\alpha \cdot \beta$, is zero, they are said to be *orthogonal* vectors.

ILLUSTRATION **4.31** The vectors $\alpha = (1, -2, 3)$, $\beta = (2, 1, 0)$, $\gamma = (3, -6, -5)$ are orthogonal in pairs, since

$$\alpha \cdot \beta = 1 \times 2 - 2 \times 1 + 3 \times 0 = 0,$$
$$\alpha \cdot \gamma = 1 \times 3 - 2 \times (-6) + 3 \times (-5) = 0,$$
$$\beta \cdot \gamma = 2 \times 3 + 1 \times (-6) + 0 \times (-5) = 0.$$

ILLUSTRATION **4.32** A manufacturer wishes to calculate the unit cost of the output of his plant. To obtain this cost, it is assumed that there are four inputs with specific amounts that make up one unit of output:

> 2 units of land
> 1.5 units of labor
> 3 units of capital
> 5 units of raw material

We write the input in vector form: $I = (2, 1.5, 3, 5)$. The next step is to compute the cost per unit of each input. Suppose that these prices are the following:

$5 per unit of land
$4 per unit of labor
$10 per unit capital
$3 per unit of raw material

The so-called price vector is $C = (5, 4, 10, 3)$. The total cost per unit of output will be the inner product of the input vector and the price vector, namely,

$$I \cdot C = 2 \times 5 + 1.5 \times 4 + 3 \times 10 + 5 \times 3 = \$61.$$

PROBLEMS

1. Given the vectors $\alpha = (1, -1, 2, 0)$, $\beta = (-2, -2, 0, 1)$, and $\gamma = (3, -4, 1, -2)$, find:
   (a) $\alpha \cdot \beta$.   (b) $\beta \cdot \alpha$.   (c) $\alpha \cdot \gamma$.   (d) $\beta \cdot \gamma$.

2. Given the vectors $\alpha = (1 - i, 2i, 1 + 2i)$, $\bar{\alpha} = (1 + i, -2i, 1 - 2i)$, $\gamma = (2 + 3i, 1 - 2i, i)$, and $\bar{\gamma} = (2 - 3i, 1 + 2i, -i)$, find:
   (a) $\alpha \cdot \bar{\alpha}$.   (b) $\gamma \cdot \bar{\gamma}$.*

3. Prove that $\alpha = (1, -2, 3)$, $\beta = (2, -2, -2)$, and $\gamma = (5, 4, 1)$ are orthogonal in pairs.

4. Given the vectors $\gamma = (1, -1, 2)$ and $\delta = (2, 0, -3)$, determine the components of $\rho = (x, y, z)$, so that ρ will be orthogonal to both γ and δ.

5. A foundary produces two alloys, A and B. Construct the input vector and the price vector for each alloy, and determine the total cost per unit of each from the following information.

	Land	Labor	Capital	Material
A	2	1.0	3	4.0
B	2	1.5	2	3.5
Unit cost ($):	7	4	12	4

With header "Units" spanning Land, Labor, Capital, Material.

6. To control a certain fungus two sprays are available. The manufacturer charges 20% of the cost per unit for profit. Determine the selling price of each spray from the following data.

---

* $\bar{\alpha}$ is called the conjugate of vector α. Note that it is obtained from α by replacing each element by its conjugate complex number.

Units

	Chemical x	Chemical y	Chemical z	Land	Labor	Overhead
Spray 1	2	1	5	2	2	1
Spray 2	3	2	2	2	1.5	1
Unit cost ($):	$1.50	0.50	0.40	4.00	4.00	0.50

7. Prove that $\alpha \cdot \beta = \beta \cdot \alpha$ for all pairs of vectors α and β in $V_n(\mathscr{F})$.

8. The expression $\sqrt{\alpha \cdot \alpha}$, is defined as the *length* of a vector α when its components are real. Find the "length" of each of the following vectors.
   (a) $\rho = (x, y, z)$.   (b) $\alpha = (2, -2, 1)$.   (c) $\beta = (1, 1, 2)$.

9. The "length" of a vector μ with complex numbers as components is defined by $\sqrt{\bar{\mu} \cdot \mu}$. Find the "length" of each of
   (a) $\mu_1 = (1, 1 - i, 2i)$.
   (b) $\mu_2 = (2 + i, -3, 1 - i)$.
   (c) $\mu_3 = (1 + i, 2, 1 - 2i)$.

10. Find the "length" of the following vectors.
    (a) $\rho_1 = (2, -3, 1, 4)$.
    (b) $\rho_2 = (1 - i, 2 + 2i, 3, -i)$.
    (c) $\rho_3 = (1 + i, 2 - i, 3 + 2i, -2 + i)$.

11. A vector μ is said to be *normalized* when each of its components is divided by $\sqrt{\bar{\mu} \cdot \mu}$. Show that the length of a normalized vector is 1.

12. Normalize the vectors of Problem 10.

Supplementary Reading

HOHN, F. E., *Elementary Matrix Algebra*, 2nd ed., Macmillan, New York, 1964.
NAHIKIAN, H. M., *A Modern Algebra for Biologists*, Univ. Chicago, Chicago, 1964.
PERLIS, S., *Theory of Matrices*, Addison-Wesley, Cambridge, Mass., 1952.

5

VECTORS AND MATRICES

5.1 INTRODUCTION

Since the early 1940's there has been a tremendous upsurge of interest in the study of matrix theory. In this chapter the reader is introduced to this important branch of mathematics which has proven to be extremely useful not only to mathematicians but also to those who are primarily interested in such diverse fields as the biological sciences, economics, the engineering sciences, physics, psychology, and statistics.

Two English mathematicians, Arthur Cayley (1821–1895) and James Joseph Sylvester (1814–1897), discovered this important area of mathematics. Their early results have furnished a broad foundation upon which the modern theory of matrices is built.

5.2 THE FORM OF A MATRIX

As we shall discover subsequently, matrices are closely related to the concept of algebraic vectors which was discussed in the preceding chapter. It was pointed out there that a vector belonging to the vector space $V_n(\mathscr{F})$ is simply an ordered n-tuple of scalars belonging to the field $\mathscr{F}$. Throughout that discussion we found it convenient to write such vectors as rows. It should be clear, however, that an ordered n-tuple could just as well be written as a column, and aside from requiring extra space its essential characteristic, order, would remain unchanged. For example, if

$$\alpha_1 = \begin{bmatrix} 1 \\ -1 \\ 2 \end{bmatrix} \quad \text{and} \quad \alpha_2 = \begin{bmatrix} 2 \\ 2 \\ -3 \end{bmatrix},$$

then

$$\alpha_1 + \alpha_2 = \begin{bmatrix} 1 + 2 \\ -1 + 2 \\ 2 - 3 \end{bmatrix} = \begin{bmatrix} 3 \\ 1 \\ -1 \end{bmatrix}.$$

The zero vector in $V_3(\mathscr{F})$ written in column form is

$$\theta = \begin{bmatrix} 0 \\ 0 \\ 0 \end{bmatrix},$$

and the unit vectors are

$$\varepsilon_1 = \begin{bmatrix} 1 \\ 0 \\ 0 \end{bmatrix}, \quad \varepsilon_2 = \begin{bmatrix} 0 \\ 1 \\ 0 \end{bmatrix}, \quad \varepsilon_3 = \begin{bmatrix} 0 \\ 0 \\ 1 \end{bmatrix}.$$

A linear combination, $x_1\varepsilon_1 + x_2\varepsilon_2 + x_3\varepsilon_3$, would appear thus:

$$x_1\varepsilon_1 + x_2\varepsilon_2 + x_3\varepsilon_3 = \begin{bmatrix} x_1 \\ 0 \\ 0 \end{bmatrix} + \begin{bmatrix} 0 \\ x_2 \\ 0 \end{bmatrix} + \begin{bmatrix} 0 \\ 0 \\ x_3 \end{bmatrix} = \begin{bmatrix} x_1 \\ x_2 \\ x_3 \end{bmatrix}.$$

In what follows we shall make use of both *row vectors* and *column vectors*. To begin with, let us consider a set of n column vectors α_j belonging to $V_m(\mathscr{F})$:

$$\alpha_1 = \begin{bmatrix} a_{11} \\ a_{21} \\ \vdots \\ a_{m1} \end{bmatrix}, \; \alpha_2 = \begin{bmatrix} a_{12} \\ a_{22} \\ \vdots \\ a_{m2} \end{bmatrix}, \ldots, \alpha_n = \begin{bmatrix} a_{1n} \\ a_{2n} \\ \vdots \\ a_{mn} \end{bmatrix}. \tag{5.1}$$

DEFINITION **5.1**   The ordered set of vectors

$$A = [\alpha_1, \alpha_2, \ldots, \alpha_n] = \begin{bmatrix} a_{11} & a_{12} & \cdots & a_{1n} \\ a_{21} & a_{22} & \cdots & a_{2n} \\ \vdots & \vdots & & \vdots \\ a_{m1} & a_{m2} & \cdots & a_{mn} \end{bmatrix},$$

is called a *matrix* with *column vectors* α_i, where $i = 1, 2, \ldots, n$.*

Alternatively, we could have chosen to write m row vectors belonging to $V_n(\mathscr{F})$

$$\begin{aligned} \beta_1 &= (a_{11}, a_{12}, \ldots, a_{1n}) \\ \beta_2 &= (a_{21}, a_{22}, \ldots, a_{2n}) \\ &\vdots \\ \beta_m &= (a_{m1}, a_{m2}, \ldots, a_{mn}) \end{aligned} \tag{5.2}$$

and formed an ordered m-tuple written as a column:

$$A = \begin{bmatrix} \beta_1 \\ \beta_2 \\ \vdots \\ \beta_m \end{bmatrix} = \begin{bmatrix} a_{11} & a_{12} & \cdots & a_{1n} \\ a_{21} & a_{22} & \cdots & a_{2n} \\ \vdots & \vdots & & \vdots \\ a_{m1} & a_{m2} & \cdots & a_{mn} \end{bmatrix}. \tag{5.3}$$

In this case we should speak of the vectors β_i as the *row vectors* of the matrix A.

Since the column vectors of the matrix A belong to $V_m(\mathscr{F})$ there are m rows, and since the row vectors belong to $V_n(\mathscr{F})$ there are n columns in the matrix.

DEFINITION **5.2**   A matrix A is said to have *dimensions m by n* (symbolically, $m \times n$) if it has m rows and n columns.

The components of the row vectors and column vectors of a given matrix are called its *elements*. The typical element located in the ith row and j^{th} column of a matrix A is designated a_{ij}, and the symbol $A = (a_{ij})$ is read "A is the matrix whose element in the ith row and j^{th} column is a_{ij}."

---

* It is customary to omit parentheses and commas inside the brackets that enclose the matrix.

ILLUSTRATION **5.1**   (a) Write the matrix whose row vectors are $(1, -1, 2)$, $(2, 0, 3)$, $(-3, 1, 1)$, $(2, 4, 0)$. The matrix is written:

$$A = \begin{bmatrix} 1 & -1 & 2 \\ 2 & 0 & 3 \\ -3 & 1 & 1 \\ 2 & 4 & 0 \end{bmatrix}.$$

(b) What are the column vectors of A? The column vectors are:

$$\alpha_1 = \begin{bmatrix} 1 \\ 2 \\ -3 \\ 2 \end{bmatrix}, \qquad \alpha_2 = \begin{bmatrix} -1 \\ 0 \\ 1 \\ 4 \end{bmatrix}, \qquad \alpha_3 = \begin{bmatrix} 2 \\ 3 \\ 1 \\ 0 \end{bmatrix}.$$

(c) What are the dimensions of A? The dimensions are 4×3.

(d) What are the following elements: a_{13}, a_{22}, a_{31}, and a_{42}? The elements are $a_{13} = 2$, $a_{22} = 0$, $a_{31} = -3$, $a_{42} = 4$.

ILLUSTRATION **5.2**   Describe the matrix whose rows are the unit vectors of $V_n(\mathscr{F})$. What are its dimensions? Will its appearance change if the unit column vectors are used instead of the row vectors?

$$I = \begin{bmatrix} \varepsilon_1 \\ \varepsilon_2 \\ \vdots \\ \varepsilon_n \end{bmatrix} = [\varepsilon_1, \varepsilon_2, \ldots, \varepsilon_n] = \begin{bmatrix} 1 & 0 & \cdots & 0 \\ 0 & 1 & \cdots & 0 \\ \vdots & \vdots & & \vdots \\ 0 & 0 & \cdots & 1 \end{bmatrix}$$

The matrix I is of dimensions $n \times n$. The matrix is the same, whether unit column vectors or unit row vectors are used.

If the dimensions of a matrix are equal (that is, $m = n$), then it is said to be *square*, and instead of describing it as $n \times n$ we sometimes say that the matrix is "n square" (n^2) or "of order n." If a matrix is square, the elements $a_{11}, a_{22}, \ldots, a_{nn}$, whose subscripts are equal, are called the *diagonal* elements.

Matrices arise in any situation that calls for an orderly array of numbers as, for example, keeping records of various kinds. They are useful in mathematics, statistics, economics, psychology, electrical engineering, civil engineering, computing science, genetics, forestry, and textiles, to mention a few. The following matrices are not important in themselves, but will serve as examples of their versatility.

ILLUSTRATION **5.3** When the coordinate axes are rotated through an angle θ about the origin in the Cartesian plane, the relationship between the old and the new coordinates of a point is given by the equations

$$x' = x \cos \theta - y \sin \theta,$$
$$y' = x \sin \theta + y \cos \theta.$$

The matrix of this transformation is

$$\begin{bmatrix} \cos \theta & -\sin \theta \\ \sin \theta & \cos \theta \end{bmatrix}.$$

ILLUSTRATION **5.4** In statistics the variance-covariance matrix that arises in a multinomial distribution is

$$\begin{bmatrix} p_1(1 - p_1) & -p_1 p_2 & -p_1 p_3 & \cdots & -p_1 p_n \\ -p_2 p_1 & p_2(1 - p_2) & -p_2 p_3 & \cdots & -p_2 p_n \\ -p_3 p_1 & -p_3 p_2 & p_3(1 - p_3) & \cdots & -p_3 p_n \\ \vdots & \vdots & \vdots & & \vdots \\ -p_n p_1 & -p_n p_2 & -p_n p_3 & \cdots & p_n(1 - p_n) \end{bmatrix}.$$

ILLUSTRATION **5.5** In a psychological experiment in which information theory is applied to the study of response to stimulus presentation the so-called "confusion matrix" is of the form

$$
\begin{array}{c}
\text{Response} \\
\text{Stimulus presentation} \begin{bmatrix} 1 & \mu & \mu^2 & \cdots & \mu^{k-1} \\ \mu & 1 & \mu & \cdots & \mu^{k-2} \\ \mu^2 & \mu & 1 & \cdots & \mu^{k-3} \\ \vdots & \vdots & \vdots & & \vdots \\ \mu^{k-1} & \mu^{k-2} & \mu^{k-3} & \cdots & 1 \end{bmatrix}.
\end{array}
$$

ILLUSTRATION **5.6** The transmission matrix for coupled circuits (see Figure 5.1) in electrical theory is determined to be

$$\begin{bmatrix} L_1/M & j\omega(L_1 L_2 - M^2)/M \\ -j/\omega M & L_2/M \end{bmatrix}.$$

where L_1 and L_2 are the self-inductances in the circuits and M is their mutual inductance.

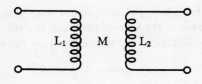

Coupled Circuits

FIGURE 5.1

5.3 OPERATIONS ON THE SET OF MATRICES

Just as we were able to develop an algebra of vectors by defining an equals relation and certain operations on a set whose elements are vectors, so are we able to construct an algebra on the set of matrices. In defining an equals relation of vectors it was necessary to take into consideration the dimension of the vector and the individual components. Because matrices are ordered arrays of vectors, we must take into consideration the number of these vectors and their dimensions. The following definition and others to be given show that ultimately the elements of the matrices must be taken into account.

DEFINITION 5.3   Two $m \times n$ matrices, $A = (a_{ij})$ and $B = (b_{ij})$, are *equal*, if and only if $a_{ij} = b_{ij}$ for all i and j, where $i = 1, 2, \ldots, m$ and $j = 1, 2, \ldots, n$.

For example, if $A = \begin{bmatrix} 1 & x \\ y & 2 \end{bmatrix}$ and $B = \begin{bmatrix} u & 3 \\ -1 & v \end{bmatrix}$, then $A = B$ if and only if $x = 3$, $y = -1$, $u = 1$, and $v = 2$.

Again, if $C = \begin{bmatrix} x - y \\ 2x + y \end{bmatrix}$ and $D = \begin{bmatrix} 1 \\ 2 \end{bmatrix}$, then $C = D$ leads to the pair of simultaneous linear equations

$$x - y = 1$$
$$2x + y = 2;$$

that is, $x = 1$ and $y = 0$.

Matrices, like vectors, are ordered arrays of scalars. It should not be surprising, therefore, that by defining certain operations on the set of matrices, as was done on the set of vectors, their usefulness is considerably enhanced. The first of several operations is defined as follows.

DEFINITION **5.4**   The *sum* of two $m \times n$ matrices, $A = (a_{ij})$ and $B = (b_{ij})$, with elements in a field, is the $m \times n$ matrix $A + B = (a_{ij} + b_{ij})$.

For example, if

$$A = \begin{bmatrix} 2 & 1 \\ -1 & 3 \\ -4 & 0 \end{bmatrix}, \qquad B = \begin{bmatrix} 5 & -2 \\ 0 & 2 \\ 1 & -2 \end{bmatrix},$$

then

$$A + B = \begin{bmatrix} 2+5 & 1-2 \\ -1+0 & 3+2 \\ -4+1 & 0-2 \end{bmatrix} = \begin{bmatrix} 7 & -1 \\ -1 & 5 \\ -3 & -2 \end{bmatrix}.$$

The definition makes it clear that two matrices can be added if and only if they have the same dimensions. In such cases we shall say that the matrices are *conformable with respect to addition*. Addition is a *binary* operation, and in order to perform it with more than two matrices involved, we should like to know whether it is associative.

THEOREM **5.1**   *If A, B, and C are $m \times n$ matrices with elements in a field, then $A + (B + C) = (A + B) + C$.*

Proof.   Let $A = (a_{ij})$, $B = (b_{ij})$, and $C = (c_{ij})$. Then, because the associative law holds for the field of scalars,

$$\begin{aligned} A + (B + C) &= (a_{ij}) + (b_{ij} + c_{ij}) \\ &= [a_{ij} + (b_{ij} + c_{ij})] \\ &= [(a_{ij} + b_{ij}) + c_{ij}] \\ &= (A + B) + C. \end{aligned}$$

The associative law for addition of matrices allows us to extend addition to any finite number of $m \times n$ matrices over the same field. We shall omit parentheses, writing $A + (B + C)$ and $(A + B) + C$ as $A + B + C$. For example, if

$$A = \begin{bmatrix} 1 & -1 & 2 \\ 2 & 0 & 1 \end{bmatrix}, \qquad B = \begin{bmatrix} 2 & 4 & 3 \\ -1 & 2 & -4 \end{bmatrix}, \qquad C = \begin{bmatrix} 1 & 1 & -1 \\ 2 & 0 & 4 \end{bmatrix},$$

then

$$A + B + C = \begin{bmatrix} 4 & 4 & 4 \\ 3 & 2 & 1 \end{bmatrix}.$$

THEOREM **5.2**   *If A and B are $m \times n$ matrices with elements in a field, then $A + B = B + A$.*

Proof. Let $A = (a_{ij})$ and $B = (b_{ij})$. Then, because the commutative law holds for the field of scalars,

$$\begin{aligned} A + B &= (a_{ij}) + (b_{ij}) \\ &= (a_{ij} + b_{ij}) \\ &= (b_{ij} + a_{ij}) \\ &= B + A. \end{aligned}$$

The second operation to be introduced into the algebra of matrices is similar to scalar multiplication of vectors.

DEFINITION **5.5** Let $A = (a_{ij})$ be a matrix with elements in a field. The *scalar product of A and an arbitrary scalar k in the field* is the matrix $kA = (ka_{ij})$ and $Ak = (a_{ij}k)$.

For example, if

$$A = \begin{bmatrix} 1 & -2 \\ 3 & 0 \end{bmatrix}, \qquad B = \begin{bmatrix} 2 & 2 \\ -4 & 3 \end{bmatrix},$$

then

$$2A + (-3)B = \begin{bmatrix} 2 & -4 \\ 6 & 0 \end{bmatrix} + \begin{bmatrix} -6 & -6 \\ 12 & -9 \end{bmatrix} = \begin{bmatrix} -4 & -10 \\ 18 & -9 \end{bmatrix}.$$

With the introduction of scalar multiplication of matrices we shall adopt the convention of writing $(-k)A = -kA$, and in the case of addition involving negative scalars we shall omit the parentheses and write, for example, $2A - 3B$ instead of $2A + (-3)B$. Thus, subtraction is introduced by the back-door method. If $A = (a_{ij})$ and $B = (b_{ij})$, then

$$A - B = A + (-1)B = (a_{ij} - b_{ij})$$

The reader can easily establish the following properties of scalar multiplication.

THEOREM **5.3** *If A and B are m × n matrices over a field, $\mathscr{F}$, and if r and s are scalars in $\mathscr{F}$, then*

(a) $r(A + B) = rA + rB = (A + B)r$,
(b) $(r + s)A = rA + sA = A(r + s)$,
(c) $(rs)A = r(sA) = s(rA) = (Ar)s = A(rs)$.

DEFINITION **5.6** The $m \times n$ matrix, each of whose elements is the additive identity of the field, is called the *zero* matrix.

The zero matrix is denoted by O if the dimension is known. Whenever this symbol is used, the context will make it clear that it is not the additive identity of the scalar field. On occasion, however, it will prove convenient to denote the zero matrix by Z or Z_{mn}. The zero matrix clearly has the property

$$A + O = (a_{ij}) + (0) = (a_{ij} + 0) = (a_{ij}) = A.$$

Moreover,

$$O + A = A.$$

In this connection we introduce the *additive inverse* of the matrix $A = (a_{ij})$ as the matrix $(-A) = (-a_{ij})$. Then,

$$A + (-A) = A - A = (a_{ij} - a_{ij}) = O.$$

PROBLEMS

1. Write out the general matrix $A = (a_{ij})$ whose dimensions are 3×2.

2. What are the row vectors of the following matrix?

$$A = \begin{bmatrix} 3 & 1 & 1 & 2 \\ -1 & 2 & 0 & 1 \\ 3 & 1 & -1 & 4 \end{bmatrix}$$

3. Determine x and y from the matrix equation:

$$2 \begin{bmatrix} x \\ y \end{bmatrix} - 3 \begin{bmatrix} y \\ x \end{bmatrix} = \begin{bmatrix} 4 \\ 5 \end{bmatrix}.$$

4. Find matrices A and B such that the following matrix equations are satisfied simultaneously:

$$A + B = \begin{bmatrix} 1 & -1 \\ 2 & 1 \end{bmatrix}, \qquad 2A - B = \begin{bmatrix} 2 & 0 \\ 1 & -2 \end{bmatrix}.$$

5. Determine x and y from the matrix equation:

$$x \begin{bmatrix} 1 \\ 3 \end{bmatrix} + y \begin{bmatrix} -2 \\ 1 \end{bmatrix} = \begin{bmatrix} -5 \\ -1 \end{bmatrix}.$$

6. Let the elements of a matrix A be in the field $\mathscr{F} = \{0, 1, 2\}$ with addition and multiplication, modulo 3 (see Problem 7, Section 4.2).
   (a) Determine matrix A, where

$$A = 2 \begin{bmatrix} 1 & 0 & 2 \\ 0 & 1 & 1 \\ 2 & 1 & 0 \end{bmatrix} + \begin{bmatrix} 1 & 0 & 2 \\ 0 & 1 & 1 \\ 2 & 1 & 0 \end{bmatrix}.$$

(b) Determine matrix B, where

$$B = 2 \begin{bmatrix} 1 & 1 & 2 \\ 0 & 2 & 1 \\ 1 & 1 & 1 \end{bmatrix} + \begin{bmatrix} 1 & 1 & 1 \\ 2 & 0 & 1 \\ 1 & 2 & 2 \end{bmatrix}.$$

7. Prove Theorem 5.3.

8. The well-known game of "stone, paper, scissors" has the following rules:
   (a) Two players call simultaneously one of three items, stone, paper, or scissors.
   (b) The combination *paper* and *stone* is a win of 1 point for the player calling *paper* (paper covers stone).
   (c) The combination *stone* and *scissors* is a win of 1 point for the player calling *stone* (stone breaks scissors).
   (d) The combination *scissors* and *paper* is a win of 1 point for the player calling *scissors* (scissors cuts paper).
   (e) If both players call the same item it is a tie.
   Denoting by 1 a win, by −1 a loss, and by 0 a tie, construct the pay-off matrix for player A:

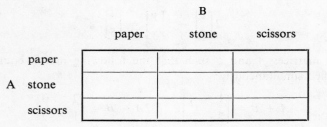

9. The game of "one, two, three" is played as follows:
   (a) Two players, A and B, call simultaneously one of the numbers one, two, or three.
   (b) The player calling the larger number *wins* 2 points if the difference between the numbers called is 1.
   (c) The player calling the larger number *loses* 4 points if the difference between the numbers called is 2.
   (d) If both players call the same number it is considered a tie and 0 points are exchanged.
   Construct a pay-off matrix for player A denoting a win by 2, a loss by −4, and a tie by 0.

10. An *incidence* matrix for a relation R defined on a set $S = \{x_1, x_2, \ldots, x_n\}$ is an $n \times n$ matrix with elements $a_{ij} = 1$ if $x_i \, R \, x_j$ (that is, if "x_i is in relation R to x_j") and with elements $a_{ij} = 0$ if $x_i \, \not{R} \, x_j$ (that is, if "x_i is not in relation to x_j"). Such $0 - 1$ matrices play an important role in certain areas of the mathematics of communications theory and of sociology. Given the set $\{x_1, x_2, x_3\}$ and the relation R, construct the incidence matrix in which $x_1 \, R \, x_2$, $x_1 \, R \, x_3$, $x_2 \, R \, x_3$, $x_3 \, R \, x_1$, and $x_3 \, R \, x_2$ are the only pairs in the relation.

5.4   OPERATIONS ON MATRICES (CONTINUED)

In the preceding section the binary operation of *matrix addition* on the set of $m \times n$ matrices over a field was defined. In addition to this operation, which maps a pair of $m \times n$ matrices into an $m \times n$ matrix, a scalar-matrix operation called *scalar multiplication* was defined. In this latter operation the set of $m \times n$ matrices is mapped into itself, not through combining the elements of two matrices, but through the multiplication of each element of the matrix by a member of the scalar field.

Before introducing a second binary operation, we shall find it convenient to define a certain *unary* operation on the set of $m \times n$ matrices, which maps such matrices into $n \times m$ matrices.

DEFINITION 5.7   The matrix $A' = (a_{ij})' = (a_{ji})$, obtained from $A = (a_{ij})$ by the unary operation of interchanging the rows of A with its columns, is called the *transpose* of A.

For example, if

$$A = \begin{bmatrix} 1 & 2 & 2 \\ 0 & -3 & 1 \\ 4 & 0 & 5 \end{bmatrix}, \qquad B = \begin{bmatrix} 1 & 1 \\ 2 & 0 \\ -1 & 1 \end{bmatrix}, \qquad C = [1, 2, 2], \qquad D = \begin{bmatrix} 1 \\ 0 \\ 4 \end{bmatrix},$$

then

$$A' = \begin{bmatrix} 1 & 0 & 4 \\ 2 & -3 & 0 \\ 2 & 1 & 5 \end{bmatrix}, \qquad B' = \begin{bmatrix} 1 & 2 & -1 \\ 1 & 0 & 1 \end{bmatrix}, \qquad C' = \begin{bmatrix} 1 \\ 2 \\ 2 \end{bmatrix}, \qquad D' = [1, 0, 4].$$

We note that the dimensions of each matrix change from $m \times n$ to $n \times m$. We note also that the element in the (i, j) position of A' is located in the (j, i) position of A.

We turn now to the second of the binary operations defined on the set of matrices with elements in a field. This operation is called *matrix multiplication*, in contrast to scalar multiplication. We shall find it convenient to define this operation in terms of a matrix A of dimensions $m \times p$, which is written in terms of its m row vectors α_i belonging to $V_p(\mathscr{F})$,

$$A = \begin{bmatrix} \alpha_1 \\ \alpha_2 \\ \vdots \\ \alpha_i \\ \vdots \\ \alpha_m \end{bmatrix}, \quad \text{where } \alpha_i = [a_{i1}, a_{i2}, \ldots, a_{ip}],$$

and of a matrix B of dimensions $p \times n$, which is written in terms of its n column vectors β_j, also belonging to $V_p(\mathscr{F})$,

$$B = [\beta_1, \beta_2, \ldots, \beta_j, \ldots, \beta_n],$$

where $\beta_{ij} = \mathrm{col}\,[b_{1j}, b_{2j}, \ldots, b_{pj}]$ is the jth column of B.

DEFINITION 5.8 The *matrix product*, AB, of the $m \times p$ matrix A and the $p \times n$ matrix B, with elements in a field, is the $m \times n$ matrix whose element in the (i, j) position is the inner product of the ith row vector of A and the jth column vector of B; that is,

$$\alpha_i \cdot \beta_j = a_{i1}b_{1j} + a_{i2}b_{2j} + \cdots + a_{ip}b_{pj} = \sum_{k=1}^{p} a_{ik}b_{kj}.$$

ILLUSTRATION 5.7 Find the product of matrices A and B, where

$$A = \begin{bmatrix} 1 & -1 \\ 2 & 0 \end{bmatrix}, \quad B = \begin{bmatrix} 2 & 4 & 1 \\ -1 & 2 & 0 \end{bmatrix}.$$

The solution is as follows:

$$AB = \begin{bmatrix} [1 & -1] \cdot \begin{bmatrix} 2 \\ -1 \end{bmatrix} & [1 & -1] \cdot \begin{bmatrix} 4 \\ 2 \end{bmatrix} & [1 & -1] \cdot \begin{bmatrix} 1 \\ 0 \end{bmatrix} \\ [2 & 0] \cdot \begin{bmatrix} 2 \\ -1 \end{bmatrix} & [2 & 0] \cdot \begin{bmatrix} 4 \\ 2 \end{bmatrix} & [2 & 0] \cdot \begin{bmatrix} 1 \\ 0 \end{bmatrix} \end{bmatrix} = \begin{bmatrix} 3 & 2 & 1 \\ 4 & 8 & 2 \end{bmatrix}.$$

ILLUSTRATION 5.8 Find the inner product of ε_i and α, where ε_i is the ith unit vector and α is an arbitrary vector in $V_n(\mathscr{F})$.

The solution follows:

$$\varepsilon_i \cdot \alpha = [0, \ldots, 1, \ldots, 0] \begin{bmatrix} a_1 \\ \vdots \\ a_i \\ \vdots \\ a_n \end{bmatrix}$$

$$= 0 \cdot a_1 + \cdots + 1 \cdot a_i + \cdots + 0 \cdot a_n$$
$$= a_i.$$

ILLUSTRATION **5.9**   Let A be an $m \times n$ matrix with elements in a field $\mathscr{F}$, and let I be the $m \times m$ matrix whose rows are the unit vectors $\varepsilon_1, \varepsilon_2, \ldots, \varepsilon_m$ in $V_m(\mathscr{F})$. Show that $IA = A$.

The solution is

$$IA = \begin{bmatrix} \varepsilon_1 \\ \varepsilon_2 \\ \vdots \\ \varepsilon_m \end{bmatrix} [\alpha_1, \alpha_2, \ldots, \alpha_n] = \begin{bmatrix} \varepsilon_1 \cdot \alpha_1 & \varepsilon_1 \cdot \alpha_2 & \cdots & \varepsilon_1 \cdot \alpha_n \\ \varepsilon_2 \cdot \alpha_1 & \varepsilon_2 \cdot \alpha_2 & \cdots & \varepsilon_2 \cdot \alpha_n \\ \vdots & \vdots & & \vdots \\ \varepsilon_m \cdot \alpha_1 & \varepsilon_m \cdot \alpha_2 & \cdots & \varepsilon_m \cdot \alpha_n \end{bmatrix},$$

where the element in the (i, j) position of IA is the inner product, $\varepsilon_i \cdot \alpha_j = a_{ij}$ from Illustration 5.8. Therefore,

$$IA = (a_{ij}) = A.$$

Note that the $m \times m$ matrix I is called the *identity* matrix of order m. If we wish to *postmultiply* the $m \times n$ matrix A by an identity matrix, we must use the identity matrix of order n, in which case $AI = (a_{ij}) = A$. However, for the set of all *square* matrices of order n we have the following theorem.

THEOREM **5.4**   *For square matrices of order n with elements in a field, $\mathscr{F}$, there is a unique identity matrix, I, of order n.*

Proof.   Let us assume that there exist two matrices, I_1 and I_2, such that $AI_1 = I_1A = A$ and $AI_2 = I_2A = A$ for all matrices A of order n. Substituting $A = I_2$ in the first relation, we have $I_2I_1 = I_1I_2 = I_2$, and placing $A = I_1$ in the second relation, we have $I_1I_2 = I_2I_1 = I_1$. Therefore, $I_1 = I_2 = I$.

If A is of dimensions $m \times p$ and B is of dimensions $p \times m$, then AB is of dimensions $m \times m$. On the other hand, BA is of dimensions $p \times p$. It is clear from the definition of equal matrices that in this case $AB \neq BA$, because the matrices do not have the same dimensions. However, even in the more favorable case in which $m = p$ it is *not generally true* that AB and BA are equal.

ILLUSTRATION **5.10**   Determine AB and BA for matrices

$$A = \begin{bmatrix} 1 & -1 \\ 2 & 0 \end{bmatrix}, \qquad B = \begin{bmatrix} 3 & 2 \\ -1 & 4 \end{bmatrix}.$$

Forming the products, we have

$$AB = \begin{bmatrix} 1 & -1 \\ 2 & 0 \end{bmatrix} \begin{bmatrix} 3 & 2 \\ -1 & 4 \end{bmatrix} = \begin{bmatrix} 4 & -2 \\ 6 & 4 \end{bmatrix},$$

$$BA = \begin{bmatrix} 3 & 2 \\ -1 & 4 \end{bmatrix} \begin{bmatrix} 1 & -1 \\ 2 & 0 \end{bmatrix} = \begin{bmatrix} 7 & -3 \\ 7 & 1 \end{bmatrix}.$$

Clearly, $AB \neq BA$ in this illustration.

ILLUSTRATION **5.11**   It is possible for AB to be zero and neither A nor B to be the zero matrix. Consider

$$A = \begin{bmatrix} a & 0 \\ b & 0 \end{bmatrix} \qquad \text{and} \qquad B = \begin{bmatrix} 0 & 0 \\ c & d \end{bmatrix},$$

where a, b, c, and d are arbitrary elements in the field F; then

$$AB = \begin{bmatrix} a & 0 \\ b & 0 \end{bmatrix} \begin{bmatrix} 0 & 0 \\ c & d \end{bmatrix} = \begin{bmatrix} 0 & 0 \\ 0 & 0 \end{bmatrix} = O.$$

Furthermore,

$$BA = \begin{bmatrix} 0 & 0 \\ c & d \end{bmatrix} \begin{bmatrix} a & 0 \\ b & 0 \end{bmatrix} = \begin{bmatrix} 0 & 0 \\ ac + bd & 0 \end{bmatrix},$$

so that $BA \neq O$ in the general case.

While it is true that matrix multiplication is not commutative in general, it is comforting to know that the associative law holds, provided that the matrices involved in the product are *conformable with respect to multiplication*. That is, if A is $m \times p$ and B is $r \times s$, then the product AB can be formed only if $p = r$, and the product BA only if $s = m$. In this case we say that the *contiguous* dimensions are equal.

THEOREM **5.5**   *If the matrices A, B, and C are conformable with respect to multiplication, then $A(BC) = (AB)C$.*

Proof. Assume A, B, and C are matrices over a field and that their respective dimensions are $m \times p$, $p \times q$, and $q \times n$. Then

$$A(BC) = (a_{is})[(b_{sr})(c_{rj})]$$

$$= (a_{is})\left(\sum_{r=1}^{q} b_{sr}c_{rj} \right)$$

$$= \left(\sum_{s=1}^{p} a_{is} \sum_{r=1}^{q} b_{sr}c_{rj} \right).$$

We can change the order of the summations in the last expression, because they are finite sums and involve elements of a field. Therefore, we conclude that

$$A(BC) = \left[\sum_{r=1}^{q} \left(\sum_{s=1}^{p} a_{is}b_{sr} \right) c_{rj} \right] = (AB)C.$$

ILLUSTRATION **5.12**   Given that

$$A = \begin{bmatrix} 1 & -1 & 1 \\ 2 & 0 & 3 \end{bmatrix}, \qquad B = \begin{bmatrix} 1 \\ -1 \\ 3 \end{bmatrix}, \qquad C = \begin{bmatrix} 1 & -5 \end{bmatrix},$$

compute the products $A(BC)$ and $(AB)C$.

$$A(BC) = \begin{bmatrix} 1 & -1 & 1 \\ 2 & 0 & 3 \end{bmatrix} \begin{bmatrix} 1 & -5 \\ -1 & 5 \\ 3 & -15 \end{bmatrix} = \begin{bmatrix} 5 & -25 \\ 11 & -55 \end{bmatrix},$$

$$(AB)C = \begin{bmatrix} 5 \\ 11 \end{bmatrix} \begin{bmatrix} 1 & -5 \end{bmatrix} = \begin{bmatrix} 5 & -25 \\ 11 & -55 \end{bmatrix}.$$

Clearly, the second product is the easier to compute of the two in this example.

Furthermore, we find that matrix multiplication is distributive over addition, as is proved in the following theorem.

THEOREM **5.6**   *The distributive laws*

$$A(B + C) = AB + AC \qquad and \qquad (B + C)A = BA + CA$$

are satisfied by matrices A, B, and C over a field, $\mathscr{F}$, whenever they are compatible with respect to the operations involved.

Proof. We prove only the first of these laws and leave the second as an exercise for the reader. Let $A = (a_{ik})$ be $m \times p$, $B = (b_{kj})$ be $p \times n$, and $C = (c_{kj})$ be $p \times n$. Then

$$
\begin{aligned}
A(B + C) &= (a_{ik})(b_{kj} + c_{kj}) \\
&= \left(\sum_{k=1}^{p} a_{ik}(b_{kj} + c_{kj}) \right) \\
&= \left(\sum_{k=1}^{p} a_{ik}b_{kj} + \sum_{k=1}^{p} a_{ik}c_{kj} \right) \\
&= AB + AC.
\end{aligned}
$$

In the following theorem we summarize the results in the algebra of matrices of order n that have been discussed up to this point.

THEOREM **5.7**   *The set of square matrices of order n over a field, $\mathscr{F}$, forms a ring with an identity.*

Proof. Assume $\{A, B, C, \ldots\}$ is the given set of matrices. The following properties of such matrices have been either defined or derived and fulfill the requirement that a system be a ring (with an identity), as set forth in Definition 4.1.

PROPERTIES OF A SQUARE MATRIX
(a)   Closure with respect to the binary operations of matrix addition and multiplication (Definitions 5.4 and 5.8).

(b)	$A + B = B + A$	(Theorem 5.2).
(c)	$A + (B + C) = (A + B) + C$	(Theorem 5.1).
(d)	$A + O = A$	(Definition 5.6).
(e)	$A + (-A) = O$	(Definition 5.6).
(f)	$A(BC) = (AB)C$	(Theorem 5.5).
(g)	$AI = IA = A$	(Theorem 5.4).
(h)	$A(B + C) = AB + AC$	(Theorem 5.6)
	$(B + C)A = BA + CA$	(Problem 11, Section 5.4).

Returning to the identity matrix I of order m, one might define it as a square matrix of dimensions $m \times m$, in which the main diagonal consists entirely of 1's and all other elements are 0. We write $I = (\delta_{ij})$, where

$$
\begin{aligned}
\delta_{ij} &= 1, \quad \text{when } i = j, \\
\delta_{ij} &= 0, \quad \text{when } i \neq j.
\end{aligned}
\tag{5.4}
$$

This function, called the *Kronecker delta*, maps the ordered pairs (i, j), where $i = 1, 2, \ldots, m$ and $j = 1, 2, \ldots, m$ into the set $\{0, 1\}$.

Now assume $A = (a_{jk})$ to be an arbitrary $m \times n$ matrix, and form the product

$$IA = (\delta_{ij})(a_{jk}) = \left(\sum_{j=1}^{m} \delta_{ij}a_{jk} \right). \tag{5.5}$$

By using Equations 5.4 the expression $\sum_{j=1}^{m} \delta_{ij}a_{jk}$ in Equation 5.5 is the sum of zero terms, except when $j = i$. In this case we obtain the single term $1 \cdot a_{ik} = a_{ik}$. Thus Equation 5.5 simplifies, to yield the earlier result (see Illustration 5.9)

$$IA = (a_{ik}) = A. \tag{5.6}$$

A square matrix of order m, in which the main diagonal consists entirely of the scalar k and all other elements are zero, is called a scalar matrix. Using the Kronecker delta (Equation 5.4), we write

$$K = (k\delta_{ij}) = \begin{bmatrix} k & 0 & \cdots & 0 \\ 0 & k & \cdots & 0 \\ \vdots & \vdots & & \vdots \\ 0 & 0 & \cdots & k \end{bmatrix}. \tag{5.7}$$

Let $A = (a_{jh})$ be an arbitrary $m \times n$ matrix; then

$$KA = (k\delta_{ij})(a_{jh}) = \left(\sum_{j=1}^{m} k\delta_{ij}a_{jh} \right) = (ka_{ih}) = kA. \tag{5.8}$$

From Equation 5.8 we see that scalar multiplication of A by the scalar k can be performed by *matrix multiplication* using the scalar matrix K of proper dimensions.

More generally, the square matrix D of order m, whose diagonal consists of the elements $(d_1, d_2, \ldots, d_m)$, not necessarily equal as in the scalar matrix K, and whose other elements are zero, is called a *diagonal matrix*. We write

$$D = \mathrm{diag}\,(d_1, d_2, \ldots, d_m) = \begin{bmatrix} d_1 & 0 & \cdots & 0 \\ 0 & d_2 & \cdots & 0 \\ \vdots & \vdots & & \vdots \\ 0 & 0 & \cdots & d_m \end{bmatrix}. \tag{5.9}$$

Premultiplying the $m \times n$ matrix $A = (a_{ij})$ by the diagonal matrix D in Equation 5.9 gives

$$DA = \mathrm{diag}\,(d_1, d_2, \ldots, d_m)(a_{ij}) = (d_i a_{ij}). \tag{5.10}$$

Clearly, the effect is to multiply each *row* of A by the corresponding diagonal element of D. In the same way, if we *postmultiply* the $m \times n$ matrix A by the diagonal matrix of order n, we find that the effect is to multiply each *column* of A by the corresponding diagonal element of D.

ILLUSTRATION **5.13**   Form the product AD, where

$$A = \begin{bmatrix} 1 & -1 & 2 \\ 2 & 0 & 3 \\ -4 & 1 & 2 \end{bmatrix}, \qquad D = \text{diag}(3, -2, 5).$$

By the result stated in the preceding paragraph we may write

$$\begin{bmatrix} 1(3) & -1(-2) & 2(5) \\ 2(3) & 0(-2) & 3(5) \\ -4(3) & 1(-2) & 2(5) \end{bmatrix} = \begin{bmatrix} 3 & 2 & 10 \\ 6 & 0 & 15 \\ -12 & -2 & 10 \end{bmatrix}.$$

DEFINITION **5.9**   If $p > 0$ is an integer, the product of p square matrices A of order n is called the pth *power of A* and is denoted by A^p. In particular, we define $A^0 = I$, the identity matrix of order n.

Let $f(x) = a_0 x^p + a_1 x^{p-1} + \cdots + a_{p-1} x + a_p$ be a polynomial of degree p in the scalar variable x with coefficients a_i in the field $\mathscr{F}$. Then $f(A)$ is a polynomial in the $n \times n$ matrix A with elements in $\mathscr{F}$, where

$$f(A) = a_0 A^p + a_1 A^{p-1} + \cdots + a_{p-1} A + a_p I. \qquad (5.11)$$

Note: The constant term a_p in $f(x)$ can be thought of as $a_p x^0$ so that the corresponding term in $f(A)$ is $a_p A^0 = a_p I$, by Definition 5.9.

ILLUSTRATION **5.14**   Given the following, find $f(A)$:

$$f(x) = x^2 - 2x + 3 \qquad \text{and} \qquad A = \begin{bmatrix} 1 & 2 \\ -1 & 0 \end{bmatrix}.$$

The solution follows:

$$f(A) = A^2 - 2A + 3I$$
$$= \begin{bmatrix} -1 & 2 \\ -1 & -2 \end{bmatrix} - 2 \begin{bmatrix} 1 & 2 \\ -1 & 0 \end{bmatrix} + 3 \begin{bmatrix} 1 & 0 \\ 0 & 1 \end{bmatrix} = \begin{bmatrix} 0 & -2 \\ 1 & 1 \end{bmatrix}.$$

PROBLEMS

1. For the following matrices find AB, CA, and $C'A$.

$$A = \begin{bmatrix} 1 & -1 & 2 \\ 0 & 1 & 1 \end{bmatrix}, \qquad B = \begin{bmatrix} 2 \\ 0 \\ -1 \end{bmatrix}, \qquad C = \begin{bmatrix} 1 & -1 \\ 4 & 0 \end{bmatrix}.$$

2. The following matrices have elements in the field $\mathscr{F} = \{0, 1, 2\}$ with addition and multiplication, modulo 3. Find the products AB, AC, and $C'A$.

$$A = \begin{bmatrix} 1 & 2 & 0 \\ 0 & 1 & 1 \\ 2 & 1 & 1 \end{bmatrix}, \qquad B = \begin{bmatrix} 1 & 1 \\ 2 & 1 \\ 0 & 2 \end{bmatrix}, \qquad C = \begin{bmatrix} 1 \\ 2 \\ 2 \end{bmatrix}.$$

3. Let $f(x) = 3x^2 + 2x - 4$; find $f(A)$ when $A = \begin{bmatrix} -6 & 3 \\ 2 & 0 \end{bmatrix}$.

4. For the matrix A in Problem 3, show that $A^2 + 6A - 6I = O$.

5. Given

$$A = \begin{bmatrix} -2 & -1 \\ -4 & -2 \end{bmatrix} \qquad \text{and} \qquad B = \begin{bmatrix} 2 & -1 \\ -4 & 2 \end{bmatrix},$$

show that $AB = BA = O$. (A and B are different from zero, but their product is zero. Such matrices are called *divisors of zero*.)

6. Given

$$A = \begin{bmatrix} 1 & 2 \\ -3 & -5 \end{bmatrix} \qquad \text{and} \qquad B = \begin{bmatrix} -5 & -2 \\ 3 & 1 \end{bmatrix},$$

show that $AB = BA = I$. (A and B are *inverses* of each other, since their product is I.)

7. Given

$$AB = \begin{bmatrix} 4 & 1 \\ 3 & 1 \end{bmatrix}\begin{bmatrix} x & y \\ u & v \end{bmatrix} = \begin{bmatrix} 1 & 0 \\ 0 & 1 \end{bmatrix},$$

solve for x, y, u, and v. That is, determine B, which is the inverse of A. Show that $BA = I$.

8. Show that $A^3 + A^2 - 2A = O$, if

$$A = \begin{bmatrix} -6 & -7 & -5 \\ 2 & 3 & 1 \\ 2 & 2 & 2 \end{bmatrix}.$$

9. Show that $A(A^2 + A - 2I) = O$ for the matrix A in Problem 8.

10. If A and B are $n \times n$ matrices over a field, under what conditions will the following relations be true?
   (a) $(A + B)^2 = A^2 + 2AB + B^2$.
   (b) $(A + B)(A - B) = A^2 - B^2$.

11. Given that $A = (a_{jk})$, $B = (b_{ij})$, and $C = (c_{ij})$ are matrices of dimensions $n \times p$, $m \times n$, and $m \times n$, respectively, prove the distributive law, $(B + C)A = BA + CA$.

12. Let $A = (a_{ij})$ and $B = (b_{jk})$ be matrices of dimensions $m \times n$ and $n \times p$, respectively. Prove that *the transpose of the product (AB) of two matrices is the product of their transposes in reverse order*, $(AB)' = B'A'$.

5.5 RANK OF A MATRIX

Let A be an $m \times n$ matrix with elements in a field $\mathscr{F}$. As was pointed out at the beginning of this chapter, a matrix of these dimensions represents both an ordered set of m row vectors belonging to $V_n(\mathscr{F})$ and an ordered set of n column vectors belonging to $V_m(\mathscr{F})$. The rows of A span a subspace of $V_n(\mathscr{F})$ called the *row space* of A, and the columns span a subspace of $V_m(\mathscr{F})$ called the *column space* of A.

DEFINITION 5.10 The dimension of the row (or the column) space of a matrix is called the *row* (or the *column*) *rank* of the matrix.

ILLUSTRATION 5.15. Let us consider the following 3×4 matrix with elements in the rational field:

$$A = \begin{bmatrix} 1 & -1 & 2 & 0 \\ 2 & 0 & 2 & 3 \\ -1 & 1 & 1 & 2 \end{bmatrix}.$$

Here the row vectors, $\alpha_1 = (1, -1, 2, 0)$, $\alpha_2 = (2, 0, 2, 3)$, and $\alpha_3 = (-1, 1, 1, 2)$ are linearly independent. Hence, the row space of A which they span is of dimension 3.

On the other hand, the column vectors are *not* independent, since there are 4 three-dimensional vectors in the set.

$$\beta_1 = \begin{bmatrix} 1 \\ 2 \\ -1 \end{bmatrix}, \qquad \beta_2 = \begin{bmatrix} -1 \\ 0 \\ 1 \end{bmatrix}, \qquad \beta_3 = \begin{bmatrix} 2 \\ 2 \\ 1 \end{bmatrix}, \qquad \beta_4 = \begin{bmatrix} 0 \\ 3 \\ 2 \end{bmatrix}.$$

Indeed, any three of these vectors are independent while the four vectors satisfy the equation $5\beta_1 + 13\beta_2 + 4\beta_3 - 6\beta_4 = \theta$. Thus, the dimension of the column space also is 3.

The result obtained in the preceding illustration is not just a coincidence. In general, the following theorem holds.*

---

*A detailed proof of this assertion can be found in H. M. Nahikian, *A Modern Algebra for Biologists*, The University of Chicago Press, Chicago, 1964, pp. 142–45.

THEOREM **5.8** *For any* $m \times n$ *matrix over a field the row rank and column rank are equal.*

We shall accept Theorem 5.8 and, instead of speaking of row rank and column rank, henceforth we shall speak of *the rank of the matrix*. Because the dimension of a vector subspace is the number of vectors in a basis (see Definition 4.14), it is possible to determine the rank of a matrix by finding the maximal number of independent rows or columns of the matrix. We shall find the following transformations useful in this matter.

DEFINITION **5.11** The *elementary* matrix transformations may be outlined as follows:
   (a)   The *interchange* of any two row vectors or column vectors.
   (b)   The *scalar product* of any row vector or column vector and a nonzero scalar in the field.
   (c)   The addition to any row vector of a scalar multiple of any other row vector, or the addition to any column vector of a scalar multiple of any other column vector.

Of course, matrices obtained from a given matrix by means of such transformations are *not* equal. We shall find, however, that their ranks and dimensions are the same (see Theorem 5.11).

DEFINITION **5.12** Matrices A and B are said to be *equivalent* if one is obtained from the other by elementary matrix transformations. We shall symbolize equivalent matrices by writing $A \sim B$.

THEOREM **5.9** *Each elementary matrix transformation has an inverse that is an elementary transformation of the same type.*

Proof. In the discussion that follows, the term *vector* will be used to designate either row or column vector.

If matrix B is obtained from A by the first type of transformation, which interchanges two vectors, then applying the *same* transformation to B restores each of these vectors to its original position, yielding A.

Assume next that matrix B is obtained from A by the transformation that multiplies the ith vector of A by the nonzero scalar k. Then A is obtained from B by the same type of transformation, which multiplies the ith vector of B by the scalar k^{-1}.

Finally, if B is obtained from A by the transformation that adds to the ith vector of A the scalar multiple k of the jth vector, then matrix A is restored by applying the transformation that adds to the ith vector of B the scalar multiple $(-k)$ of the jth vector.

THEOREM **5.10**   *The relation* $\sim$ *is an equivalence relation on the set of* $m \times n$ *matrices*.

Proof.   Reflexive property, $A \sim A$: trivially true! For the type (a) transformation (see Definition 5.11) interchange any vector with itself. For the type (b), multiply the ith vector by 1. For the type (c), multiply the jth vector by 0 and add to the ith vector. In each case A is obtained by applying an elementary transformation to A. Hence, by Definition 5.12, $A \sim A$.

Symmetric property, $A \sim B \rightarrow B \sim A$: this follows immediately from Theorem 5.9.

Transitive property, $A \sim B$ and $B \sim C \rightarrow A \sim C$: by assumption, B is obtained from A by elementary transformations, and C is obtained in turn from B by elementary transformations. By applying the entire sequence of transformations to A, the matrix C can be obtained directly from A. Thus, $A \sim C$.

ILLUSTRATION **5.16**   Given the following matrix,

$$A = \begin{bmatrix} 1 & -1 & 2 \\ 0 & 5 & 3 \\ 2 & 4 & -2 \end{bmatrix}.$$

(a)   Perform the indicated elementary transformation on A:

(new 3rd row) = (old 3rd row) $-$ 2(old 1st row)

$$r_3' = r_3 - 2r_1.$$

Then A is equivalent to matrix B, where

$$A \sim B = \begin{bmatrix} 1 & -1 & 2 \\ 0 & 5 & 3 \\ 0 & 6 & -6 \end{bmatrix}.$$

(b)   Perform the following elementary transformation on B:

(new 3rd row) = $\frac{1}{6}$(old 3rd row)

$$r_3' = \tfrac{1}{6}r_3.$$

Then B is equivalent to C, where

$$B \sim C = \begin{bmatrix} 1 & -1 & 2 \\ 0 & 5 & 3 \\ 0 & 1 & -1 \end{bmatrix}.$$

(c)   Perform the indicated elementary transformation on C:

interchange 2nd row with 3rd row

$$r_2' = r_3$$
$$r_3' = r_2.$$

Then matrix C is equivalent to matrix D, where

$$C \sim D = \begin{bmatrix} 1 & -1 & 2 \\ 0 & 1 & -1 \\ 0 & 5 & 3 \end{bmatrix}.$$

(d)   Because of the transitivity of the relation $\sim$ we may write $A \sim D$.

THEOREM **5.11**   *Equivalent matrices have the same rank.*

Proof.   Clearly, the effect of elementary transformations on the vectors of a matrix is to produce linear combinations of these vectors. By Theorem 4.5 these new vectors lie in the space spanned by the rows (or columns) of A. Thus, if $A \sim B$, the row (or column) space of B lies in the corresponding space of A. It follows that the dimension of B cannot exceed that of A; that is, $r_B \leqslant r_A$, where r_A and r_B are the respective ranks of A and B. However, because each of the elementary transformations has an inverse of the same type (Theorem 5.9), the matrix A can be restored by performing these inverse transformations on the rows (or columns) of B. Hence, we may argue that $r_A \leqslant r_B$. It follows that the equality holds, and we may write $r_A = r_B$.

THEOREM **5.12**   *Any row (column) vector of a matrix that is linearly dependent on the row (column) vectors that precede it can be replaced with a zero vector without any altering of the rank of the matrix.*

Proof.   Let the given matrix be of dimensions $m \times n$, and assume its rank to be $r(< m)$. By using elementary transformations of type (a) we can obtain a matrix, B, equivalent to the given matrix, whose first r row vectors are independent while the $(r + 1)^{th}$ row, α_{r+1}, is dependent on those that precede it (see Theorem 4.4), say $\alpha_{r+1} = c_1\alpha_1 + c_2\alpha_2 + \cdots + c_r\alpha_r$. Therefore, if we add $-c_1\alpha_1, -c_2\alpha_2, \ldots, -c_r\alpha_r$ in succession to α_{r+1}, using type (c) elementary transformations, we obtain a maxtrix C whose $(r + 1)^{th}$ row is a zero vector. By the transitivity of the equivalence relation, the matrix C is equivalent to the given matrix and therefore has the same rank. The same argument applies to the columns of the given matrix.

COROLLARY OF THEOREM 5.12   *Every m × n matrix of rank r is equivalent to a matrix whose first r rows and first r columns are independent and whose remaining m − r rows and n − r columns are zero vectors.*

ILLUSTRATION 5.17   Let us determine the rank of

$$A = \begin{bmatrix} -1 & 0 & 2 & -2 \\ 2 & -1 & 1 & 0 \\ 0 & -1 & 5 & -4 \\ 1 & -1 & 3 & -2 \end{bmatrix}.$$

In the solution of this problem we use elementary transformations on the rows to produce a sequence of equivalent matrices. In each case the necessary transformations are indicated above the new matrix.

$$\begin{array}{ll} r_2' = r_2 + 2r_1 & \\ r_3' = r_3 & r_3' = r_3 - r_2 \\ r_4' = r_4 + r_1 & r_4' = r_4 - r_2 \end{array}$$

$$\begin{bmatrix} -1 & 0 & 2 & -2 \\ 2 & -1 & 1 & 0 \\ 0 & -1 & 5 & -4 \\ 1 & -1 & 3 & -2 \end{bmatrix} \sim \begin{bmatrix} -1 & 0 & 2 & -2 \\ 0 & -1 & 5 & -4 \\ 0 & -1 & 5 & -4 \\ 0 & -1 & 5 & -4 \end{bmatrix} \sim \begin{bmatrix} -1 & 0 & 2 & -2 \\ 0 & -1 & 5 & -4 \\ 0 & 0 & 0 & 0 \\ 0 & 0 & 0 & 0 \end{bmatrix}$$

Since the first two rows of the last matrix are independent and the remaining rows are zero, we conclude that this matrix is of rank 2. Therefore, A is of rank 2.

The problem of determining the rank of A is solved. However, if we wish, we may now use elementary operations on the columns of the last matrix to obtain a matrix equivalent to A that has zero vectors for its last two columns.

$$\begin{array}{ll} c_3' = c_3 + 2c_1 + 5c_2 & c_1' = -c_1 \\ c_4' = c_4 - 2c_1 - 4c_2 & c_2' = -c_2 \end{array}$$

$$A \sim \begin{bmatrix} -1 & 0 & 0 & 0 \\ 0 & -1 & 0 & 0 \\ 0 & 0 & 0 & 0 \\ 0 & 0 & 0 & 0 \end{bmatrix} \sim \begin{bmatrix} 1 & 0 & 0 & 0 \\ 0 & 1 & 0 & 0 \\ 0 & 0 & 0 & 0 \\ 0 & 0 & 0 & 0 \end{bmatrix}$$

The method used in Illustration 5.17 is called by some authors the method of *pivotal condensation*. The row used for reducing the elements of a column to zero is called the *pivotal row*, and the column used for reducing the elements of a row to zero is called the *pivotal column*.

In Theorem 1.1 it was shown that an equivalence relation on a set partitions it into disjoint subsets, whose union is the set. It can be proven that the equivalence relation $\sim$ partitions the set of $m \times n$ matrices of rank r over a field $\mathscr{F}$ into equivalence classes $[N_r]$ of matrices equivalent to the *canonical* matrices of the type

$$N_r = \begin{bmatrix} I_r & Z_{12} \\ Z_{21} & Z_{22} \end{bmatrix},$$

where I_r is the identity matrix of order r and each of the Z_{ij} is a zero sub-matrix of appropriate dimensions.

For example, all 2×3 matrices over a field $\mathscr{F}$ that are of rank 2 belong to the equivalence class $[N_2]$, where

$$N_2 = \begin{bmatrix} 1 & 0 & 0 \\ 0 & 1 & 0 \end{bmatrix}.$$

By this we mean that all 2×3 matrices of rank 2 with elements in a field can be reduced to a matrix of type N_2 by means of elementary transformations. Similarly, all 2×3 matrices of rank 1 belong to the equivalence class $[N_1]$, where

$$N_1 = \begin{bmatrix} 1 & 0 & 0 \\ 0 & 0 & 0 \end{bmatrix},$$

and, of course, those of rank zero belong to $[N_0]$, where

$$N_0 = \begin{bmatrix} 0 & 0 & 0 \\ 0 & 0 & 0 \end{bmatrix}.$$

For the general case we have the following theorem.*

THEOREM **5.13**   *All $m \times n$ matrices over a field $\mathscr{F}$ of rank r are equivalent to the $m \times n$ canonical matrix N_r. Two $m \times n$ matrices A and B with elements in $\mathscr{F}$ are equivalent, if and only if $A \in [N_r]$ and $B \in [N_r]$ for some positive or zero integer r.*

DEFINITION **5.13**   An $m \times m$ matrix E is an *elementary matrix*, if and only if it is obtained from the identity matrix of order m by means of a single elementary transformation.

* For a more complete discussion see Nahikian, *op. cit.*, pp. 148–49.

For example, the following elementary matrices were obtained by using elementary row transformations on the identity matrix of order 2:

$$E_{12} = \begin{bmatrix} 0 & 1 \\ 1 & 0 \end{bmatrix}, \qquad E_1(k) = \begin{bmatrix} k & 0 \\ 0 & 1 \end{bmatrix}, \qquad E_2(k) = \begin{bmatrix} 1 & 0 \\ 0 & k \end{bmatrix},$$

$$E_{21}(k) = \begin{bmatrix} 1 & 0 \\ k & 1 \end{bmatrix}, \qquad E_{12}(k) = \begin{bmatrix} 1 & k \\ 0 & 1 \end{bmatrix}.$$

It is of more than passing interest to note that each elementary transformation on the rows of a matrix A can be performed by means of the matrix product EA, where E is an appropriate elementary matrix, and each elementary transformation on the columns of the matrix can be performed by means of the product AF, where F is an elementary matrix obtained by performing an elementary transformation on the columns of the identity matrix of appropriate dimensions.

ILLUSTRATION **5.18**   Carry out the elementary transformations on the rows of the 3×2 matrix, using for this purpose elementary matrices.

$$A = \begin{bmatrix} a_{11} & a_{12} \\ a_{21} & a_{22} \end{bmatrix}.$$

Using the elementary matrices shown in the example following Definition 5.13, we have

$$E_{12}A = \begin{bmatrix} a_{21} & a_{22} \\ a_{11} & a_{12} \end{bmatrix}, \quad E_1(k)A = \begin{bmatrix} ka_{11} & ka_{12} \\ a_{21} & a_{22} \end{bmatrix}, \quad E_2(k)A = \begin{bmatrix} a_{11} & a_{12} \\ ka_{21} & ka_{22} \end{bmatrix},$$

$$E_{21}(k)A = \begin{bmatrix} a_{11} & a_{12} \\ a_{21} + ka_{11} & a_{22} + ka_{12} \end{bmatrix}, \quad E_{12}(k)A = \begin{bmatrix} a_{11} + ka_{21} & a_{12} + ka_{22} \\ a_{21} & a_{22} \end{bmatrix}.$$

PROBLEMS

1. Find the rank of each of the following matrices.

(a) $\begin{bmatrix} 1 & -1 \\ 2 & 2 \\ 1 & 2 \end{bmatrix}$

(b) $\begin{bmatrix} 1 & -1 & 1 \\ 1 & 1 & 1 \\ 3 & -2 & 1 \end{bmatrix}$

(c) $\begin{bmatrix} 1 & -2 & 2 & 1 \\ 2 & -4 & 4 & 2 \\ 1 & 1 & 2 & 0 \end{bmatrix}$

(d) $\begin{bmatrix} 1 \\ 2 \\ 2 \end{bmatrix}$

(e) $[1, -1, 2]$

(f) $\begin{bmatrix} 1 & -1 & 2 & 1 \\ 2 & 1 & 1 & 5 \\ 1 & -2 & 3 & 0 \end{bmatrix}.$

2. Show that the given matrices are equivalent by reducing them all to the same canonical matrix.

(a) $\begin{bmatrix} 1 & -1 & 2 & 0 \\ 2 & 1 & 1 & 1 \\ 0 & 3 & -3 & 1 \end{bmatrix}$ (c) $\begin{bmatrix} 2 & 1 & 1 & -1 \\ 1 & 0 & 1 & 0 \\ 0 & 1 & -1 & -1 \end{bmatrix}$.

(b) $\begin{bmatrix} 1 & 1 & 3 & -1 \\ 0 & 1 & 1 & 2 \\ 2 & 1 & 5 & -4 \end{bmatrix}$

3. Write out the canonical matrices under equivalence for 3×3 matrices over a field.

4. Write out the 2×2 elementary matrices, using elementary column transformations.

5. Perform the elementary column transformations on the general 2×2 matrix

$$\begin{bmatrix} a_{11} & a_{12} \\ a_{21} & a_{22} \end{bmatrix},$$

using the matrices found in Problem 4.

5.6 SYSTEMS OF LINEAR EQUATIONS

An important application of matrix theory is that which pertains to the analysis and solution of systems of linear equations. A system of m linear equations over a field $\mathscr{F}$ in the n symbols $x_1, x_2, \ldots, x_n$ appears thus:

$$
\begin{aligned}
a_{11}x_1 &+ a_{12}x_2 + \cdots + a_{1n}x_n = b_1 \\
a_{21}x_1 &+ a_{22}x_2 + \cdots + a_{2n}x_n = b_2 \\
&\vdots \qquad \vdots \qquad\qquad \vdots \qquad \vdots \\
a_{i1}x_1 &+ a_{i2}x_2 + \cdots + a_{in}x_n = b_i \\
&\vdots \qquad \vdots \qquad\qquad \vdots \qquad \vdots \\
a_{m1}x_1 &+ a_{m2}x_2 + \cdots + a_{mn}x_n = b_m
\end{aligned}
\tag{5.12}
$$

where a_{ij} and b_i are scalars belonging to $\mathscr{F}$. Written in summation form this system becomes

$$\sum_{j=1}^{n} a_{ij}x_j = b_i, \qquad i = 1, 2, \ldots, n. \tag{5.13}$$

DEFINITION **5.14** By a *solution* of Equations 5.12 is meant any ordered *n*-tuple $(x_1, x_2, \ldots, x_n)$ of scalars in $\mathcal{F}$ for which each of the *m* equations of the system is satisfied.

For example, it is easily verified by actual substitution that the system

$$
\begin{aligned}
x_1 - x_2 + 2x_3 &= 1 \\
x_2 - x_3 &= -2
\end{aligned}
$$

has among its solutions $(-1, -2, 0)$, $(-2, -1, 1)$, and $(0, -3, -1)$.

If we define ξ and β as the vectors

$$
\xi = \begin{bmatrix} x_1 \\ x_2 \\ \vdots \\ x_n \end{bmatrix}, \qquad \beta = \begin{bmatrix} b_1 \\ b_2 \\ \vdots \\ b_m \end{bmatrix},
$$

and the *matrix of coefficients* of the system of Equations 5.12 as

$$
A = \begin{bmatrix} a_{11} & a_{12} & \cdots & a_{1n} \\ a_{21} & a_{22} & \cdots & a_{2n} \\ \vdots & \vdots & & \vdots \\ a_{m1} & a_{m2} & \cdots & a_{mn} \end{bmatrix},
$$

then the system can be written compactly in the form of a matrix equation:

$$
A\xi = \beta. \tag{5.14}
$$

It is important to note also that the system of Equations 5.12 can be expressed in terms of its *column* vectors in the following manner. Let us denote by α_j the jth column of A; then

$$
\alpha_j = \begin{bmatrix} a_{1j} \\ a_{2j} \\ \vdots \\ a_{mj} \end{bmatrix}, \qquad j = 1, 2, \ldots, n,
$$

and the system becomes

$$
x_1\alpha_1 + x_2\alpha_2 + \cdots + x_n\alpha_n = \beta. \tag{5.15}
$$

This vector equation makes it clear that a very important relation exists between the columns of the coefficient matrix A, the constant vector β, and the *n*-tuple $(x_1, x_2, \ldots, x_n)$ that we call a solution of the system, namely β *is a linear combination of the vectors α_j, where $j = 1, 2, \ldots, n$, that span the* *column space of A.* A solution $(x_1, x_2, \ldots, x_n)$ of Equations 5.12, when it exists, is a set of scalar multipliers which enables us to express the constant vector β as a linear combination of the column vectors α_j. Hence, we may state the following result of our investigation.

THEOREM **5.14** *A necessary and sufficient condition that there exist a solution $\xi = (x_1, x_2, \ldots, x_n)$ of the system of linear equations $A\xi = \beta$ is that the column vector, β, of constants belong to the column space of the matrix of coefficients A.*

DEFINITION **5.15** The system of linear equations, Equations 5.12, is said to be *consistent* if and only if a solution exists; otherwise it is said to be *inconsistent.*

DEFINITION **5.16** The *augmented matrix* of the system of linear equations (Equations 5.12) is the matrix $[A, \beta]$ formed by appending the column β to the matrix of coefficients.

Thus, for example, the system of equations,

$$
\begin{aligned}
3x_1 - 2x_2 + x_3 &= 1 \\
x_1 \qquad\quad + 2x_3 &= 0 \\
2x_1 + x_2 \qquad\quad &= -1,
\end{aligned}
$$

has the augmented matrix

$$
[A, \beta] = \begin{bmatrix} 3 & -2 & 1 & \vdots & 1 \\ 1 & 0 & 2 & \vdots & 0 \\ 2 & 1 & 0 & \vdots & -1 \end{bmatrix}.
$$

In order that β may belong to the column space of A, it is necessary and sufficient that β be linearly dependent on the column vectors α_j, where $j = 1, \ldots, n,$ of A. Hence, the dimensions of the vector subspaces spanned by the vectors $\{\alpha_1, \ldots, \alpha_n\}$ and $\{\alpha_1, \ldots, \alpha_n, \beta\}$, respectively, must be the same. In terms of the matrix defined above and the notion of rank introduced in the previous section we restate Theorem 5.14:

THEOREM **5.15** *A necessary and sufficient condition that a system of linear equations $A\xi = \beta$ have a solution ξ is that the rank of the coefficient matrix A and that of the augmented matrix $[A, \beta]$ be equal.*

Rather than determine both the rank of A and the rank of the augmented matrix $[A, \beta]$ in order to compare them, we shall find it more efficient to determine the rank of the matrix $[A, \beta]$ by using elementary transformations *on the rows only.* In this way we shall obtain, not only a set of matrices which are equivalent to $[A, \beta]$, but whose submatrices consisting of the first n columns are each equivalent to the matrix A. Hence, we shall be able to compare the ranks of A and $[A, \beta]$ at any stage of the simplifying process, which we have termed "pivotal condensation."

ILLUSTRATION **5.19** Show that the given system of linear equations is consistent:
$$
\begin{aligned}
x_1 - 2x_2 + x_3 - x_4 &= 1 \\
2x_1 \quad\quad - 2x_3 \quad\quad &= -1 \\
x_1 + 2x_2 - 3x_3 + x_4 &= -2.
\end{aligned}
$$

We construct the augmented matrix, and use elementary row operations on it to determine the rank of A and of $[A, \beta]$, respectively:

$$
\begin{aligned}
&\quad\quad\quad\quad\quad\quad\quad\quad\quad\quad\quad\quad r_2' = r_2 - 2r_1 \\
&\quad\quad\quad\quad\quad\quad\quad\quad\quad\quad\quad\quad r_3' = r_3 - r_1
\end{aligned}
$$

$$
[A, \beta] = \begin{bmatrix} 1 & -2 & 1 & -1 & \vdots & 1 \\ 2 & 0 & -2 & 0 & \vdots & -1 \\ 1 & 2 & -3 & 1 & \vdots & -2 \end{bmatrix} \sim \begin{bmatrix} 1 & -2 & 1 & -1 & \vdots & 1 \\ 0 & 4 & -4 & 2 & \vdots & -3 \\ 0 & 4 & -4 & 2 & \vdots & -3 \end{bmatrix}
$$

$$
\quad\quad\quad\quad\quad\quad\quad\quad\quad\quad\quad\quad r_3' = r_3 - r_2
$$

$$
\sim \begin{bmatrix} 1 & -2 & 1 & -1 & \vdots & 1 \\ 0 & 4 & -4 & 2 & \vdots & -3 \\ 0 & 0 & 0 & 0 & \vdots & 0 \end{bmatrix}.
$$

In the last of these matrices the submatrix to the left of the dotted line is equivalent to A. The rank of this submatrix and, hence, that of A, is 2. The entire matrix is equivalent to the augmented matrix $[A, \beta]$ and has rank 2 also. Therefore, by Theorem 5.15 the system is consistent.

Using additional row operations we can further simplify, to obtain the following equivalent matrix:

$$
[A, \beta] \sim \begin{bmatrix} 1 & 0 & -1 & 0 & \vdots & -\tfrac{1}{2} \\ 0 & 1 & -1 & \tfrac{1}{2} & \vdots & -\tfrac{3}{4} \\ 0 & 0 & 0 & 0 & \vdots & 0 \end{bmatrix}.
$$

Of course, our principal concern is not to determine whether a system is consistent or inconsistent but, rather, to *solve the system if it is consistent*. The method generally employed in solving a system of m equations of rank r in n unknowns is to find an *equivalent system*, that is, one that has solutions identical with those of the original system, in which r of the symbols x_i are isolated in the form

$$x_{i_1} = b_1^* + f_1(x)$$
$$x_{i_2} = b_2^* + f_2(x)$$
$$\vdots \qquad \vdots \qquad \vdots \tag{5.16}$$
$$x_{i_r} = b_r^* + f_r(x)$$

where $i_1, i_2, \ldots, i_r$ are distinct integers in the set $\{1, 2, \ldots, n\}$, the b_k^* are scalars, and the functions $f_k(x)$ are linear combinations of the remaining $n - r$ variables x_i. The solutions of the original system, Equations 5.12, are obtained from the equivalent system, Equations 5.16, by assigning arbitrary values to the symbols x_i in the functions $f_k(x)$.

The operations used to obtain equivalent systems are similar to the elementary row operations that were introduced in the previous section.

DEFINITION **5.17** The elementary operations leading to equivalent systems of linear equations are the following:

(a)   Interchange of any two equations.

(b)   Multiplication of any equation by a nonzero scalar.

(c)   Addition of one equation to another.

That these three operations yield systems having identical solutions may be seen in the following:

(a)   It is apparent that the solution of the system will not be altered by the interchange of any two equations.

(b)   Denote by $L_j(\xi) = b_j$ an arbitrary equation in the system of Equations 5.12. Then any solution of this arbitrary equation will likewise satisfy the equation $kL_j(\xi) = kb_j$, where k is any scalar.

(c)   If the vector ξ satisfies $L_j(\xi) = b_j$ and $L_k(\xi) = b_k$, then $L_j(\xi) + L_k(\xi) = b_j + b_k$. That is, the sum of two equations has the same solution as that common to the two equations.

The method we employ to obtain the equivalent system, Equations 5.16, is a variation of the *Gaussian elimination method* and is essentially the method of pivotal condensation.

In the augmented matrix $[A, \beta]$ of Equations 5.12 we permute the rows, if necessary, so that a nonzero element is located in the $(1, 1)$-position. The first row is then divided by this element and is used as the pivotal row to replace each of the remaining elements in the first column with 0. The matrix $[A, \beta]^{(1)}$ of the equivalent system is

$$[A, \beta]^{(1)} = \begin{bmatrix} 1 & a_{12}^{(1)} & \cdots & a_{1n}^{(1)} & b_1^{(1)} \\ 0 & a_{22}^{(1)} & \cdots & a_{2n}^{(1)} & b_2^{(1)} \\ \vdots & \vdots & & \vdots & \vdots \\ 0 & a_{m2}^{(1)} & \cdots & a_{mn}^{(1)} & b_m^{(1)} \end{bmatrix}. \tag{5.17}$$

If there is a nonzero element in the second column in any row other than the first, it is placed in the $(2, 2)$-position by interchanging rows, if necessary. The second row is then divided by this element and is used as the pivotal row to replace all of the other elements in the second column with 0. The matrix $[A, \beta]^{(2)}$ of the equivalent system is

$$[A, \beta]^{(2)} = \begin{bmatrix} 1 & 0 & a_{13}^{(2)} & \cdots & a_{1n}^{(2)} & b_1^{(2)} \\ 0 & 1 & a_{23}^{(2)} & \cdots & a_{2n}^{(2)} & b_2^{(2)} \\ \vdots & \vdots & \vdots & & \vdots & \vdots \\ 0 & 0 & a_{m3}^{(2)} & \cdots & a_{mn}^{(2)} & b_m^{(2)} \end{bmatrix}. \tag{5.18}$$

This procedure is continued through consecutive rows and columns as long as possible. If at some point a row, say the kth, is reached, and it is found that $a_{kk}^{(k)}, a_{k+1,k}^{(k)}, \ldots, a_{mk}^{(k)}$ are all zero, then the process is continued by moving to the $(k + 1)^{\text{th}}$ column.

If the system of equations is *consistent* and the rank of the system is r, the reduction will stop with an augmented matrix whose first r rows are nonzero and remaining $m - r$ rows are zero vectors. The corresponding set of equations will appear as follows:

$$
\begin{aligned}
x_{i_1} & & + a_{1, i_r+1}^{(r)} x_{i_r+1} + \cdots + a_{1, i_n}^{(r)} x_{i_n} = b_{i_1}^{(r)} \\
& x_{i_2} & + a_{2, i_r+1}^{(r)} x_{i_r+1} + \cdots + a_{2, i_n}^{(r)} x_{i_n} = b_{i_2}^{(r)} \\
& \qquad \cdot \\
& \qquad \cdot \\
& \qquad \cdot \\
& \quad x_{i_r} + a_{r, i_r+1}^{(r)} x_{i_r+1} + \cdots + a_{r, i_n}^{(r)} x_{i_n} = b_{i_r}^{(r)}
\end{aligned}
\tag{5.19}
$$

In these equations we may assign arbitrary values to the $n - r$ variables, $x_{i_r+1}, x_{i_r+2}, \ldots, x_{i_n}$, which serve as parameters, and the remaining r variables, $x_{i_1}, x_{i_2}, \ldots, x_{i_r}$, are then determined by Equations 5.19. Because this system is equivalent to the original system (Equations 5.12), there will be infinitely many solutions to it when $r < n$.

If the system is *inconsistent*, the rank of $[A, \beta]$ is greater than that of A. It follows that at some point in the reduction just outlined a row vector of the type $(0, 0, \ldots, 0, b_i)$ must appear. The corresponding equation is

$$0x_1 + 0x_2 + \cdots + 0x_n = b_i, \qquad b_i \neq 0,$$

which clearly has no solution. This indicates that this system and, hence, the equivalent system (Equations 5.12) are inconsistent.

ILLUSTRATION **5.20** The final form of the augmented matrix in Illustration 5.19 is

$$[A, \beta] \sim \begin{bmatrix} 1 & 0 & -1 & 0 & | & -\frac{1}{2} \\ 0 & 1 & -1 & \frac{1}{2} & | & -\frac{3}{4} \\ 0 & 0 & 0 & 0 & | & 0 \end{bmatrix}.$$

This is the augmented matrix of a system of linear equations equivalent to the original system. It appears thus:

$$\begin{array}{rcl} x_1 \quad - x_3 & = & -\frac{1}{2} \\ x_2 - x_3 + \frac{1}{2}x_4 & = & -\frac{3}{4}. \end{array}$$

Values for x_1 and x_2 may be obtained by assigning values to $\{x_3, x_4\}$. For example, $\xi_1 = (\frac{1}{2}, \frac{1}{4}, 1, 0)$ is the solution obtained by setting $x_3 = 1$ and $x_4 = 0$, and $\xi_2 = (-\frac{1}{2}, -\frac{5}{4}, 0, 1)$ is obtained by setting $x_3 = 0$ and $x_4 = 1$.

ILLUSTRATION **5.21** Determine, if possible, a solution of the system

$$\begin{array}{rcl} x_1 - 2x_2 - x_3 & = & -2 \\ 3x_1 + x_2 + 2x_3 & = & -1 \\ x_1 + 5x_2 + 4x_3 & = & 2. \end{array}$$

We construct the augmented matrix and proceed to the augmented matrices of equivalent systems:

$$[A, \beta] = \begin{bmatrix} 1 & -2 & -1 & | & -2 \\ 3 & 1 & 2 & | & -1 \\ 1 & 5 & 4 & | & 2 \end{bmatrix} \sim \begin{bmatrix} 1 & -2 & -1 & | & -2 \\ 0 & 7 & 5 & | & 5 \\ 0 & 7 & 5 & | & 4 \end{bmatrix}$$

$$\sim \begin{bmatrix} 1 & -2 & -1 & | & -2 \\ 0 & 7 & 5 & | & 5 \\ 0 & 0 & 0 & | & -1 \end{bmatrix}.$$

The last row $(0, 0, 0, -1)$ of the final matrix indicates that the system is inconsistent.

DEFINITION **5.18** A *homogeneous linear equation* is of the form

$$a_{i1}x_1 + a_{i2}x_2 + \cdots + a_{in}x_n = 0,$$

where the coefficients a_{ij} are scalars and the constant term on the right is zero. A *system of homogeneous linear equations* is of the form

$$\begin{array}{l} a_{11}x_1 + a_{12}x_2 + \cdots + a_{1n}x_n = 0 \\ a_{21}x_1 + a_{22}x_2 + \cdots + a_{2n}x_n = 0 \\ \vdots \qquad \vdots \qquad \qquad \vdots \\ a_{m1}x_1 + a_{m2}x_2 + \cdots + a_{mn}x_n = 0. \end{array}$$

A system such as that in Definition 5.18 *is always consistent*, because, as may be easily seen, $x_1 = x_2 = \cdots = x_n = 0$ is a solution. However, in most applications such a solution is of no great importance and is usually referred to as the *trivial* solution.

The problem in the homogeneous case, then, is to determine whether or not there are nontrivial solutions and, if there are any, to find them. By using the method of pivotal condensation outlined for the nonhomogeneous case we find that the system of homogeneous linear equations is equivalent to the following system:

$$x_{i_1} \qquad\qquad + a^{(r)}_{1,\,i_r+1}x_{i_r+1} + \cdots + a^{(r)}_{1,\,i_n}x_{i_n} = 0$$
$$\qquad x_{i_2} \qquad + a^{(r)}_{2,\,i_r+1}x_{i_r+1} + \cdots + a^{(r)}_{2,\,i_n}x_{i_n} = 0$$
$$\tag{5.20}$$
$$x_{i_r} + a^{(r)}_{r,\,i_r+1}x_{i_r+1} + \cdots + a^{(r)}_{r,\,i_n}x_{i_n} = 0.$$

As in the nonhomogeneous case, the variables

$$x_{i_r+1}, x_{i_r+2}, \ldots, x_{i_n}$$

are treated as parameters and are assigned arbitrary values. The values of the variables

$$x_{i_1}, x_{i_2}, \ldots, x_{i_r}$$

are determined from Equations 5.20, and the set $\{x_1, \ldots, x_n\}$ will then reduce each of these equations identically to zero.

If $r = n$, the only solution to the system of Equations 5.20 and, hence, to that of Definition 5.18 is the trivial one, because the former reduces simply to

$$x_{i_k} = 0, \qquad k = 1, 2, \ldots, n.$$

If $r < n$, there are infinitely many solutions, as we have found. The results are summarized in the following theorem.

THEOREM **5.16** *A system of homogeneous linear equations has a nontrivial solution if and only if the number of unknowns exceeds the rank of the coefficient matrix.*

Since the rank cannot exceed the smaller of the dimensions of a matrix, we have immediately the following result.

COROLLARY *A system of homogeneous linear equations always has a nontrivial solution if the number of equations is less than the number of unknowns.*

ILLUSTRATION **5.22**   Determine a nontrivial solution of the system of homogeneous linear equations,

$$
\begin{aligned}
x_1 - 2x_2 + x_3 \quad\quad &= 0 \\
x_1 \quad\quad - 2x_3 + 2x_4 &= 0 \\
x_2 - x_3 - x_4 &= 0.
\end{aligned}
$$

The following chain of equivalent matrices consists of the matrix of coefficients of the given system and the respective coefficient matrices of equivalent systems:

$$
\begin{bmatrix} 1 & -2 & 1 & 0 \\ 1 & 0 & -2 & 2 \\ 0 & 1 & -1 & -1 \end{bmatrix}
\sim
\begin{bmatrix} 1 & -2 & 1 & 0 \\ 0 & 2 & -3 & 2 \\ 0 & 1 & -1 & -1 \end{bmatrix}
\sim
\begin{bmatrix} 1 & 0 & -1 & -2 \\ 0 & 0 & -1 & 4 \\ 0 & 1 & -1 & -1 \end{bmatrix}
$$

$$
\sim
\begin{bmatrix} 1 & 0 & 0 & -6 \\ 0 & 0 & -1 & 4 \\ 0 & 1 & 0 & -5 \end{bmatrix}
\sim
\begin{bmatrix} 1 & 0 & 0 & -6 \\ 0 & 1 & 0 & -5 \\ 0 & 0 & 1 & -4 \end{bmatrix}.
$$

The last matrix is the matrix of the equivalent system,

$$
\begin{aligned}
x_1 \quad &= 6x_4 \\
x_2 \quad &= 5x_4 \\
x_3 &= 4x_4.
\end{aligned}
$$

Hence, all the nontrivial solutions of the original system are of the form $(6k, 5k, 4k, k)$, where k is any real number.

PROBLEMS

1. Determine the solutions of the following systems of linear equations whenever they exist.

(a) $x_1 + 2x_2 - x_3 = -1$
     $2x_1 - x_2 \quad = -3$
     $\quad x_2 + 2x_3 = 5.$

(c) $x_1 + 2x_2 \quad = 2$
     $x_1 - x_2 + 2x_3 = 4$
     $\quad 3x_2 - 2x_3 = 1.$

(b) $x_1 + 2x_2 - x_3 = -1$
     $2x_1 - x_2 \quad = -3$
     $x_1 - 3x_2 + x_3 = -2.$

(d) $x_1 + 2x_2 + 3x_3 - x_4 = 0$
     $3x_1 \quad - x_3 \quad = 4$
     $\quad x_2 - x_3 - x_4 = 2.$

2. Find nontrivial solutions when they exist.

(a) $x_1 + 2x_2 + 3x_3 - x_4 = 0$
     $3x_1 \quad - x_3 \quad = 0$
     $\quad x_2 - x_3 - x_4 = 0.$

(c) $2x_1 - x_2 - x_3 + x_4 = 0$
     $x_1 + 2x_2 - x_3 - x_4 = 0$
     $x_1 - 3x_2 \quad + 2x_4 = 0$
     $\quad 5x_2 - x_3 - 3x_4 = 0.$

(b) $2x_1 - x_2 + x_3 = 0$
     $\quad x_2 - x_3 = 0$
     $x_1 \quad + x_3 = 0.$

(d) $a_{11}x_1 + a_{12}x_2 = 0$
     $a_{21}x_1 + a_{22}x_2 = 0,$
     where $a_{11}a_{22} - a_{21}a_{12} \neq 0.$

5.7 NONSINGULAR MATRICES, AND THE INVERSE OF A MATRIX

We begin this section by recalling that the set of $n \times n$ matrices with elements in a field is a ring with an identity with respect to the binary operations of matrix addition and multiplication (see Theorem 5.7). Those elements of such systems that have an inverse are called the *units* of the ring. In general, not every element is a unit.

DEFINITION **5.19** A matrix A is said to be *nonsingular* if there is a matrix B such that

$$AB = I = BA.$$

Any such matrix B is called an *inverse* of A. If there is no such matrix B, then A is said to be *singular*.

THEOREM **5.17** *If A is a nonsingular matrix, it is necessarily square, and it has one and only one inverse.*

Proof. Let A be $m \times n$ and assume that B is an inverse of A of dimensions $n \times p$. Clearly, if $AB = I$, then B must be of dimension $n \times m$, since I is a square matrix. Definition 5.19 gives us $AB = I = BA$, and so we must conclude that the dimensions of A and B are $m \times m$; that is, A is a square matrix.

Now assume that the $m \times m$ matrix A has two inverses, B and C. Then we can write, using the associative law wherever necessary,

$$C(AB) = C(I) = C = (CA)B = (I)B = B$$
$$\therefore \ C = B.$$

Henceforth we shall speak of *the* inverse of a nonsingular matrix A and denote it by the symbol A^{-1}.

ILLUSTRATION **5.23** Show that

$$A = \begin{bmatrix} -1 & -2 \\ 3 & 5 \end{bmatrix}$$

is nonsingular by determining A^{-1}.

Let us assume that the inverse of A is

$$A^{-1} = \begin{bmatrix} x & y \\ z & w \end{bmatrix}$$

and determine the elements w, x, y, z from the matrix equation $AA^{-1} = I$:

$$AA^{-1} = \begin{bmatrix} -1 & -2 \\ 3 & 5 \end{bmatrix}\begin{bmatrix} x & y \\ z & w \end{bmatrix} = \begin{bmatrix} -x - 2z & -y - 2w \\ 3x + 5z & 3y + 5w \end{bmatrix} = \begin{bmatrix} 1 & 0 \\ 0 & 1 \end{bmatrix}.$$

Equating elements, we obtain two sets of linear equations:

$$-x - 2z = 1, \qquad -y - 2w = 0$$
$$3x + 5z = 0, \qquad 3y + 5w = 1.$$

The solutions of these equations are $x = 5$, $z = -3$, $y = 2$, $w = -1$, giving

$$A^{-1} = \begin{bmatrix} 5 & 2 \\ -3 & -1 \end{bmatrix}.$$

The reader should show that $AA^{-1} = A^{-1}A = I$.

In the discussion that follows, we shall develop a more efficient method of computing the inverse of a given nonsingular matrix.

THEOREM **5.18**   *Elementary matrices are nonsingular.*

Proof.   In Theorem 5.9 it is shown that each elementary transformation has an inverse that is itself an elementary transformation. Since each such transformation can be accomplished by means of an elementary matrix, such matrices have inverses and are therefore nonsingular.

ILLUSTRATION **5.24**   Write out the inverse of each of the given elementary matrices:

$$E_{12} = \begin{bmatrix} 0 & 1 \\ 1 & 0 \end{bmatrix}, \qquad E_{12}(k) = \begin{bmatrix} 1 & k \\ 0 & 1 \end{bmatrix}, \qquad E_2(k) = \begin{bmatrix} 1 & 0 \\ 0 & k \end{bmatrix}.$$

The solution is as follows:

$$E_{12}^{-1} = \begin{bmatrix} 0 & 1 \\ 1 & 0 \end{bmatrix}, \qquad E_{12}(k)^{-1} = \begin{bmatrix} 1 & -k \\ 0 & 1 \end{bmatrix}, \qquad E_2(k)^{-1} = \begin{bmatrix} 1 & 0 \\ 0 & 1/k \end{bmatrix}.$$

The reader should verify that these matrices are actually the inverses.

THEOREM **5.19**   *The product AB of two nonsingular matrices A and B is nonsingular, and* $(AB)^{-1} = B^{-1}A^{-1}$.

Proof.   The inverse of a matrix is unique. Hence, we need only to verify that the matrices $B^{-1}A^{-1}$ and AB have the identity matrix as a product:

$$(AB)(B^{-1}A^{-1}) = A(BB^{-1})A^{-1} = AIA^{-1} = AA^{-1} = I,$$
$$(B^{-1}A^{-1})(AB) = B^{-1}(A^{-1}A)B = B^{-1}IB = B^{-1}B = I.$$

The theorem can be extended by mathematical induction to the product of any finite number of square matrices of order n.

COROLLARY OF THEOREM **5.19** $(A_1 A_2 \cdots A_k)^{-1} = A_k^{-1} A_{k-1}^{-1} \cdots A_2^{-1} A_1^{-1}.$

The inverse of a nonsingular matrix has been defined and its uniqueness proved. We are now in a position to present a method of obtaining the inverse of a nonsingular matrix A by using the technique for solving a system of linear equations $A\xi = \beta$, demonstrated in the previous section.

Since the matrix A in question is nonsingular, it is square, say $n \times n$. We write

$$AX = I, \tag{5.21}$$

where the $n \times n$ matrix X is the undetermined inverse of A and I is the identity matrix of order n. Writing both X and I in terms of their column vectors, we have $X = (\xi_1, \xi_2, \ldots, \xi_n)$ and $I = (\varepsilon_1, \varepsilon_2, \ldots, \varepsilon_n)$, and we may write $AX = I$ in the form

$$A\xi_i = \varepsilon_i, \qquad i = 1, 2, \ldots, n, \tag{5.22}$$

that is, n systems of n equations in n unknowns.

Now multiplying Equations 5.22 by A^{-1}, we have

$$A^{-1}A\xi_i = A^{-1}\varepsilon_i, \qquad i = 1, 2, \ldots, n$$

or

$$I\xi_i = A^{-1}\varepsilon_i, \qquad i = 1, 2, \ldots, n. \tag{5.23}$$

All the systems of Equation 5.22 have the same coefficient matrix, so we associate with them the $n \times 2n$ augmented matrix,

$$[A, \varepsilon_1, \varepsilon_2, \ldots, \varepsilon_n] = [A, I], \tag{5.24}$$

and we can obtain the solutions, ξ_i, where $i = 1, 2, \ldots, n$, to all n systems *simultaneously* by transforming this last matrix to the following equivalent matrix,

$$[I, A^{-1}\varepsilon_1, \ldots, A^{-1}\varepsilon_n] = [A, I], \tag{5.25}$$

using only elementary *row* transformations. This now is the augmented matrix of the systems in Equation 5.23. Essentially, then, we obtain A^{-1} from the $n \times n$ matrix of Equation 5.25 by reading off the last n columns. The following illustration will serve to clarify these above remarks.

ILLUSTRATION **5.25**   Find the inverse of

$$A = \begin{bmatrix} 1 & 1 & 2 \\ 2 & 1 & 0 \\ 1 & 2 & 2 \end{bmatrix}.$$

We write the augmented matrix corresponding to Equation 5.24. Then, using elementary row operations, we find an equivalent matrix corresponding to Equation 5.25:

$$[A, I] = \begin{bmatrix} 1 & 1 & 2 & \vdots & 1 & 0 & 0 \\ 2 & 1 & 0 & \vdots & 0 & 1 & 0 \\ 1 & 2 & 2 & \vdots & 0 & 0 & 1 \end{bmatrix} \sim \begin{bmatrix} 1 & 1 & 2 & \vdots & 1 & 0 & 0 \\ 0 & -1 & -4 & \vdots & -2 & 1 & 0 \\ 0 & 1 & 0 & \vdots & -1 & 0 & 1 \end{bmatrix}$$

$$\sim \begin{bmatrix} 1 & 0 & 2 & \vdots & 2 & 0 & -1 \\ 0 & 0 & -4 & \vdots & -3 & 1 & 1 \\ 0 & 1 & 0 & \vdots & -1 & 0 & 1 \end{bmatrix} \sim \begin{bmatrix} 1 & 0 & 2 & \vdots & 2 & 0 & -1 \\ 0 & 1 & 0 & \vdots & -1 & 0 & 1 \\ 0 & 0 & 1 & \vdots & \frac{3}{4} & -\frac{1}{4} & -\frac{1}{4} \end{bmatrix}$$

$$\sim \begin{bmatrix} 1 & 0 & 0 & \vdots & \frac{1}{2} & \frac{1}{2} & -\frac{1}{2} \\ 0 & 1 & 0 & \vdots & -1 & 0 & 1 \\ 0 & 0 & 1 & \vdots & \frac{3}{4} & -\frac{1}{4} & -\frac{1}{4} \end{bmatrix}$$

$$\therefore A^{-1} = \begin{bmatrix} \frac{1}{2} & \frac{1}{2} & -\frac{1}{2} \\ -1 & 0 & 1 \\ \frac{3}{4} & -\frac{1}{4} & -\frac{1}{4} \end{bmatrix}.$$

The reader should verify that $AA^{-1} = I$.

PROBLEMS

1. What is the inverse of the identity matrix I of order n?

2. Show that the inverse of A^{-1} is A.

3. Show that, if A is nonsingular, its transpose, A', is nonsingular and $(A')^{-1} = (A^{-1})'$.

4. Find the inverse of

$$A = \begin{bmatrix} 2 & 1 \\ 4 & 3 \end{bmatrix}$$

over the rational field.

5. Find the inverse of

$$A = \begin{bmatrix} 1 & 1 & -1 \\ 2 & 1 & 1 \\ 1 & 0 & 1 \end{bmatrix}$$

over the rational field.

6. Show that the following matrix is singular.

$$A = \begin{bmatrix} 1 & 1 & -1 \\ 2 & 1 & 1 \\ 1 & 0 & 2 \end{bmatrix}.$$

7. Solve $AX = B$ and $YA = B$ for

$$A = \begin{bmatrix} 1 & -1 \\ 2 & -3 \end{bmatrix}, \qquad B = \begin{bmatrix} 1 & -5 \\ 2 & 2 \end{bmatrix}$$

over the rational field. *Note*: $X = A^{-1}B$.

8. Solve $AX = B$ and $YA = B$ for

$$A = \begin{bmatrix} 1 & -1 & 2 \\ 2 & 0 & 1 \\ 1 & 1 & 1 \end{bmatrix}, \qquad B = \begin{bmatrix} 3 & 1 & 1 \\ 1 & 0 & -2 \\ 2 & -2 & 1 \end{bmatrix}.$$

9. Find the inverse of

$$A = \begin{bmatrix} 1 & 2 & 2 \\ 0 & 1 & 2 \\ 2 & 0 & 1 \end{bmatrix},$$

where the elements of A belong to the finite field $\{0, 1, 2\}$ with addition and multiplication, modulo 3.

10. (a) Show that the matrix

$$A = \begin{bmatrix} 1 & 2 & 2 \\ 0 & 1 & 2 \\ 2 & 1 & 1 \end{bmatrix}$$

is singular when the elements of A belong to the finite field $\{0, 1, 2\}$ with addition and multiplication, modulo 3.

(b) Show that A is nonsingular when its elements belong to the rational field. Find A^{-1} in this case.

Supplementary Reading

BIRKHOFF, G., and S. MACLANE, *A Survey of Modern Algebra*, 3rd ed., Macmillan, New York, 1965.

BROWNE, E. T., *An Introduction to the Theory of Determinants and Matrices*, Univ. North Carolina, Chapel Hill, N.C., 1958.

NAHIKIAN, H. M., *A Modern Algebra for Biologists*, Univ. Chicago, Chicago, 1964.

PERLIS, S., *Theory of Matrices*, Addison-Wesley, Cambridge, Mass., 1952.

6

FUNCTIONS WITH VECTOR ARGUMENTS

6.1 INTRODUCTION

The concept of mapping one set of elements into another set not necessarily distinct was introduced in Chapter 1 and has proven useful throughout this text. It will be recalled that the special type of mapping called a *function* is a rule that pairs with each element of the domain set a unique element of the range set. This definition does not put any limitation on the kind of elements that are placed in correspondence, nor does it state how the correspondence is realized. The function may, for example, map a set of scalars into a set of scalars. On the other hand, the domain may be a set of m-dimensional vectors and the function a correspondence that pairs each vector uniquely with an n-dimensional vector. The function may be specified by a subset of the product set $D \times R$, where D is the domain set and R the range, or it may be defined by an open statement such as $f = a^2 - 2a + 5$, where $a \in D$.

In this chapter we shall be concerned with functions on vector domains, that is to say, functions with vector arguments.

ILLUSTRATION **6.1** (*Linear Forms*) The first function of this type that we shall consider is called a *linear form*. Let us first select a domain set consisting of three-dimensional vectors whose components belong to the real field. For convenience, we shall write these vectors as column vectors:

$$\xi = \text{col}\,(x_1, x_2, x_3) = \begin{bmatrix} x_1 \\ x_2 \\ x_3 \end{bmatrix}.$$

In the same vector space from which the domain set is constructed let us select a known, or fixed, vector $\alpha = \text{col}\,(a_1, a_2, a_3)$. Then a linear form involving α as a *vector of coefficients* is written

$$f(\xi) = \alpha \cdot \xi = [a_1, a_2, a_3] \begin{bmatrix} x_1 \\ x_2 \\ x_3 \end{bmatrix} = a_1 x_1 + a_2 x_2 + a_3 x_3.$$

Thus a linear form is the *inner product*, or *dot product*, of ξ with α (see Definition 5.8).

In particular, if $\alpha = \text{col}\,(2, -1, 1)$, then the function is the open statement $f(\xi) = \alpha \cdot \xi = 2x_1 - x_2 + x_3$. Because we are assuming that the vectors $\xi = \text{col}\,(x_1, x_2, x_3)$ have components belonging to the real field, it is clear that f maps each vector ξ into a unique real number. For example,

$$f(1, 2, 3) = [2, -1, 1] \begin{bmatrix} 1 \\ 2 \\ 3 \end{bmatrix} = 2(1) + (-1)(2) + 1(3) = 3,$$

$$f(-1, 2, -4) = [2, -1, 1] \begin{bmatrix} -1 \\ 2 \\ -4 \end{bmatrix} = 2(-1) + (-1)(2) + 1(-4) = -8;$$

$$f(0, 1, -1) = [2, -1, 1] \begin{bmatrix} 0 \\ 1 \\ -1 \end{bmatrix} = 2(0) + (-1)(1) + 1(-1) = -2.$$

The *general linear form* is the inner product of a fixed n-dimensional vector $\alpha = \text{col}\,(a_1, a_2, \ldots, a_n)$ with arbitrary vectors $\xi = \text{col}\,(x_1, x_2, \ldots, x_n)$. That is,

$$f(\xi) = \alpha \cdot \xi = a_1 x_1 + a_2 x_2 + \cdots + a_n x_n,$$

where the components a_i and x_i belong to a field.

A somewhat more complex function is the subject of the next illustration.

ILLUSTRATION **6.2** (*Quadratic Forms*).   Again let us take as the domain the set of three-dimensional vectors $\xi = \text{col}\,(x_1, x_2, x_3)$, whose components x_i are real numbers, and write the open statement

$$h(\xi) = a_{11} x_1^2 + a_{22} x_2^2 + a_{33} x_3^2 + 2a_{12} x_1 x_2 + 2a_{13} x_1 x_3 + 2a_{23} x_2 x_3,$$

where the coefficients a_{ij} are scalars in the real field. A function such as $h(\xi)$ is called a *quadratic form* over the real field.

Matrices provide a convenient way of writing and computing the values of such forms. To this end we first arrange the terms of $h(\xi)$ in the following way:

$$
\begin{aligned}
h(\xi) = \quad & a_{11}x_1^2 \quad + a_{12}x_1x_2 + a_{13}x_1x_3 \\
+ \; & a_{21}x_2x_1 \; + a_{22}x_2^2 \;\; + a_{23}x_2x_3 \\
+ \; & a_{31}x_3x_1 \; + a_{32}x_3x_2 + a_{33}x_3^2,
\end{aligned}
$$

where $a_{ij} = a_{ji}$. Then $h(\xi)$ can be written as the product of a 3×3 matrix A, the vector $\xi = \text{col}\,(x_1, x_2, x_3)$, and the transpose vector $\xi' = [x_1, x_2, x_3]$ thus:

$$
h(\xi) = \xi'A\xi = [x_1, x_2, x_3]
\begin{bmatrix}
a_{11} & a_{12} & a_{13} \\
a_{21} & a_{22} & a_{23} \\
a_{31} & a_{32} & a_{33}
\end{bmatrix}
\begin{bmatrix}
x_1 \\
x_2 \\
x_3
\end{bmatrix}.
$$

Consider the numerical example

$$
h(\xi) = 3x_1^2 - 2x_2^2 + 2x_3^2 - 4x_1x_2 + x_1x_3 - 5x_2x_3,
$$

which may be written as the matrix product:

$$
h(\xi) = \xi'A\xi = [x_1, x_2, x_3]
\begin{bmatrix}
3 & -2 & 1/2 \\
-2 & -2 & -5/2 \\
1/2 & -5/2 & 2
\end{bmatrix}
\begin{bmatrix}
x_1 \\
x_2 \\
x_3
\end{bmatrix}.
$$

The matrix A is called the *coefficient* matrix of the quadratic form. We note that, since $a_{ij} = a_{ji}$, it follows that $A' = A$. Matrices with this property are called *symmetric* matrices. The concept outlined in the foregoing may be extended in an obvious way to quadratic forms involving n-dimensional vectors.

ILLUSTRATION **6.3** (*Bilinear Forms*) Just as we have functions of two *scalar* arguments (see Definition 1.6), we have the concept of functions of two *vector* arguments. Let $\xi = \text{col}\,(x_1, x_2, \ldots, x_n)$ and $\eta = \text{col}\,(y_1, y_2, \ldots, y_m)$ be vectors in $V_n(\mathscr{F})$ and $V_m(\mathscr{F})$, respectively, and consider the open statement

$$
\begin{aligned}
g(\xi, \eta) = \quad & b_{11}x_1y_1 + b_{12}x_1y_2 + \cdots + b_{1n}x_1y_n \\
+ \; & b_{21}x_2y_1 + b_{22}x_2y_2 + \cdots + b_{2n}x_2y_n \\
+ \; & \vdots \qquad\qquad \vdots \qquad\qquad\quad \vdots \\
+ \; & b_{m1}x_my_1 + b_{m2}x_my_2 + \cdots + b_{mn}x_my_n,
\end{aligned}
$$

where the coefficients b_{ij} are assumed to be scalars in $\mathscr{F}$. We note that $g(\xi, \eta)$ can be written as the following matrix product:

$$g(\xi, \eta) = \xi'B\eta = [x_1, x_2, \ldots, x_m]\begin{bmatrix} b_{11} & b_{12} & \cdots & b_{1n} \\ b_{21} & b_{22} & \cdots & b_{2n} \\ \vdots & & & \vdots \\ b_{m1} & b_{m2} & \cdots & b_{mn} \end{bmatrix}\begin{bmatrix} y_1 \\ y_2 \\ \vdots \\ y_n \end{bmatrix}$$

Consider the numerical example

$$g(\xi, \eta) = \begin{matrix} 3x_1y_1 - & x_1y_2 + 2x_1y_3 \\ + x_2y_1 - & 2x_2y_2 + x_2y_3 \end{matrix} = [x_1, x_2]\begin{bmatrix} 3 & -1 & 2 \\ 1 & -2 & 1 \end{bmatrix}\begin{bmatrix} y_1 \\ y_2 \\ y_3 \end{bmatrix}$$

ILLUSTRATION **6.4** (*Determinants*)   Let us choose as the domain the set of 2×2 matrices with typical elements:

$$A = \begin{bmatrix} a_{11} & a_{12} \\ a_{21} & a_{22} \end{bmatrix}.$$

Such matrices may be thought of as four-dimensional vectors. Associated with them is a well-known function that maps each such matrix into a scalar. It is called the *determinant* of A and is denoted here by the symbol "det A," although a more common notation, perhaps, is $|A|$. This function is defined by the rule

$$\det \begin{bmatrix} a_{11} & a_{12} \\ a_{21} & a_{22} \end{bmatrix} = a_{11}a_{22} - a_{12}a_{21}.$$

For a 3×3 matrix the determinant is defined by

$$\det \begin{bmatrix} a_{11} & a_{12} & a_{13} \\ a_{21} & a_{22} & a_{23} \\ a_{31} & a_{32} & a_{33} \end{bmatrix}$$
$$= a_{11}a_{22}a_{33} + a_{13}a_{21}a_{32} + a_{12}a_{23}a_{31} - a_{13}a_{22}a_{31} - a_{11}a_{23}a_{32} - a_{12}a_{21}a_{33}.$$

Using the above definition, we find

$$\det \begin{bmatrix} 1 & -1 & 2 \\ 3 & 0 & 1 \\ -1 & 2 & 3 \end{bmatrix} = 0 + 12 + 1 - 0 - 2 + 9 = 20.$$

These determinants are special cases of a function that may be defined on square matrices of any order. It should be noted that, if the elements of the matrices belong to a field, this function maps each matrix into a unique element of the field.

The determinant associated with the matrix $A = (a_{ij})$ of order n is the function

$$\det A = \sum \varepsilon_j a_{1j_1} a_{2j_2} \cdots a_{nj_n},$$

where the summation extends over all $n!$ permutations $j_1, j_2, \ldots, j_n$ of the subscripts $1, 2, \ldots, n$ and ε_j has the value $+1$ or -1 according as the permutation $j_1, j_2, \ldots, j_n$ has an even or odd number of inversions.

PROBLEMS

1. Write each of the following linear forms in terms of vectors. Find the value of the function in each case for the vector $\xi = \text{col}\,(2, -2, 2)$.
   (a) $-2x_1 + x_2 + 3x_3$.　　　　　　(c) $3x_1 + x_2 - x_3$.
   (b) $x_1 - 4x_2 - 2x_3$.

2. Write as a matrix product each of the following quadratic forms. Find the value of the function in each case for the vectors $\xi_1 = \text{col}\,(1, -2, 3)$ and $\xi_2 = \text{col}\,(2, 1, 0, -2)$, respectively.
   (a) $-2x_1^2 + x_2^2 - 3x_3^2 + 2x_1x_2 - 4x_1x_3 - 6x_2x_3$.
   (b) $x_1^2 + 4x_2^2 - x_3^2 - 2x_4^2 + 3x_1x_2 - 4x_1x_3 + x_2x_4 - 4x_3x_4$.

3. Write as a matrix product each of the given bilinear forms. Find the value of (a) when $\xi_1 = \text{col}\,(2, -1)$ and $\eta_1 = \text{col}\,(3, 1, 4)$. Find the value of (b) when $\xi_2 = \text{col}\,(1, -1, 2, 4)$ and $\eta_2 = \text{col}\,(2, -3)$.
   (a) $2x_1y_1 - 3x_1y_2 + 2x_1y_3 - x_2y_1 - 2x_2y_2 - 3x_2y_3$.
   (b) $x_1y_1 + 2x_1y_2 - x_2y_2 - 4x_3y_1 + 2x_3y_2 - 2x_4y_1$.

4. Evaluate the determinant function for each of the given matrices.
   (a) $\begin{bmatrix} 1 & -1 \\ 2 & 0 \end{bmatrix}$.　　　　　　(c) $\begin{bmatrix} 5 & 2 \\ -1 & -2 \end{bmatrix}$.

   (b) $\begin{bmatrix} 3 & -2 \\ 1 & 1 \end{bmatrix}$.　　　　　　(d) $\begin{bmatrix} a & b \\ c & d \end{bmatrix}$.

5. Evaluate the determinant function for each of the following matrices.
   (a) $\begin{bmatrix} 1 & -2 & 2 \\ 2 & 1 & 3 \\ -1 & 1 & 2 \end{bmatrix}$.　　　　　(c) $\begin{bmatrix} 2 & 2 & -1 \\ 3 & -1 & 2 \\ 5 & 1 & -1 \end{bmatrix}$.

   (b) $\begin{bmatrix} 2 & 1 & 0 \\ 3 & 2 & -5 \\ 1 & 1 & -5 \end{bmatrix}$.

6. Verify the following properties of the determinant function, using for this purpose the matrix

$$A = \begin{bmatrix} a_{11} & a_{12} \\ a_{21} & a_{22} \end{bmatrix}.$$

(a) Det $A = $ det A', where A' is the transpose of A.
(b) If B is formed from A by interchanging two rows (or columns), det $B = -$det A.
(c) If two rows (or columns) of A are identical, det $A = 0$.
(d) If B is formed from A by multiplying a row (or column) by a scalar k, then det $B = k$ (det A).
(e) If a row (or column) of A consists of zeros, det $A = 0$.
(f) If B is formed from A by adding to any row (or column) a scalar multiple of any other row (or column), then det $B = $ det A.

7. In the determinant of a 4×4 matrix $A = (a_{ij})$, what sign precedes each of the following terms?
(a) $a_{13}a_{22}a_{31}a_{44}$.   (b) $a_{12}a_{23}a_{31}a_{44}$.   (c) $a_{13}a_{24}a_{32}a_{41}$.

8. Evaluate the determinant function for the given matrices.

(a) $\begin{bmatrix} 1 & 0 & 0 & 0 \\ 0 & 1 & 0 & 0 \\ 0 & 0 & 1 & 0 \\ 0 & 0 & 0 & 1 \end{bmatrix}.$ (c) $\begin{bmatrix} 0 & 0 & 0 & a_{14} \\ 0 & 0 & a_{23} & 0 \\ 0 & a_{32} & 0 & 0 \\ a_{41} & 0 & 0 & 0 \end{bmatrix}.$

(b) $\begin{bmatrix} 1 & 1 & 1 & 1 \\ 0 & 2 & 2 & 2 \\ 0 & 0 & 3 & 3 \\ 0 & 0 & 0 & 4 \end{bmatrix}.$

6.2 LINEAR TRANSFORMATIONS

In this section we shall discuss an important class of functions whose domain and range both are linear vector spaces. Let us denote by $V_n(\mathscr{F})$ a linear vector space of dimension n over a field $\mathscr{F}$. It will be recalled that $V_n(\mathscr{F})$ is a set of ordered n-tuples, whose components belong to $\mathscr{F}$ and which is closed with respect to vector addition and scalar multiplication.

DEFINITION 6.1 *A linear transformation defined on the vector space,* $V_n(\mathscr{F})$, *is a function* $T: V_n(\mathscr{F}) \to V_n(\mathscr{F})$ *whose domain is* $V_n(\mathscr{F})$ *and whose* range is a subset of $V_n(\mathscr{F})$, such that for any two vectors ξ and η in the domain the following conditions are satisfied:

(a) $T(\xi + \eta) = T(\xi) + T(\eta)$.

(b) $T(k\xi) = kT(\xi), \qquad k \in F$.

The definition states that a linear transformation, T, is a rule by which each n-tuple, $\xi \in V_n(\mathscr{F})$, corresponds to a unique element, $T(\xi) \in V_n(\mathscr{F})$. Such a transformation can be thought of as a device by which each vector ξ is *mapped into* a unique image vector, $T(\xi)$. Although there are many ways in which such a mapping may be realized, two conditions must be satisfied for the transformation to be classified as *linear*. The first is that *the image of the sum of two vectors of $V_n(\mathscr{F})$ is the sum of their images*. The second is that *the image of a scalar multiple of a vector in $V_n(\mathscr{F})$ is the scalar multiple of the image of the vector*.

Conditions (a) and (b) of Definition 6.1 can be combined into a single relationship:

(c) $T(k_1\xi + k_2\eta) = k_1T(\xi) + k_2T(\eta)$,

for, if k_1 and k_2 are chosen as 1, the condition (c) reduces to condition (a) and if $k_1 = k$ while $k_2 = 0$, it reduces to condition (b).

By using mathematical induction condition (c) can be extended to the case of a linear combination of r vectors, where r is a positive integer:

$$T(k_1\xi_1 + k_2\xi_2 + \cdots + k_r\xi_r) = k_1T(\xi_1) + k_2T(\xi_2) + \cdots + k_rT(\xi_r). \qquad (6.1)$$

That the set of linear transformations is not void may be seen by the following examples.

ILLUSTRATION **6.5** Consider a transformation $I: V_n(\mathscr{F}) \rightarrow V_n(\mathscr{F})$ which *maps each vector of $V_n(\mathscr{F})$ into itself*. Thus, if $\xi \in V_n(\mathscr{F})$, then $I(\xi) = \xi$.

To establish that the transformation I is linear, we shall show that it satisfies condition (c); that is,

$$I(k_1\xi + k_2\eta) = k_1I(\xi) + k_2I(\eta). \qquad (6.2)$$

Now, if we assume that ξ and η are vectors in $V_n(\mathscr{F})$ then, $V_n(\mathscr{F})$ being a linear vector space, the linear combination $k_1\xi + k_2\eta$ lies in $V_n(\mathscr{F})$. It follows at once from the definition of the transformation I that

$$I(k_1\xi + k_2\eta) = k_1\xi + k_2\eta = k_1I(\xi) + k_2I(\eta).$$

Thus I is a linear transformation defined on $V_n(\mathscr{F})$. For obvious reasons I is called the *identity transformation* defined on $V_n(\mathscr{F})$.

ILLUSTRATION 6.6 Assume the domain of the transformation T to be the set $V_2(\mathcal{R})$ of two-dimensional vectors over the real number field, that is, ordered pairs $\xi = (x_1, x_2)$ and $\eta = (y_1, y_2), \ldots$, whose components are real numbers. Let T be a transformation such that

$$T\xi = T(x_1, x_2) = (x_1 + 2x_2, 2x_1 - x_2);$$

then T is a linear transformation.

First, we investigate the behavior of T as it operates on the sum $(\xi + \eta)$ of two vectors, ξ and η:

$$\begin{aligned}
T(\xi + \eta) &= T(x_1 + y_1, x_2 + y_2) \\
&= [x_1 + y_1 + 2(x_2 + y_2), 2(x_1 + y_1) - (x_2 + y_2)] \\
&= [(x_1 + 2x_2) + (y_1 + 2y_2), (2x_1 - x_2) + (2y_1 - y_2)] \\
&= (x_1 + 2x_2, 2x_1 - x_2) + (y_1 + 2y_2, 2y_1 - y_2) \\
&= T(\xi) + T(\eta).
\end{aligned}$$

Second, we consider the image of $k\xi$ under T:

$$\begin{aligned}
T(k\xi) = T(kx_1, kx_2) &= (kx_1 + 2kx_2, 2kx_1 - kx_2) \\
&= k(x_1 + 2x_2, 2x_1 - x_2) \\
&= kT(\xi).
\end{aligned}$$

Since T satisfies both the requirements of Definition 6.1, it is a linear transformation.

Not all transformations on $V_n(\mathcal{F})$ are linear, as may be seen by the following example.

ILLUSTRATION 6.7 Assume $V_2(\mathcal{R})$ is the domain and range of T, and let $T\xi = T(x_1, x_2) = (e^{x_1}, e^{x_2})$; then

$$T(\xi + \eta) = T(x_1 + y_1, x_2 + y_2) = (e^{x_1 + y_1}, e^{x_2 + y_2}).$$

On the other hand,

$$\begin{aligned}
T(\xi) + T(\eta) &= (e^{x_1}, e^{x_2}) + (e^{y_1}, e^{y_2}) \\
&= (e^{x_1} + e^{y_1}, e^{x_2} + e^{y_2}) \\
T(\xi + \eta) &\neq T(\xi) + T(\eta).
\end{aligned}$$

Thus, *T is not a linear transformation.*

Having defined a linear transformation in complete generality, we now propose to use Definition 6.1 to show that *all such transformations can be represented by matrices.* We shall confine our discussion at first to the three-dimensional case, although it will be clear that the theory extends to the n-dimensional vector space in an obvious way.

We have seen in Chapter 4 that the set of unit vectors $\{\varepsilon_1, \varepsilon_2, \varepsilon_3\}$ is a basis of $V_3(\mathscr{F})$. Writing $\varepsilon_1 = \text{col}\ (1, 0, 0)$, $\varepsilon_2 = \text{col}\ (0, 1, 0)$, and $\varepsilon_3 = \text{col}\ (0, 0, 1)$, we may then write an arbitrary vector $\xi = \text{col}\ (x_1, x_2, x_3)$ in $V_3(\mathscr{F})$:

$$\xi = x_1\varepsilon_1 + x_2\varepsilon_2 + x_3\varepsilon_3. \tag{6.3}$$

Let T be a linear transformation defined on $V_3(\mathscr{F})$, and assume the images of ε_1, ε_2, and ε_3 are known to be, respectively,

$$T\varepsilon_1 = \begin{bmatrix} a_{11} \\ a_{21} \\ a_{31} \end{bmatrix}, \qquad T\varepsilon_2 = \begin{bmatrix} a_{12} \\ a_{22} \\ a_{32} \end{bmatrix}, \qquad T\varepsilon_3 = \begin{bmatrix} a_{13} \\ a_{23} \\ a_{33} \end{bmatrix}. \tag{6.4}$$

We shall show that with this information—namely, that T is a linear transformation defined on $V_3(\mathscr{F})$ and that the images of the vectors, ε_1, ε_2, and ε_3 are specified—it is possible to determine the effect of T on all the vectors in $V_3(\mathscr{F})$. Thus, the transformation T will be *completely characterized*, or *identified*.

Operating by T on the vector ξ of Equation 6.3 and using Equations 6.4, we have

$$\begin{aligned} T(\xi) &= T(x_1\varepsilon_1 + x_2\varepsilon_2 + x_3\varepsilon_3) \\ &= T(x_1\varepsilon_1) + T(x_2\varepsilon_2) + T(x_3\varepsilon_3) \\ &= x_1T(\varepsilon_1) + x_2T(\varepsilon_2) + x_3T(\varepsilon_3). \end{aligned} \tag{6.5}$$

Replacing the vectors $T(\varepsilon_1)$, $T(\varepsilon_2)$, and $T(\varepsilon_3)$ in Equation 6.5 with their values from Equation 6.4, we obtain

$$T(\xi) = x_1\begin{bmatrix} a_{11} \\ a_{21} \\ a_{31} \end{bmatrix} + x_2\begin{bmatrix} a_{12} \\ a_{22} \\ a_{32} \end{bmatrix} + x_3\begin{bmatrix} a_{13} \\ a_{23} \\ a_{33} \end{bmatrix} = \begin{bmatrix} a_{11}x_1 + a_{12}x_2 + a_{13}x_3 \\ a_{21}x_1 + a_{22}x_2 + a_{23}x_3 \\ a_{31}x_1 + a_{32}x_2 + a_{33}x_3 \end{bmatrix} \tag{6.6}$$

This last vector, Equation 6.6, can be written as the product of a matrix $A = (a_{ij})$ and the vector $\xi = \text{col}\ (x_1, x_2, x_3)$, namely,

$$T(\xi) = \begin{bmatrix} a_{11} & a_{12} & a_{13} \\ a_{21} & a_{22} & a_{23} \\ a_{31} & a_{32} & a_{33} \end{bmatrix}\begin{bmatrix} x_1 \\ x_2 \\ x_3 \end{bmatrix} = A\xi. \tag{6.7}$$

It is worth noting that if the images of the basis vectors, ε_1, ε_2, and ε_3, are denoted by $T(\varepsilon_1)$, $T(\varepsilon_2)$, and $T(\varepsilon_3)$, then the matrix A which characterizes T is

$$A = [T(\varepsilon_1), T(\varepsilon_2), T(\varepsilon_3)]. \tag{6.8}$$

This matrix is called the matrix of the *linear transformation T*.

From Equation 6.7 it is clear that the image, $T(\xi)$, of an arbitrary vector ξ is determined by multiplying the vector by matrix A of the transformation. If the image $T(\xi)$ is the vector col (y_1, y_2, y_3), then from Equation 6.6 we have

$$
\begin{aligned}
y_1 &= a_{11}x_1 + a_{12}x_2 + a_{13}x_3 \\
y_2 &= a_{21}x_1 + a_{22}x_2 + a_{23}x_3 \\
y_3 &= a_{31}x_1 + a_{32}x_2 + a_{33}x_3.
\end{aligned}
\tag{6.9}
$$

A numerical example may help to clarify the discussion.

ILLUSTRATION **6.8**   Let T be a linear transformation defined on $V_3(\mathscr{R})$ such that the unit vectors ε_1, ε_2, and ε_3 are mapped into

$$
T(\varepsilon_1) = \begin{bmatrix} 1 \\ -1 \\ 2 \end{bmatrix}, \qquad T(\varepsilon_2) = \begin{bmatrix} 0 \\ 1 \\ 2 \end{bmatrix}, \qquad T(\varepsilon_3) = \begin{bmatrix} 1 \\ 0 \\ 1 \end{bmatrix}.
$$

Determine the matrix of the transformation, and the image of each of the following vectors:

$$
\xi_1 = \begin{bmatrix} 1 \\ -1 \\ 1 \end{bmatrix}, \qquad \xi_2 = \begin{bmatrix} 2 \\ 2 \\ -1 \end{bmatrix}, \qquad \xi = \begin{bmatrix} x_1 \\ x_2 \\ x_3 \end{bmatrix}.
$$

The matrix of T is the 3×3 matrix A whose columns are the vectors $T(\varepsilon_1)$, $T(\varepsilon_2)$, and $T(\varepsilon_3)$. Therefore,

$$
A = \begin{bmatrix} 1 & 0 & 1 \\ -1 & 1 & 0 \\ 2 & 2 & 1 \end{bmatrix}.
$$

Multiplying each of the vectors ξ_1, ξ_2, and ξ in turn by A, we have the respective images

$$
T(\xi_1) = A\xi_1 = \begin{bmatrix} 2 \\ -2 \\ 1 \end{bmatrix}, \qquad T(\xi_2) = A\xi_2 = \begin{bmatrix} 1 \\ 0 \\ 7 \end{bmatrix},
$$

$$
T(\xi) = A\xi = \begin{bmatrix} x_1 && + x_3 \\ -x_1 + & x_2 & \\ 2x_1 + & 2x_2 & + x_3 \end{bmatrix}.
$$

Turning now to the general case, we consider a linear transformation, $T \colon V_n(\mathscr{F}) \to V_m(\mathscr{F})$, which maps n-dimensional vectors over a field $\mathscr{F}$ into m-dimensional vectors over the same field. Conditions (a) and (b) are postulated for T as they were for the more restricted case given in Definition 6.1.

Assuming that the vectors $\alpha_1, \alpha_2, \ldots, \alpha_n$ constitute a basis of $V_n(\mathscr{F})$, we shall show that *a knowledge of the effect of T on these basis vectors is sufficient to characterize completely the linear transformation T*. The image $T\alpha_i$ of a vector α_i is a vector in $V_m(\mathscr{F})$, and we assume these images are known:

$$T(\alpha_1) = \begin{bmatrix} a_{11} \\ a_{21} \\ \vdots \\ a_{m1} \end{bmatrix}, \qquad T(\alpha_2) = \begin{bmatrix} a_{12} \\ a_{22} \\ \vdots \\ a_{m2} \end{bmatrix}, \ldots, T(\alpha_n) = \begin{bmatrix} a_{1n} \\ a_{2n} \\ \vdots \\ a_{mn} \end{bmatrix}. \qquad (6.10)$$

An arbitrary vector $\xi = \operatorname{col}(x_1, x_2, \ldots, x_n)$ in $V_n(\mathscr{F})$ may be written as the following linear combination of the vectors α_i, where $i = 1, 2, \ldots, n$:

$$\xi = x_1\alpha_1 + x_2\alpha_2 + \cdots + x_n\alpha_n. \qquad (6.11)$$

Applying the transformation T to ξ in Equation 6.11 and using the linear properties of T, we have

$$T(\xi) = x_1 T(\alpha_1) + x_2 T(\alpha_2) + \cdots + x_n T(\alpha_n). \qquad (6.12)$$

Substituting in this from Equation 6.10 gives the relationship

$$T(\xi) = x_1 \begin{bmatrix} a_{11} \\ a_{21} \\ \vdots \\ a_{m1} \end{bmatrix} + x_2 \begin{bmatrix} a_{12} \\ a_{22} \\ \vdots \\ a_{m2} \end{bmatrix} + \cdots + x_n \begin{bmatrix} a_{1n} \\ a_{2n} \\ \vdots \\ a_{mn} \end{bmatrix}. \qquad (6.13)$$

Making use of matrix multiplication, we may write this equation in the form

$$T(\xi) = \begin{bmatrix} a_{11} & a_{12} & \cdots & a_{1n} \\ a_{21} & a_{22} & \cdots & a_{2n} \\ \vdots & \vdots & & \vdots \\ a_{m1} & a_{m2} & \cdots & a_{mn} \end{bmatrix} \begin{bmatrix} x_1 \\ x_2 \\ \vdots \\ x_n \end{bmatrix} = A\xi. \qquad (6.14)$$

Hence, the matrix of the transformation in the general case, $T: V_n(\mathscr{F}) \to V_m(\mathscr{F})$, is

$$A = \begin{bmatrix} a_{11} & a_{12} & \cdots & a_{1n} \\ a_{21} & a_{22} & \cdots & a_{2n} \\ \vdots & \vdots & & \vdots \\ a_{m1} & a_{m2} & \cdots & a_{mn} \end{bmatrix}. \qquad (6.15)$$

The components of the image of ξ under the linear transformation T are, respectively,

$$
\begin{aligned}
y_1 &= a_{11}x_1 + a_{12}x_2 + \cdots + a_{1n}x_n \\
y_2 &= a_{21}x_1 + a_{22}x_2 + \cdots + a_{2n}x_n \\
&\vdots \qquad \vdots \qquad \vdots \qquad \qquad \vdots \\
y_m &= a_{m1}x_1 + a_{m2}x_2 + \cdots + a_{mn}x_n
\end{aligned}
\qquad (6.16)
$$

ILLUSTRATION **6.9**   Given a linear transformation, $T: V_3(\mathscr{R}) \to V_2(\mathscr{R})$, which maps a basis, $\{\alpha_1, \alpha_2, \alpha_3\}$, into the respective images

$$
T(\alpha_1) = \begin{bmatrix} 1 \\ -1 \end{bmatrix}, \qquad T(\alpha_2) = \begin{bmatrix} 0 \\ 2 \end{bmatrix}, \qquad T(\alpha_3) = \begin{bmatrix} 3 \\ 1 \end{bmatrix},
$$

find the matrix of T and the components of $T(\xi)$, where $\xi = \text{col}\,(x_1, x_2, x_3)$ relative to the given basis.

The matrix of T is the 2×3 matrix with columns $T(\alpha_1)$, $T(\alpha_2)$, and $T(\alpha_3)$. Hence,

$$
A = \begin{bmatrix} 1 & 0 & 3 \\ -1 & 2 & 1 \end{bmatrix}.
$$

An arbitrary vector, $\xi = \text{col}\,(x_1, x_2, x_3)$ is mapped into

$$
T(\xi) = A\xi = \begin{bmatrix} 1 & 0 & 3 \\ -1 & 2 & 1 \end{bmatrix} \begin{bmatrix} x_1 \\ x_2 \\ x_3 \end{bmatrix} = \begin{bmatrix} x_1 & & + 3x_3 \\ -x_1 & + 2x_2 & + x_3 \end{bmatrix}.
$$

Therefore, if $T(\xi) = \text{col}\,(y_1, y_2)$, then

$$
\begin{aligned}
y_1 &= x_1 + 3x_3 \\
y_2 &= -x_1 + 2x_2 + x_3.
\end{aligned}
$$

PROBLEMS

1. Determine which of the following transformations defined on V are linear. In each case, $\xi = \text{col}\,(x_1, x_2)$.

   (a) $T(\xi) = \text{col}\,(\sqrt{x_1}, \sqrt{x_2})$

   (b) $T(\xi) = \text{col}\,(x_2, x_1)$

   (c) $T(\xi) = \text{col}\,(x_1 - x_2, x_1 + x_2)$

   (d) $T(\xi) = \text{col}\,(x_1 + 1, x_2 - 1)$

   (e) $T(\xi) = \text{col}\,(2^{x_1}, 2^{x_2})$

   (f) $T(\xi) = \text{col}\,(2x_1 + x_2, -x_1 + 3x_2)$

2. Find the matrix of the linear transformation

$$T: V_3(\mathscr{R}) \to V_3(\mathscr{R})$$

for

$$T(\varepsilon_1) = \begin{bmatrix} 2 \\ 1 \\ 3 \end{bmatrix}, \qquad T(\varepsilon_2) = \begin{bmatrix} 1 \\ 0 \\ 0 \end{bmatrix}, \qquad T(\varepsilon_3) = \begin{bmatrix} 3 \\ 3 \\ 0 \end{bmatrix},$$

where $\{\varepsilon_1, \varepsilon_2, \varepsilon_3\}$ is a basis of $V_3(\mathscr{R})$. Determine the images of

$$\xi_1 = \begin{bmatrix} 1 \\ 1 \\ 5 \end{bmatrix}, \qquad \xi_2 = \begin{bmatrix} 1 \\ -1 \\ -2 \end{bmatrix}, \qquad \xi = \begin{bmatrix} x_1 \\ x_2 \\ x_3 \end{bmatrix}.$$

3. Given that a linear transformation, $T: V_2(\mathscr{R}) \to V_3(\mathscr{R})$, maps an appropriate basis, $\{\alpha_1, \alpha_2\}$ of $V_2(\mathscr{R})$ into $T(\alpha_1) = \text{col}\,(3, 0, 2)$ and $T(\alpha_2) = \text{col}$ $(4, -1, -2)$, find the images of $\xi_1 = \text{col}\,(1, -1)$, $\xi_2 = \text{col}\,(2, 5)$, and $\xi = (x_1, x_2)$.

4. Given that $T: V_3(\mathscr{R}) \to V_3(\mathscr{R})$ is a linear transformation which maps an appropriate basis, $\{\alpha_1, \alpha_2, \alpha_3\}$, into $T(\alpha_1) = \text{col}\,(1, 0, 6)$, $T(\alpha_2) = \text{col}\,(-1, 0, 0)$, and $T(\alpha_3) = (0, 1, 1)$, find the matrix of the transformation and the image, $T(\xi) = \text{col}\,(y_1, y_2, y_3)$, in terms of the components of the vector, $\xi = \text{col}\,(x_1, x_2, x_3)$; also find the inverse, T^{-1}, of T such that $T^{-1}(\eta) = \text{col}\,(x_1, x_2, x_3)$, where $\eta = \text{col}\,(y_1, y_2, y_3)$.

5. Given that $T: V_4(\mathscr{R}) \to V_4(\mathscr{R})$ is a linear transformation which maps an appropriate basis, $\{\alpha_1, \alpha_2, \alpha_3, \alpha_4\}$, into the vectors $T(\alpha_1) = (1, -1, 0, 0)$, $T(\alpha_2) = (1, 0, 1, 0)$, $T(\alpha_3) = (2, -1, 2, 1)$, and $T(\alpha_4) = (0, 0, 0, 1)$, find the matrix of the transformation and the matrix of the inverse transformation.

6.3   THE USE OF MATRICES IN CRYPTOGRAPHY

Cryptography offers many examples of transformations. For instance, a message might be encoded by the simple device of mapping each letter of the alphabet into the one that follows: $A \to B$, $B \to C$, ..., $Y \to Z$, $Z \to A$; so that, for instance, $\text{DOG} \to \text{EPH}$. Or first the code may be made numerical by assigning integers in a one-to-one manner to the letters of the alphabet, as

A	B	C	⋯	Y	Z
1	2	3	⋯	25	26

and then by some arbitrary but fixed scheme these integers be reordered before the message is encoded, as

A	B	C	D	E	F	G	H	I	J	K	L	M	N	O	P	$\cdots$	Z
2	4	6	8	10	12	14	16	18	20	22	24	26	1	3	5	$\cdots$	25

so that in this code DOG $\to$ 8 3 14.

Decoding an enciphered message is equivalent to applying the inverse transformation. Clearly, *an important prerequisite of a good code is that it be nonsingular* for, if it is singular, the inverse transformation does not exist and the message cannot be decoded, at least not without some ambiguity. An example of a singular transformation in this connection is a code that assigns the same code symbol to several letters of the alphabet.

Simple substitutions of the type just presented offer no great challenge to an experienced cryptographer. The substitution of new symbols for the alphabet of the message does not alter the frequency of occurrence of the letters in the message. Frequency of occurrence of the letters of alphabets in various languages have been the object of much research and are well known to those who deal in such matters. Thus, if a text is sufficiently long, certain key letters—vowels and some consonants—are quickly identified by the expert.

How to avoid this difficulty in writing coded messages has been a subject of interest to cryptographers for many years, and some highly effective methods have been produced. One scheme of particular interest to us involves the concept of a nonsingular linear transformation of a vector space.

The first step in this method of encoding is to assign integers to the letters of the alphabet: for example, A = 1, B = 2, C = 3, ..., Z = 26. The next is to divide the message into groups of n letters each. Thus the dimension of the vectors is n, and the matrix of the linear transformation involved is $n \times n$.

Suppose the message to be encoded is

$$\text{THIS MATH COURSE IS TOO DIFFICULT,}$$

and it is decided to divide it into triplets. The message appears thus:

$$\text{THI SMA THC OUR SEI STO ODI FFI CUL TYZ,}$$

where YZ is added in order that each group may have three letters. Assigning the integers to the letters of the message, we have the vectors,

$$\begin{bmatrix} T \\ H \\ I \end{bmatrix} = \begin{bmatrix} 20 \\ 8 \\ 9 \end{bmatrix}, \quad \begin{bmatrix} S \\ M \\ A \end{bmatrix} = \begin{bmatrix} 19 \\ 13 \\ 1 \end{bmatrix}, \quad \begin{bmatrix} T \\ H \\ C \end{bmatrix} = \begin{bmatrix} 20 \\ 8 \\ 3 \end{bmatrix}, \quad \begin{bmatrix} O \\ U \\ R \end{bmatrix} = \begin{bmatrix} 15 \\ 21 \\ 18 \end{bmatrix}, \text{ etc.}$$

Next we choose a nonsingular matrix of order 3, preferably one that has integral elements and whose inverse also has integral elements. The following matrices will do for purposes of illustration:

$$A = \begin{bmatrix} 1 & 1 & 1 \\ 1 & 2 & 2 \\ 1 & 2 & 3 \end{bmatrix}, \qquad A^{-1} = \begin{bmatrix} 2 & -1 & 0 \\ -1 & 2 & -1 \\ 0 & -1 & 1 \end{bmatrix}.$$

We now proceed to transform each of these vectors by the linear transformation whose matrix is A. The first three vectors and their corresponding images are as follows:

$$\begin{bmatrix} T \\ H \\ I \end{bmatrix} \to A \begin{bmatrix} 20 \\ 8 \\ 9 \end{bmatrix} = \begin{bmatrix} 37 \\ 54 \\ 63 \end{bmatrix},$$

$$\begin{bmatrix} S \\ M \\ A \end{bmatrix} \to A \begin{bmatrix} 19 \\ 13 \\ 1 \end{bmatrix} = \begin{bmatrix} 33 \\ 47 \\ 48 \end{bmatrix},$$

$$\begin{bmatrix} T \\ H \\ C \end{bmatrix} \to A \begin{bmatrix} 20 \\ 8 \\ 3 \end{bmatrix} = \begin{bmatrix} 31 \\ 42 \\ 45 \end{bmatrix}.$$

The decoding proceeds in a similar manner with the use of the inverse matrix A^{-1}:

$$A^{-1} \begin{bmatrix} 37 \\ 54 \\ 63 \end{bmatrix} = \begin{bmatrix} 20 \\ 8 \\ 9 \end{bmatrix} = \begin{bmatrix} T \\ H \\ I \end{bmatrix},$$

$$A^{-1} \begin{bmatrix} 33 \\ 47 \\ 48 \end{bmatrix} = \begin{bmatrix} 19 \\ 13 \\ 1 \end{bmatrix} = \begin{bmatrix} S \\ M \\ A \end{bmatrix},$$

$$A^{-1} \begin{bmatrix} 31 \\ 42 \\ 45 \end{bmatrix} = \begin{bmatrix} 20 \\ 8 \\ 3 \end{bmatrix} = \begin{bmatrix} T \\ H \\ C \end{bmatrix}.$$

There is a class of linear transformations that is characterized by the property that, when a transformation T is applied successively to the vector ξ and its image $T(\xi)$, the final image is the initial vector, ξ. Thus, $T[T(\xi)] = \xi$.

In short, T^2 is the identity transformation and its matrix is $B^2 = I$. Linear transformations and matrices that have this property are called *involutory*.

The obvious advantage of using an involutory matrix for the encoding of a message is that $B^2 = BB = I$, which means that $B^{-1} = B$. Hence, the same matrix B is used for both encoding and decoding. An example of such an involutory matrix is the following:

$$B^2 = \begin{bmatrix} -1 & -2 & -2 \\ 1 & 2 & 1 \\ -1 & -1 & 0 \end{bmatrix} \begin{bmatrix} -1 & -2 & -2 \\ 1 & 2 & 1 \\ -1 & -1 & 0 \end{bmatrix} = \begin{bmatrix} 1 & 0 & 0 \\ 0 & 1 & 0 \\ 0 & 0 & 1 \end{bmatrix}.$$

PROBLEMS

1. Complete the encoding of the message

    THIS MATH COURSE IS TOO DIFFICULT

    using the matrix A of the text.

2. Use the involutory matrix

$$B = \begin{bmatrix} -1 & -2 & -2 \\ 1 & 2 & 1 \\ -1 & -1 & 0 \end{bmatrix}$$

    to encode the message

    I MUST PREPARE FOR MY EXAM

3. Verify that the given matrix C is involutory, and use that fact to decode the coded message which for convenience is given as the columns of the matrix M:

$$C = \begin{bmatrix} 0 & 1 & -1 \\ 3 & -2 & 3 \\ 2 & -2 & 3 \end{bmatrix},$$

$$M = \begin{bmatrix} 0 & -9 & -4 & 10 & 1 & -17 \\ 36 & 51 & 32 & 37 & 78 & 123 \\ 29 & 47 & 29 & 23 & 57 & 102 \end{bmatrix}.$$

6.4 MARKOV CHAINS AND STOCHASTIC MATRICES

As an introduction to the terminology and notation of this section, let us consider the following hypothetical situation.

In a psychology laboratory a maze consisting of nine cells (see Figure 6.1) is constructed for a learning experiment on rats. A rat has partially

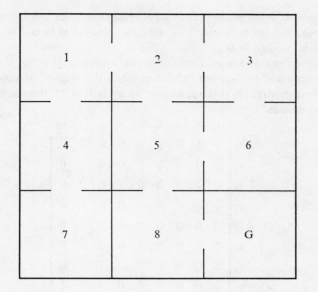

Learning Maze.

FIGURE 6.1

learned the maze in which G is the goal. For various reasons the following learning pattern exists: if the rat is in cell 1, 2, 3, or 4, it moves with equal probability to those cells that the maze permits; if it is in cell 5, 6, or 8, it moves directly from cell to cell toward G; if it is in cell 7 or G, it remains there.

We shall call the maze and rat a *system*, $\mathscr{S}$. The system changes as the rat moves from cell to cell. The *state* of the system at any step n (or instant t, if time is involved) is denoted by $s_i(n)$ if the rat is in cell i at the nth step, or by $s_i(t)$ if at instant t. The compound event, S_{ij}, is read, "The rat is in cell i in the $(n-1)^{\text{th}}$ step [or at time $t-1$] and is in cell j in the nth step [or at time t]."

The probability of the event S_{ij} is denoted by q_{ij}. These nonnegative numbers are called the *transition probabilities* and are determined by the observed frequency of each of the compound events S_{ij} of the experiment. This information is summarized in the description of the learning pattern. For example, according to the rat's observed pattern, $q_{11} = 0$, $q_{12} = \frac{1}{2}$, and $q_{14} = \frac{1}{2}$, while the remaining probabilities $q_{1j} = 0$ because of the physical characteristics of the maze. Further, according to the observed frequencies, it is found that if the rat is in cell 5, it always moves to cell 8; that is, $q_{58} = 1$

and, of course, all other probabilities $q_{5j} = 0$. On the other hand, it is observed that whenever the rat is in cell 7, it remains there; that is, $q_{77} = 1$, and all other probabilities $q_{7j} = 0$.

It is convenient and useful to construct a matrix $Q = (q_{ij})$, called the *transition matrix* of the system, which exhibits the transition probabilities. The transition matrix of this rat-and-maze system is of dimensions 9×9 and may be written

$$Q = s_5 \begin{array}{c} \\ \end{array} \begin{array}{ccccccccc} s_1 & s_2 & s_3 & s_4 & s_5 & s_6 & s_7 & s_8 & s_G \\ \begin{array}{c} s_1 \\ s_2 \\ s_3 \\ s_4 \\ s_5 \\ s_6 \\ s_7 \\ s_8 \\ s_G \end{array} \begin{bmatrix} 0 & \frac{1}{2} & 0 & \frac{1}{2} & 0 & 0 & 0 & 0 & 0 \\ \frac{1}{3} & 0 & \frac{1}{3} & 0 & \frac{1}{3} & 0 & 0 & 0 & 0 \\ 0 & \frac{1}{2} & 0 & 0 & 0 & \frac{1}{2} & 0 & 0 & 0 \\ \frac{1}{2} & 0 & 0 & 0 & 0 & 0 & \frac{1}{2} & 0 & 0 \\ 0 & 0 & 0 & 0 & 0 & 0 & 0 & 1 & 0 \\ 0 & 0 & 0 & 0 & 1 & 0 & 0 & 0 & 0 \\ 0 & 0 & 0 & 0 & 0 & 0 & 1 & 0 & 0 \\ 0 & 0 & 0 & 0 & 0 & 0 & 0 & 0 & 1 \\ 0 & 0 & 0 & 0 & 0 & 0 & 0 & 0 & 1 \end{bmatrix} \end{array}.$$

Because the elements q_{ij} of the ith row of Q are the probabilities that $\mathscr{S}$ was in state s_i at step $n - 1$ and in state s_j at step n, we have $0 \leqslant q_{ij} \leqslant 1$. Moreover, row i contains *all* of the probabilities of the compound event S_{ij} and, accordingly, we have

$$\sum_{j=1}^{n} q_{ij} = 1.$$

A matrix of this type is classified a *stochastic* matrix. A sequence of states of this type, in which the transition probabilities are independent of the step n or time t, is called a *finite Markov chain*.

In the general problem leading to a finite Markov chain we assume an undefined biological or physical system $\mathscr{S}$ which is capable of functioning in n states s_i.

For the purposes of this discussion we shall assume the following:

1. The states s_i are mutually exclusive.

2. The state of the system $\mathscr{S}$ is recorded at regular intervals, say at times $t - 1, t, t + 1, t + 2, \ldots$.

3. No change of state occurs at the precise times $t - 1, t, t + 1, t + 2, \ldots$

4. Not more than one change of state takes place during any one of the unit intervals $(t - 1, t), (t, t + 1), \ldots$.

The *state of the system at time t*, denoted by $s_i(t)$, may arise in n different ways, depending on which one of the states $s_1(t - 1), s_2(t - 1), \ldots, s_n(t - 1)$

precedes $s_i(t)$. That is to say, $\mathscr{S}$ is assumed to have been in some one of the n possible states during time $t - 1$ and to have changed to state $s_i(t)$ during the interval $(t - 1, t)$. Furthermore, in the general problem the possibility that $\mathscr{S}$ remains in a given state is not ruled out. Assume $p_i(t)$ to be probability that $\mathscr{S}$ is in state $s_i(t)$.

Let us denote by S_{ij} the compound event, in which the system $\mathscr{S}$ is in state $s_j(t)$ at time t and was in state $s_i(t - 1)$ at time $t - 1$. Then, according to the theory of probability developed in Sections 3.4 and 3.5, the probability p, of such an event is

$$p(s_{ij}) = p[s_i(t - 1)] \cdot p[s_j(t) \mid s_i(t - 1)]. \tag{6.17}$$

The expression $p[s_j(t) \mid s_i(t - 1)]$ is the conditional probability that $\mathscr{S}$ is in state s_j at time t when it is known that $\mathscr{S}$ was in state s_i at time $t - 1$. This is the transitional probability q_{ij} introduced earlier for the rat-maze system. Hence, we write

$$q_{ij} = p[s_j(t) \mid s_i(t - 1)] \tag{6.18}$$

and also

$$p_i(t - 1) = p[s_i(t - 1)]. \tag{6.19}$$

Substituting from Equations 6.18 and 6.19 into Equation 6.17, we have

$$p(s_{ij}) = p_i(t - 1)q_{ij}, \qquad i = 1, \ldots, n \quad \text{and} \quad j = 1, \ldots, n. \tag{6.20}$$

That is, the probability that a system $\mathscr{S}$ is in state s_j at time t and was in s_i at time $t - 1$ is the product of the probability that $\mathscr{S}$ was in state $s_i(t - 1)$, and the probability that $\mathscr{S}$ changed from state s_i to s_j in the interval $(t - 1, t)$.

Now note that $\mathscr{S}$ is in state $s_j(t)$ when and only when S_{1j} or $S_{2j}, \ldots,$ or S_{nj} takes place. These n compound events are mutually exclusive, since the states were so assumed. Hence, we have

$$p[s_j(t)] = p(S_{1j}) + p(S_{2j}) + \cdots + p(S_{nj}). \tag{6.21}$$

Using the relationships established in Equations 6.19 and 6.20, we may write Equation 6.21 in the form

$$p_j(t) = p_1(t - 1)q_{1j} + p_2(t - 1)q_{2j} + \cdots + p_n(t - 1)q_{nj} \tag{6.22}$$

Let us write col $(q_{1j}, q_{2j}, \ldots, q_{nj})$ as the jth column, Q_j, of the transition matrix, Q,

$$Q = \begin{bmatrix} q_{11} & q_{12} & \cdots & q_{1j} & \cdots & q_{1n} \\ q_{21} & q_{22} & \cdots & q_{2j} & \cdots & q_{2n} \\ \vdots & \vdots & & \vdots & & \vdots \\ q_{n1} & q_{n2} & \cdots & q_{nj} & \cdots & q_{nn} \end{bmatrix},$$

and write $p_1(t-1), p_2(t-1), \ldots, p_n(t-1)$ as the components of the row vector $P(t-1)$, called the *status vector* of $\mathcal{S}$ at time $t-1$:

$$P(t-1) = [p_1(t-1), p_2(t-1), \ldots, p_n(t-1)]. \qquad (6.23)$$

Then, from Equation 6.22, we may write

$$p_j(t) = P(t-1) \cdot Q_j, \qquad j = 1, 2, \ldots, n. \qquad (6.24)$$

That is, *the probability that $\mathcal{S}$ is in state s_j at time t is the inner product of the jth column of the transition matrix of the system $\mathcal{S}$ and the status vector of $\mathcal{S}$ at time $t-1$.*

As an immediate consequence of the rule for multiplying vectors and matrices, we have, by using Equations 6.23 and 6.24,

$$\begin{aligned}
P(t) &= [p_1(t), p_2(t), \ldots, p_n(t)] \\
&= [p(t-1) \cdot Q_1, p(t-1) \cdot Q_2, \ldots, p(t-1) \cdot Q_n] \\
&= p(t-1)Q.
\end{aligned}$$

Verbally, *the status vector of a system $\mathcal{S}$ at time t is the product of the status vector at time $t-1$ and the transition matrix.* *

ILLUSTRATION **6.10**   Assume a system $\mathcal{S}$ which has four possible states s_i, where $i = 1, 2, 3, 4$. It is known that $\mathcal{S}$ cannot remain in its present state, s_i, but changes with *equal probability* from s_i to "adjacent" states, indicated in Figure 6.2. In this case, the transition matrix Q is of the form

$$Q = \begin{array}{c} \\ s_1 \\ s_2 \\ s_3 \\ s_4 \end{array} \begin{array}{c} \begin{array}{cccc} s_1 & s_2 & s_3 & s_4 \end{array} \\ \left[\begin{array}{cccc} 0 & \frac{1}{2} & 0 & \frac{1}{2} \\ \frac{1}{2} & 0 & \frac{1}{2} & 0 \\ 0 & \frac{1}{2} & 0 & \frac{1}{2} \\ \frac{1}{2} & 0 & \frac{1}{2} & 0 \end{array} \right] \end{array}.$$

If we assume the status vector $P(t-1) = (1, 0, 0, 0)$, then

$$P(t) = p(t-1)Q = (0, \tfrac{1}{2}, 0, \tfrac{1}{2}).$$

If we use this last vector, we determine the status vector of $\mathcal{S}$ at time $t+1$ to be

$$P(t+1) = P(t)Q = (\tfrac{1}{2}, 0, \tfrac{1}{2}, 0).$$

Similarly, the status vector at time $t+2$ is

$$P(t+2) = P(t+1)Q = (0, \tfrac{1}{2}, 0, \tfrac{1}{2}).$$

* It seems more convenient to postmultiply a row vector by Q than to premultiply a column vector by the *transpose* matrix Q'.

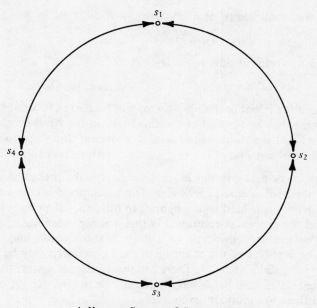

Adjacent States of System S.

FIGURE 6.2

Because it is apparent that the status vectors $(\frac{1}{2}, 0, \frac{1}{2}, 0)$ and $(0, \frac{1}{2}, 0, \frac{1}{2})$ alternate at consecutive units of time, we may conclude that, regardless of what state $\mathscr{S}$ is in at any given instant, it will be in either of two adjacent states with equal probability during the next instant.

ILLUSTRATION **6.11**   Assume that a system $\mathscr{S}$ can either remain in its present state or change to adjacent states all with equal probability. The transitional matrix is

$$Q = \begin{bmatrix} \frac{1}{3} & \frac{1}{3} & 0 & \frac{1}{3} \\ \frac{1}{3} & \frac{1}{3} & \frac{1}{3} & 0 \\ 0 & \frac{1}{3} & \frac{1}{3} & \frac{1}{3} \\ \frac{1}{3} & 0 & \frac{1}{3} & \frac{1}{3} \end{bmatrix}.$$

If we assume that the status vector of $\mathscr{S}$ at time $t - 1$ is

$$P(t - 1) = (\tfrac{1}{4}, 0, \tfrac{1}{2}, \tfrac{1}{4}),$$

then the status vector of $\mathscr{S}$ at time t is

$$P(t) = P(t - 1)Q = (\tfrac{1}{6}, \tfrac{1}{4}, \tfrac{1}{4}, \tfrac{1}{3}).$$

Similarly, the status vector of $\mathscr{S}$ at time $t + 1$ is

$$P(t + 1) = P(t)Q = (\tfrac{1}{4}, \tfrac{4}{18}, \tfrac{5}{18}, \tfrac{1}{4}),$$

and the status vector at time $t + 2$ is

$$P(t + 2) = P(t + 1)Q = (\tfrac{13}{54}, \tfrac{1}{4}, \tfrac{1}{4}, \tfrac{14}{54}).$$

Although the initial probability vector was biassed in favor of the state s_3, it is apparent that by the end of the third step in the Markov chain, it can be predicted that the status of the system $\mathscr{S}$ over a "long" period of time is that it will be in any one of the four states s_i with equal probability.

ILLUSTRATION 6.12   In this example, we apply the preceding theory to a genetic problem of *continued crossings*. The assumption is that an animal of unknown genotype is bred with a hybrid. In turn, the offspring is bred with a hybrid, and the process is continued in this manner indefinitely.

That this problem gives rise to a finite Markov chain may be seen as follows. The genotype of the offspring in each generation may be considered to be the biological system $\mathscr{S}$. There are three possible states: the genotype in each generation can be *dominant*, $\{G, G\}$, or *hybrid*, $\{G, g\}$, or *recessive* $\{g, g\}$, and these are mutually exclusive.

In the computations of transitional probabilities it will be assumed that the following genetic principle is valid: *The offspring of a dominant genotype and a hybrid is either dominant or hybrid with equal probability, and the offspring of a recessive genotype and a hybrid is either recessive or hybrid with equal probability.*

Accordingly, if the elements of the first row of the transitional matrix Q are selected as the respective probabilities q_{1j} that $\mathscr{S}$ will change from $\{G, G\}$ to $\{G, G\}$, $\{G, g\}$, or $\{g, g\}$, then $q_{11} = \tfrac{1}{2}$, $q_{12} = \tfrac{1}{2}$, and $q_{13} = 0$. If the entries in the third row are the respective probabilities q_{3j} that $\mathscr{S}$ will change from $\{g, g\}$ to $\{G, G\}$, $\{g, G\}$, or $\{g, g\}$, then $q_{31} = 0$, $q_{32} = \tfrac{1}{2}$, and $q_{33} = \tfrac{1}{2}$.

The computation of the elements of the second row, which are the probabilities that $\mathscr{S}$ will change from $\{G, g\}$ to $\{G, G\}$, $\{g, G\}$, or $\{g, g\}$, is as follows. The probability that one parent will contribute a dominant gene is $p\{G\} = \tfrac{1}{2}$. Hence, the probability that both parents will contribute a dominant gene is $q_{21} = p(\{G\} \cap \{G\}) = p(G) \times p\{G\} = \tfrac{1}{2} \times \tfrac{1}{2} = \tfrac{1}{4}$. Similarly, the event $\{g, g\}$ has probability $q_{23} = \tfrac{1}{4}$. The probability of the event $\{g, G\} = \{G, g\}$ is $q_{22} = 2 \times \tfrac{1}{2} \times \tfrac{1}{2} = \tfrac{1}{2}$. Therefore, the transitional matrix for this problem is

$$Q = \begin{array}{c} \\ d \\ h \\ r \end{array} \begin{array}{ccc} d & h & r \\ \left[\begin{array}{ccc} \tfrac{1}{2} & \tfrac{1}{2} & 0 \\ \tfrac{1}{4} & \tfrac{1}{2} & \tfrac{1}{4} \\ 0 & \tfrac{1}{2} & \tfrac{1}{2} \end{array}\right]. \end{array}$$

Suppose at some step in the experiment the genotype is dominant. This is equivalent to the statement that the status vector of $\mathscr{S}$ at this step is $P_0 = (1, 0, 0)$. The following computations are easily verified:

$$P_1 = P_0 Q = (\tfrac{1}{2}, \tfrac{1}{2}, 0)$$
$$P_2 = P_1 Q = (\tfrac{3}{8}, \tfrac{1}{2}, \tfrac{1}{8})$$
$$P_3 = P_2 Q = (\tfrac{5}{16}, \tfrac{1}{2}, \tfrac{3}{16})$$
$$P_4 = P_3 Q = (\tfrac{9}{32}, \tfrac{1}{2}, \tfrac{7}{32}).$$

It appears that, starting with a dominant genotype, the status vector after four generations is almost equal to the vector $(\tfrac{1}{4}, \tfrac{1}{2}, \tfrac{1}{4})$. It is easily verified that, starting with a recessive genotype, the status vector after four generations is $(\tfrac{7}{32}, \tfrac{1}{2}, \tfrac{9}{32})$ and, starting with a hybrid, it becomes $(\tfrac{1}{4}, \tfrac{1}{2}, \tfrac{1}{4})$ after one generation and remains unchanged thenceforth. Our conclusion is that, no matter what genotype we start with, after continued crossbreeding with a hybrid it is twice as likely that we will obtain a hybrid genotype than either a dominant or a recessive type, which are equally likely.

We have noted that if the initial status vector in this problem is $(\tfrac{1}{4}, \tfrac{1}{2}, \tfrac{1}{4})$, then $(\tfrac{1}{4}, \tfrac{1}{2}, \tfrac{1}{4})Q^n = (\tfrac{1}{4}, \tfrac{1}{2}, \tfrac{1}{4})$. Such a vector is called a *fixed-point probability vector* of the Markov chain. When it exists, it is unique and is the *limiting* probability vector, assuming that the Markov process is continued indefinitely.

PROBLEMS

1. A certain three-state system $\mathscr{S}$ has the transitional matrix

$$Q = \begin{array}{c} \\ s_1 \\ s_2 \\ s_3 \end{array} \begin{array}{c} \begin{array}{ccc} s_1 & s_2 & s_3 \end{array} \\ \left[\begin{array}{ccc} \tfrac{1}{4} & \tfrac{3}{4} & 0 \\ \tfrac{3}{4} & 0 & \tfrac{1}{4} \\ 0 & \tfrac{1}{4} & \tfrac{3}{4} \end{array} \right]. \end{array}$$

(a) If $\mathscr{S}$ is in state s_1, is it probable that it will change states? If so, how?
(b) If $\mathscr{S}$ is in state s_2, is it likely to remain in that state?
(c) Does $\mathscr{S}$ ever change from state s_3 to state s_1?

2. A fly wanders around a room containing a piece of flypaper, a warm stove, a piece of candy, and a bald-headed man dozing in a rocking chair. If the fly stops on the flypaper, it remains there. It if lands on the warm stove, it moves with equal likelihood to the candy or the bald head. If it lights on the candy, it is equally likely to remain there or move to the bald head. If the fly stops on the bald head, it is equally likely to move to the flypaper or the candy or the stove. Construct the corresponding transition matrix.

3. Three Common Market countries, F, G, and N, have the following financial agreement. F keeps half the U.S. dollars available to her and sends one fourth of the remainder to each of her neighbors, G and N. G keeps half the U.S. dollars available to her and sends one fourth of the remainder to each of her neighbors, F and N. N ships all her U.S. dollars to F and G, splitting the amount equally between them. Construct a transition matrix ("flow" matrix). Starting with the initial status vector, $P_0 = (\frac{1}{3}, \frac{1}{3}, \frac{1}{3})$, determine the status vector after three steps. Can you predict a trend?

4. Assume an undefined system $\mathscr{S}$ with four states such that, when $\mathscr{S}$ is in state s_1 or s_4, it remains in that state. If $\mathscr{S}$ is in state s_2 or s_3, it changes with equal probability to an adjacent state (see Figure 6.2). Determine a transition matrix for $\mathscr{S}$. Starting with the status vector $(\frac{1}{4}, \frac{1}{4}, \frac{1}{4}, \frac{1}{4})$, compute the status vector after two steps. What is your prediction for the status of the system over a "long" period of time?

5. What is the transition matrix, if an unknown genotype is bred with a dominant individual and the offspring is in turn crossed with a dominant type, and so on? Show that after a "long" period of this sort of cross-breeding it is almost certain that the offspring will be a dominant type.

6. Prove that the product of two Markov matrices is a Markov matrix.

6.5   GAME THEORY

Game theory is *truly* modern mathematics, because it was proposed in 1921 by Emil Borel and established in 1928 by John von Neumann, and the first comprehensive work on the subject and on its application to economic behavior was published in 1944 by von Neumann and Morgenstern.*

The principal concern of the theory of games is the following problem: If n players, $P_1, P_2, \ldots,$ and P_n play a given game, $\mathscr{G}$, how must the ith player, P_i, play to achieve the most favorable result? While it is true that much of the language of game theory and many of its situations are patterned on actual games, such as bridge and poker, the importance of this mathematical theory lies in its applications to economics, sociology, psychology, politics, and war, in which gamelike problems arise.

We make the following assumptions in this discussion of game theory:
1. There exists a set of rules and conventions for *playing* the game $\mathscr{G}$.
2. There is an arbitrary (but fixed) number n of players, P_i, where $i = 1, 2, \ldots, n$.

* J. von Neumann and O. Morgenstern, *Theory of Games and Economic Processes*, 2nd ed., Princeton Univ., Princeton, 1947.

3. A possible realization of the rules and conventions is a *play*.

4. At the end of each play of $\mathscr{G}$, each player, P_i, receives an amount of money, v_i, called the *pay-off to player* P_i.

5. The only objective a player is assumed to have in determining his *strategy* is that of maximizing the amount of pay-off he receives.

In summary, then, this mathematical discussion is limited to the following situation. There are n players, each of whom must make one choice from a well-defined set of choices, and it is assumed it is made without knowledge of the choices of the other players. Given the choices of each of the players, there is a certain outcome which determines the player's reaction and strategy for the next play or plays. The guiding principle of each player is to make the choice that will benefit him most. We shall illustrate these ideas with some well-known games and their variations.

ILLUSTRATION **6.13**   The first game to be considered is that of *matching coins*. Basically, this is a two-player game, although there are variations that will allow more than two players. Let P_1 be the player who is to match. Then P_1 wins if the coins are revealed as (h, h) or (t, t). The second player, P_2, wins if the ordered pair (h, t) or (t, h) occurs. It is assumed that each player can control only his own coin and that each has the same chance of winning, so the game is said to be a *fair* one.

In this game a play consists of a toss or selection of heads or tails by P_1 and a similar play by P_2 without knowledge of the choice of P_1. After the play is completed, P_2 pays 1 unit to P_1, if they match, or -1 unit if they do not. These pay-off values of 1 and -1 are termed a *gain* or a *loss*, respectively, for P_1. The corresponding *pay-off* matrix is

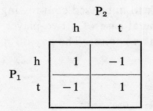

The rows of the pay-off matrix represent the possible selections for player P_1, and the columns correspond to the possible choices for P_2. The elements of the matrix correspond to the point of view of P_1, whose gains are positive values and whose losses are negative. P_1 is called the *maximizing player* and P_2, whose gains and losses are negative and positive values, respectively, is called the *minimizing player*. Since the algebraic sum of each player's winnings is zero, this is called a *zero-sum* game.

The *mathematical expectation* of an event is defined as the product of the probability of the event and the pay-off value of the event. If the coins are flipped, the probability that P_1 will choose heads is $\frac{1}{2}$, and the probability that he will choose tails is $\frac{1}{2}$. If P_2 selects heads also, then the mathematical expectation for P_1 is obtained by multiplying each element of the first column by $\frac{1}{2}$ and adding, to obtain

$$\tfrac{1}{2}(1) + \tfrac{1}{2}(-1) = 0.$$

If P_2 selects tails, P_1 has the mathematical expectation

$$\tfrac{1}{2}(-1) + \tfrac{1}{2}(1) = 0.$$

Under the given circumstances, P_1's strategy has zero expectation against his opponent's choice of head and also against his choice of tail. Therefore, it does not make any difference to P_1 what P_2 does, since he should come out even in the long run.

It is possible for P_1 to improve his strategy by changing the proportion of heads tossed? For example, suppose the probability is p that a head will occur and, therefore, the probability that a tail will occur is $(1 - p)$. What is the mathematical expectation in this case? If P_2 tosses a head, the mathematical expectation of P_1 is

$$E_1 = p(1) + (1 - p)(-1) = 2p - 1,$$

and if P_2 tosses a tail, the mathematical expectation of P_1 is

$$E_2 = p(-1) + (1 - p)(1) = 1 - 2p.$$

Hence, if P_1 elects to bias his tosses, so that $0 \leqslant p < \frac{1}{2}$, then E_1 is negative, and if $\frac{1}{2} < p \leqslant 1$, then E_2 is negative. Therefore P_1 cannot improve his strategy and should stick to unbiassed coin-tossing.

We consider the general case of a two-player game in which player P_1 has m choices and P_2 has n choices. The pay-off matrix is the $m \times n$ matrix

$$P_1 \begin{array}{c} \quad\quad\quad\quad P_2 \\ \begin{bmatrix} a_{11} & a_{12} & \cdots & a_{1j} & \cdots & a_{1n} \\ a_{21} & a_{22} & \cdots & a_{2j} & \cdots & a_{2n} \\ \vdots & \vdots & & \vdots & & \vdots \\ a_{i1} & a_{i2} & \cdots & a_{ij} & \cdots & a_{in} \\ \vdots & \vdots & & \vdots & & \cdots & \vdots \\ a_{m1} & a_{m2} & \cdots & a_{mj} & \cdots & a_{mn} \end{bmatrix} \end{array},$$

where the elements a_{ij} are any real numbers. The m rows represent the m choices available to P_1, and the n columns correspond to the n choices available to P_2. If we assume P_1 is the maximizing player, a_{ij} represents the amount P_1 wins if he makes the ith selection and P_2 makes the jth ($-a_{ij}$ is the amount P_2 wins).

According to our assumptions, P_1 is supposed to choose a row which in his opinion will *maximize his winnings*. A conservative strategy for P_1 is to choose row i, as then he will be sure of being paid at least the minimum of the elements in the ith row, that is, the $\min_j a_{ij}$. Therefore, if he chooses the row that contains the largest of these elements $\min_j a_{ij}$, then *the least that P_1 can win by using this strategy is* $\max_i \min_j a_{ij}$.

In the meantime P_2, without knowledge of P_1's choice, should select a column that in his opinion will *minimize his losses to* P_1. The strategy of P_2 is to choose column j, knowing that the most he can lose to P_1 is the maximum element in the jth column, that is, $\max_i a_{ij}$. Therefore, if P_2 chooses the column that has the least of the elements, $\max_i a_{ij}$, then *the most that P_2 can lose is* $\min_j \max_i a_{ij}$, *if he uses this strategy*.

ILLUSTRATION 6.14 Consider the game defined by the matrix

$$A = \begin{bmatrix} 1 & 0 & 2 & 1 \\ -1 & 1 & 1 & 0 \\ 2 & 1 & -2 & 1 \end{bmatrix}.$$

The least that P_1 can win in row 1 is $a_{12} = \quad 0$.
"   "   " P_1 "   "   " row 2 " $a_{21} = -1$.
"   "   " P_1 "   "   " row 3 " $a_{33} = -2$.

Therefore, P_1's best strategy is to choose row 1, since

$$\max_i \min_j a_{ij} = a_{12} = 0.$$

The most that P_2 can lose in column 1 is $a_{31} = 2$.
"   "   " P_2 "   "   " column 2 " $a_{22} = a_{32} = 1$.
"   "   " P_2 "   "   " column 3 " $a_{13} = 2$.
"   "   " P_2 "   "   " column 4 " $a_{14} = a_{34} = 1$.

Since $\min_j \max_i a_{ij} = a_{22} = a_{32} = a_{14} = a_{34} = 1$, it follows that P_2 should choose either column 2 or column 4.

If these min-max strategies are followed by P_1 and P_2, then P_1 can be sure of winning at least 0 units, and he can be prevented from winning more than 1 unit.

A *mixed strategy* for the maximizing player P_1 is a row vector,

$$\xi = (x_1, x_2, \ldots, x_m),$$

where $x_i \geqslant 0$ and $x_1 + x_2 + \cdots + x_m = 1$. Correspondingly, a mixed strategy for the minimizing player, P_2, is a column vector,

$$\eta = \mathrm{col}\,(y_1, y_2, \ldots, y_n),$$

where $y_j \geqslant 0$ and $y_1 + y_2 + \cdots + y_n = 1$.

Clearly, these vectors are probability vectors (similar to the status vectors of the Markov process). The components, x_i and y_j, of the vectors ξ and η represent, respectively, the frequencies with which P_1 chooses row i in his strategy of play and P_2 selects column j.

In particular, if $x_i = 1$ and all other components in ξ are zero, the vector is termed a *pure strategy* for P_1. In this case player P_1 selects only row i.

In Illustration 6.14 the pure strategy for P_1 is $(1, 0, 0)$, if he wishes to follow the min-max procedure, for in this case we have $(1, 0, 0)A = (1, 0, 2, 1)$ the first row in A. On the other hand, P_2 has two possible pure strategies which he may follow in carrying out the min-max strategy in this same game, namely col $(0, 1, 0, 0)$ and col $(0, 0, 0, 1)$, because $A[\mathrm{col}\,(0, 1, 0, 0,)] = \mathrm{col}\,(0, 1, 1)$ and $A[\mathrm{col}\,(0, 0, 0, 1)] = \mathrm{col}\,(1, 0, 1)$, the second and fourth columns of A, respectively.

ILLUSTRATION **6.15**   In the game defined by the matrix

$$A = \begin{bmatrix} 1 & -1 & 2 \\ 2 & 1 & 2 \end{bmatrix},$$

the maximizing player, P_1, can win at least 1 unit by following the pure strategy $(0, 1)$, which selects $i = 2$ (row 2). Player P_2, realizing that he must lose unless he chooses $j = 2$ (column 2) decides to minimize his loss by following this strategy. Thus by electing the pure strategy col $(0, 1, 0)$, P_2 prevents P_1 from winning more than 1 unit, and by following the pure strategy $(0, 1)$, P_1 assures himself of a gain of 1 unit.

In Illustration 6.15 we have the situation

$$\max_i \min_j a_{ij} = a_{22} = 1 = \min_j \max_i a_{ij}.$$

In this case the matrix game is said to be *strictly determined*, since any other choice on the part of P_1 will result in less gain, assuming that his opponent plays correctly, and any other choice on the part of P_2 will result in a greater loss, assuming that P_1 plays correctly (that is, according to assumption 5 of our original assumptions).

Whenever, as in the last example, it happens that an element a_{ij} in a matrix game is both minimal in its row position and maximal in its column position, it is referred to as a *saddle point*, and the corresponding i^{th} pure strategy of P_1 and the jth pure strategy of P_2 are called *optimal pure strategies*.

When the pay-off matrix is of dimensions 2×2, it is possible to determine necessary and sufficient conditions that the game be *nonstrictly determined*.

THEOREM **6.1**   *The matrix game defined by the matrix*

$$A = \begin{bmatrix} a_{11} & a_{12} \\ a_{21} & a_{22} \end{bmatrix}$$

is nonstrictly determined if and only if:

(a) $a_{11} < a_{12}, a_{11} < a_{21}, a_{22} < a_{21}$, and $a_{22} < a_{12}$.

or

(b) $a_{11} > a_{12}, a_{11} > a_{21}, a_{22} > a_{21}$, and $a_{22} > a_{12}$.

The theorem states that the matrix game is nonstrictly determined, if and only if each of the elements of the principal diagonal is less than each of the elements of the secondary diagonal, or else each of the elements of the principal diagonal is greater than the remaining elements.

Proof. If either condition (a) or condition (b) holds, it is impossible for any element of A to be both minimal in a row and maximal in a column. Therefore, the game is nonstrictly determined, and the sufficiency of the conditions is established.

To show also that these conditions are necessary, we shall assume that the game is nonstrictly determined and demonstrate that the inequalities (a) and (b) are a result of this assumption.

Suppose first that $a_{11} < a_{12}$ and so a_{11} is minimal in row 1. Since A is assumed nonstrictly determined, we have $a_{11} < a_{21}$; otherwise, we should have the contradiction that a_{11} is minimal in row 1 and maximal in column 1, and the game would be strictly determined. Similar arguments show that the game is always strictly determined when we have any equalities among the elements. Hence, the inequalities (a) and (b) are necessary and sufficient conditions that the 2×2 matrix game A be nonstrictly determined.

COROLLARY OF THEOREM 6.1   *If a 2×2 matrix game, $A = (a_{ij})$, is nonstrictly determined, then $(a_{11} + a_{22}) - (a_{12} + a_{21}) \neq 0$.*

ILLUSTRATION **6.16**   Which of the following matrix games are nonstrictly determined?

$$A = \begin{bmatrix} 1 & -1 \\ 2 & 2 \end{bmatrix}, \qquad B = \begin{bmatrix} 0 & -1 \\ 1 & 2 \end{bmatrix}, \qquad C = \begin{bmatrix} 2 & 3 \\ 4 & 2 \end{bmatrix}.$$

A is strictly determined, since $a_{21} = a_{22} = 2$. The value of the game is 2.

B is strictly determined, since $b_{11} > b_{12}$ but $b_{11} < b_{21}$. Therefore, $b_{11} = 0$ is a saddle point, and the value of the game is 0.

C is nonstrictly determined, since $c_{11} < c_{12}$, $c_{11} < c_{21}$, $c_{22} < c_{12}$, and $c_{22} < c_{21}$.

As we have seen in the illustrations preceding this one, not all matrix games can be played in an optimal manner by means of pure strategies. In order to generalize this concept, we need to consider the notion of *optimal mixed strategies*.

Let $A = (a_{ij})$ be an $m \times n$ matrix game, and assume that

$$\xi = (x_1, x_2, \ldots, x_m)$$

and $\eta = \text{col}(y_1, y_2, \ldots, y_n)$ are arbitrary mixed strategies of P_1 and P_2, respectively. The bilinear form (see Illustration 6.3),

$$f(\xi, \eta) = \xi A \eta = \sum_{i=1}^{m} \sum_{j=1}^{n} a_{ij} x_i y_j,$$

is defined as the *pay-off function* for P_1 with respect to strategies ξ and η.

ILLUSTRATION 6.17   Let the matrix game be defined by

$$A = \begin{bmatrix} 1 & 2 & 1 \\ -2 & 0 & 2 \\ -1 & -2 & 1 \end{bmatrix}.$$

The pay-off function for P_1 is

$$f(\xi, \eta) = (x_1, x_2, x_3) \begin{bmatrix} 1 & 2 & 1 \\ -2 & 0 & 2 \\ -1 & -2 & 1 \end{bmatrix} \begin{bmatrix} y_1 \\ y_2 \\ y_3 \end{bmatrix}$$

$$= (x_1 - 2x_2 - x_3)y_1 + (2x_1 - 2x_3)y_2 + (x_1 + 2x_2 + x_3)y_3.$$

In particular, if $\xi_1 = (0.2, 0.5, 0.3)$ and $\eta_1 = \text{col}(0.3, 0.3, 0.4)$, then

$$f(\xi_1, \eta_1) = (0.2, 0.5, 0.3) \begin{bmatrix} 1 & 2 & 1 \\ -2 & 0 & 2 \\ -1 & -2 & 1 \end{bmatrix} \begin{bmatrix} 0.3 \\ 0.3 \\ 0.4 \end{bmatrix}$$

$$= (-1.1, -0.2, 1.5) \begin{bmatrix} 0.3 \\ 0.3 \\ 0.4 \end{bmatrix}$$

$$= 0.21.$$

On the other hand, if P_1 elects to play the strategy $\xi_2 = (0, 0.5, 0.5)$, while P_2 continues to use the strategy $\eta_1 = \text{col}(0.3, 0.3, 0.4)$, we have the following computation:

$$f(\xi_2, \eta_1) = (0, 0.5, 0.5)A \begin{bmatrix} 0.3 \\ 0.3 \\ 0.4 \end{bmatrix}$$

$$= (-1.5, -1, 1.5) \begin{bmatrix} 0.3 \\ 0.3 \\ 0.4 \end{bmatrix}$$

$$= -0.15.$$

Thus, by using the first strategy P_1 expects to gain 0.21 unit over a "long" period, and by using the second strategy he expects to lose 0.15 unit.

In the general matrix game, $A = (a_{ij})$, if P_1 plays a mixed strategy, $\xi = (x_1, x_2, \ldots, x_m)$, against the jth pure strategy of P_2, the expected gain of P_1 is

$$f(\xi, j) = \sum_{i=1}^{m} x_i a_{ij} = x_1 a_{1j} + x_2 a_{2j} + \cdots + x_m a_{mj};$$

that is, the inner product of ξ and the jth column of A. Likewise, if $\eta = \text{col}(y_1, y_2, \ldots, y_n)$ is a mixed strategy of P_2, then the inner product of η and the ith row of A,

$$f(i, \eta) = \sum_{j=1}^{n} a_{ij} y_j = a_{i1} y_1 + a_{i2} y_2 + \cdots + a_{in} y_n,$$

is P_2's expected loss against the ith pure strategy of P_1.

The first player, P_1, knows that if his opponent plays as skillfully as possible, then his strategy, $\xi = (x_1, x_2, \ldots, x_m)$, should be evaluated on the basis of

$$\min_j f(\xi, j) = \min_j \sum_{i=1}^{m} x_i a_{ij}, \quad j = 1, 2, \ldots, n.$$

On the average, this is the amount he should expect to win per game. Therefore, the first player should choose his strategy so as to maximize his minimum expected gain. P_1 *wants to max-min his gains.*

The second player, P_2, computes his losses against the rows of the pay-off matrix. If his strategy is $\eta = \text{col}(y_1, y_2, \ldots, y_n)$, it should be evaluated against

$$\max_i f(i, \eta) = \max_i \sum_{j=1}^{n} a_{ij} y_j, \quad i = 1, 2, \ldots, m.$$

Therefore, the goal of the second player, P_2, is to choose his strategy so that it will minimize his maximum expected losses. Thus, P_2 *wants to min-max his losses.*

In short, the first player's strategy is to place as high a floor as possible under his expected gains. On the other hand, the second player plans his strategy in such manner as to place as low a ceiling as possible on his losses. In this connection, it was John von Neumann* who first established that not only do such *minimax* numbers exist in matrix games, but the number which is the floor for P_1's gains is at the same time the ceiling for P_2's losses. This number, v, is called the *minimax value* of the game. This important result is stated formally as follows:

THEOREM **6.2** (The Fundamental Theorem of Matrix Games)   *Given the game defined by the $m \times n$ matrix $A = (a_{ij})$, there exist optimal strategy vectors, $\hat{\xi} = (\hat{x}_1, \hat{x}_2, \ldots, \hat{x}_m)$ and $\hat{\eta} = \text{col}\,(\hat{y}_1, \hat{y}_2, \ldots, \hat{y}_n)$, of players P_1 and P_2, respectively, and a real number v such that*:

(a) $f(\hat{\xi}, j) = \sum_{k=1}^{m} a_{kj}\hat{x}_k \geqslant v, \quad j = 1, 2, \ldots, n.$
(b) $f(i, \hat{\eta}) = \sum_{k=1}^{n} a_{ik}\hat{y}_k \leqslant v, \quad i = 1, 2, \ldots, m.$

We cannot in this brief discussion prove this theorem in general,† but we shall discuss in some detail its application to games defined by 2×2 matrices.

First, let us consider 2×2 matrix games that are *strictly determined*. We lose no generality in assuming a_{11} to be the saddle point. By definition, a_{11} is minimal in row 1 and maximal in column 1. With $v = a_{11}$, $\hat{\xi} = (1, 0)$, and $\hat{\eta} = \begin{bmatrix} 1 \\ 0 \end{bmatrix}$ the matrix inequalities are satisfied:

$$f(\hat{\xi}, 1) = (1, 0) \begin{bmatrix} a_{11} \\ a_{21} \end{bmatrix} = a_{11} = v,$$

$$f(\hat{\xi}, 2) = (1, 0) \begin{bmatrix} a_{12} \\ a_{22} \end{bmatrix} = a_{12} > v,$$

$$f(1, \hat{\eta}) = (a_{11}, a_{12}) \begin{bmatrix} 1 \\ 0 \end{bmatrix} = a_{11} = v,$$

$$f(2, \hat{\eta}) = (a_{21}, a_{22}) \begin{bmatrix} 1 \\ 0 \end{bmatrix} = a_{21} < v.$$

Turning now to 2×2 matrix games defined by $A = (a_{ij})$ that are *non-strictly determined*, we shall prove the following theorem.

---

* J. von Neumann "Zur Theorie der Gesellschaftsspiele," *Mathematische Annalen*, Vol. 100, pp. 295–320, 1928.
† For a proof the reader is referred to H. W. Kuhn, *Lectures on the Theory of Games*, Annals of Mathematics Studies, 37, Princeton Univ., Princeton, 1957.

THEOREM **6.3** *If the* 2×2 *matrix game defined by* $A = (a_{ij})$ *is non-strictly determined, then the minimax value* v *and the optimal mixed strategies* $\hat{\xi} = (\hat{x}_1, \hat{x}_2)$ *and* $\hat{\eta} = \text{col}\,(\hat{y}_1, \hat{y}_2)$ *of players* P_1 *and* P_2, *respectively, are*:

$$v = \frac{a_{11}a_{22} - a_{12}a_{21}}{d}, \qquad \hat{x}_1 = \frac{a_{22} - a_{21}}{d}, \qquad \hat{x}_2 = \frac{a_{11} - a_{12}}{d},$$

$$\hat{y}_1 = \frac{a_{22} - a_{12}}{d}, \qquad \hat{y}_2 = \frac{a_{11} - a_{21}}{d}, \qquad d = a_{11} + a_{22} - a_{12} - a_{21}.$$

Proof. By assumption, the game is nonstrictly determined. Hence, by Theorem 6.1, we have either (a) or (b), as follows:

(a) $a_{11} < a_{12}, \quad a_{11} < a_{21}, \quad a_{22} < a_{12}, \quad a_{22} < a_{21}$
(b) $a_{11} > a_{12}, \quad a_{11} > a_{21}, \quad a_{22} > a_{12}, \quad a_{22} > a_{21}$

In case (a) we have $d = a_{11} + a_{22} - (a_{12} + a_{21}) < 0$, and in case (b) we have $d = a_{11} + a_{22} - (a_{12} + a_{21}) > 0$. Hence,

$$\hat{x}_1 = \frac{a_{22} - a_{21}}{d} > 0, \qquad \hat{x}_2 = \frac{a_{11} - a_{12}}{d} > 0, \qquad \hat{x}_1 + \hat{x}_2 = 1.$$

Similarly, $\hat{y}_1 > 0$, $\hat{y}_2 > 0$, and $\hat{y}_1 + \hat{y}_2 = 1$. Furthermore, the minimax relations are satisfied as *equalities*. We verify those that involve $\hat{\xi} = (\hat{x}_1, \hat{x}_2)$, leaving those that involve $\hat{\eta} = \text{col}\,(\hat{y}_1, \hat{y}_2)$ for the reader to verify:

$$a_{11}\hat{x}_1 + a_{21}\hat{x}_2 = \frac{a_{11}a_{22} - a_{11}a_{21} + a_{11}a_{21} - a_{12}a_{21}}{d}$$

$$= \frac{a_{11}a_{22} - a_{12}a_{21}}{d}$$

$$= v,$$

$$a_{12}\hat{x}_1 + a_{22}\hat{x}_2 = \frac{a_{12}a_{22} - a_{12}a_{21} + a_{11}a_{22} - a_{12}a_{22}}{d}$$

$$= \frac{a_{11}a_{22} - a_{12}a_{21}}{d}$$

$$= v.$$

The reader may have noted that the minimax value of the nonstrictly determined matrix game is $v = \det A/d$, which is easily remembered. It may be easier to solve such problems directly from the minimax equations by using this value of v than to memorize four more formulas. The following example may help to clarify this point.

ILLUSTRATION **6.18** Find the value of the game defined by the matrix A and determine the optimal strategy vectors for P_1 and P_2:

$$A = \begin{bmatrix} 2 & 5 \\ 3 & 1 \end{bmatrix}.$$

We first compute the minimax value of the game:

$$v = \frac{\det A}{d} = \frac{2 - 15}{3 - 8} = \frac{13}{5}.$$

Using this value, we find the corresponding optimal strategies $\hat{\xi}$ and $\hat{\eta}$:

$$f(\hat{\xi}, 1) = v: \quad 2\hat{x}_1 + 3\hat{x}_2 = \tfrac{13}{5}$$
$$f(\hat{\xi}, 2) = v: \quad 5\hat{x}_1 + \hat{x}_2 = \tfrac{13}{5}$$
$$\overline{\qquad\qquad\qquad}$$
$$-13\hat{x}_1 = -\tfrac{26}{5}$$
$$\hat{x}_1 = \tfrac{2}{5}$$
$$\hat{x}_2 = 1 - \hat{x}_1 = \tfrac{3}{5}$$
$$\therefore \ \hat{\xi} = (\tfrac{2}{5}, \tfrac{3}{5}).$$

$$f(1, \hat{\eta}) = v: \quad 2\hat{y}_1 + 5\hat{y}_2 = \tfrac{13}{5}$$
$$f(2, \hat{\eta}) = v: \quad 3\hat{y}_1 + \hat{y}_2 = \tfrac{13}{5}$$
$$\overline{\qquad\qquad\qquad}$$
$$-13\hat{y}_1 = -\tfrac{52}{5}$$
$$\hat{y}_1 = \tfrac{4}{5}$$
$$\hat{y}_2 = 1 - \hat{y}_1 = \tfrac{1}{5}$$
$$\therefore \ \hat{\eta} = \begin{bmatrix} \tfrac{4}{5} \\ \tfrac{1}{5} \end{bmatrix}.$$

The minimax value of the game in this illustration being $v = \tfrac{13}{5}$, the game favors P_1 to the extent that it will pay him 2.6 units per game on the average. Hence, P_1 should pay P_2 this much for the privilege of playing it as the maximizing player.

The following game from Kuhn* is an example of one that appears to be fair—that is, value $v = 0$—but can be shown to favor the maximizing player.

ILLUSTRATION 6.19   Players P_1 and P_2 are each provided with an ace of diamonds and an ace of clubs. P_1 also has a two of diamonds and P_2 has a two of clubs. The rules of the game are:

1. On the first play P_1 chooses a card, and P_2, ignorant of P_1's choice, selects a card.
2. The players then show their choices.
3. P_1 wins if the suits match. P_2 wins if they do not.
4. The amount of pay-off is the numerical value of the card shown by the winner.

* *Loc. cit.*

5. If two deuces are shown, the pay-off is zero.
The pay-off matrix is

$$
\begin{array}{ccc}
 & A_d & A_c & 2_c \\
A_d & \begin{bmatrix} 1 \\ -1 \\ 2 \end{bmatrix} & \begin{matrix} -1 \\ 1 \\ -1 \end{matrix} & \begin{matrix} -2 \\ 1 \\ 0 \end{matrix} \end{array}.
$$

For P_1 minimum gain row 1 is -2
  „ P_1 „   „   row 2 „ -1
  „ P_1 „   „   row 2 „   0.

Therefore, P_1 plays either $i = 2$ or $i = 3$ pure strategies but never plays $i = 1$. Since the values of the elements in the first row are in each case either less than or equal to the corresponding elements in the third row, the third row is said to *dominate* the first row. Therefore, player P_1 eliminates row 1 as a possible pure strategy, and the pay-off matrix becomes

$$
\begin{bmatrix} -1 & 1 & 1 \\ 2 & -1 & 0 \end{bmatrix}.
$$

Concerning the strategies of P_2, column 2 is a better strategy for the minimizing player than column 3, because each of its elements is less than or equal to the corresponding elements of column 3. Therefore, P_2 plays either $j = 1$ or $j = 2$, and the pay-off matrix becomes

$$
\begin{bmatrix} -1 & 1 \\ 2 & -1 \end{bmatrix}.
$$

This is nonstrictly determined, so we may determine the minimax value of the game and the optimal mixed strategies by the results of Theorem 6.3 and obtain

$$
v = \tfrac{1}{5}, \qquad \hat{\xi} = (0, \tfrac{2}{3}, \tfrac{3}{5}), \qquad \hat{\eta} = \mathrm{col}\,(\tfrac{2}{5}, \tfrac{3}{5}, 0).
$$

Since the value of the game is $1/5$, it clearly favors P_1.

PROBLEMS

1. Determine the value of each of the following matrix games and the optimal strategies of both players:

(a) $\begin{bmatrix} 1 & 2 \\ 0 & -1 \end{bmatrix}$.

(b) $\begin{bmatrix} 1 & 2 \\ 0 & 2 \end{bmatrix}$.

(c) $\begin{bmatrix} 2 & 5 \\ 3 & 1 \end{bmatrix}$.

(d) $\begin{bmatrix} 3 & -2 \\ 2 & 4 \end{bmatrix}$.

(e) $\begin{bmatrix} 4 & 2 \\ 3 & 1 \end{bmatrix}$.

(f) $\begin{bmatrix} 0 & -1 \\ 1 & 1 \end{bmatrix}$.

2. A version of two-finger Marra is played by the following rules:
   1. Each player holds up one or two fingers.
   2. If the sum is even, P_1 wins, and the pay-off is equal to the number of fingers showing.
   3. If the sum is odd, P_2 wins and receives a pay-off equal to the number of fingers showing.
   Construct the pay-off matrix. Determine the minimax value of the game and the optimal strategies of the players.

3. If the following matrix is nonstrictly determined, what is the value, $v = (\det A)/d$, assuming that the minimax relations are the *equations*
   $f(\hat{\xi}, 1) = v, f(\hat{\xi}, 2) = v, f(1, \hat{\eta}) = v, f(2, \hat{\eta}) = v, \hat{x}_1 + \hat{x}_2 = 1, \hat{y}_1 + \hat{y}_2 = 1$

4. Construct the pay-off matrix for the game of "Stone, Paper, Scissors" (Problem 8, Section 5.2). Set up the expectation functions for P_1 and P_2, and verify the optimal strategy $\hat{\xi} = (1/3, 1/3, 1/3)$.

5. The following inequalities occur in applying minimax strategies to a matrix game. What is the pay-off matrix in the game? What are the corresponding inequalities for the second player's strategy?

$$x_1 > 0, \qquad x_2 > 0, \qquad x_3 > 0$$
$$x_1 + x_2 + x_3 = 1$$
$$x_1 + 2x_2 - x_3 \geqslant v,$$
$$- 2x_2 + x_3 \geqslant v,$$
$$2x_1 \qquad - x_3 \geqslant v.$$

Supplementary Reading

GASS, S. I., *Linear Programming*, McGraw-Hill, New York, 1958.

HILL, L. S., "Concerning certain linear transformation apparatus of cryptography," *American Mathematics Monthly*, Vol. 38, p. 135.

KEMENY, J. G., and J. L. SNELL, *Finite Markov Chains*, Van Nostrand, Princeton, 1960.

KEMENY, J. G., J. L. SNELL, and G. L. THOMPSON, *Finite Mathematics*, Prentice-Hall, Englewood Cliffs, N.J., 1957.

KUHN, H. W., *Lectures on the Theory of Games*, Annals of Mathematics Studies 37, Princeton Univ., Princeton, 1957.

KUHN, H. W., and A. W. TUCKER, *Linear Inequalities and Related Systems*, Annals of Mathematics Studies 38, Princeton Univ., Princeton, 1956.

LEVINE, J., "Some elementary cryptanalysis of algebraic cryptography," *American Mathematics Monthly*, Vol. 68, p. 411.

NAHIKIAN, H. M., *A Modern Algebra for Biologists*, Univ. Chicago, Chicago, 1964.

VON NEUMANN, J., and O. MORGENSTERN, *Theory of Games and Economic Processes*, 2nd ed., Princeton Univ., Princeton, 1947.

WILLIAMS, J., *The Compleat Strategyst*, McGraw-Hill, New York, 1954.

ANSWERS TO SELECTED PROBLEMS

SECTION **1.2**

1. (a), (c), (d), (e), (i).
2. (b), (c), (d), (e), (f).
3. (a) {3}. (b) {0, 3}. (c) {0}. (d) $\varnothing$. (e) {0, 3/2}. (f) {1, 2, 3, 4, 5}.
4. (a) $\{x \mid x \in I, -2 < x \leqslant 3\}$, or $\{-1, 0, 1, 2, 3\}$.
   (b) $\{x \mid x \in Q, (3x - 2)(x + 1) = 0\}$, or $\{2/3, -1\}$.
   (c) $\{x \mid x = 2n - 1, n \in Z^+, 1 \leqslant n \leqslant 4\}$, or $\{1, 3, 5, 7\}$.
5. (a) $Q = \{x \mid x = p/q, p \in I, q \in I, q \neq 0\}$.
   (b) $E = \{x \mid x \in I, x \equiv 0 \pmod 2\}$.
   $O = \{x \mid x \in I, x \equiv 1 \pmod 2\}$.
6. (b), (c), (f).

SECTION **1.3**

1. (a), (c), (e).
3. $\{\varnothing, \{a_1\}, \{a_2\}, \{a_3\}, \{a_1, a_2\}, \{a_1, a_3\}, \{q_2, a_3\}, A\}$.
6. 2^4 has 4 elements, therefore the power set of 2^4 has $2^4 = 16$ elements.
10. (a) Equivalent. (b) Equal and equivalent. (c) Equal and equivalent.

Section 1.4

1. (a) A; (c) $\varnothing$; (e) A; (g) U.
2. Even natural numbers. (b) Consonants. (c) Rational fractions that do not reduce to integers.
4. (a) {r}; (b) {d, o, g, m, a, i}. (c) {b, o, a, t, c, e, n}. (d) {t}.
   (e) {a, i, o, r, t}. (f) {o, a}.
7. $X \cap Y'$; $X' \cap Y$; $X \cap Y$; $(X \cup Y)' = X' \cap Y'$.
9. $(A - B) \cup (B - A) = (A \cap B') \cup (B \cap A')$.
11. B and C are closest together; A and B, A and C, are equally far apart.

Section 1.5

3. $A \times B = \{(1, 1), (1, 2), (1, 3), (2, 1), (2, 2), (2, 3)\}$.
   $B \times A = \{(1, 1), (1, 2), (2, 1), (2, 2), (3, 1), (3, 2)\}$.
   $A \times A = \{(1, 1), (1, 2), (2, 1), (2, 2)\}$.
   $B \times B = \{(1, 1), (1, 2), (1, 3), (2, 1), (2, 2), (2, 3), (3, 1), (3, 2), (3, 3)\}$.
4. mn, nm, m^2, n^2.
5. (a) $\{(1, 1), (1, 2), (1, 3), (2, 1), (2, 2), (2, 3)\}$.
7. $\{(1, 1), (1, 0), (0, 1), (0, 0)\}$.
   $\{(1, 1, 1), (1, 1, 0), (1, 0, 1), (1, 0, 0), (0, 1, 1), (0, 1, 0), (0, 0, 1), (0, 0, 0)\}$.
8. $f(1, 1) = 0, f(1, 0) = 2, f(0, 1) = -3, f(0, 0) = 0$.

Section 1.6

1. (a) Transitive. (b) Reflexive, antisymmetric, transitive.
2. Transitive in some cases.
5. (a) Reflexive, symmetric. (b) Reflexive, symmetric, transitive.
   (c) Transitive. (d) Reflexive, antisymmetric, transitive.

Section 1.7

1. (a) Equivalence relation. (b) Not symmetric. (c) Equivalence relation.
   (d) Not transitive. (e) Not transitive.
2. $[0] = \{\ldots, -4, 0, 4, 8, \ldots\}$; $[1] = \{\ldots, -3, 1, 5, 9, \ldots\}$;
   $[2] = \{\ldots, -2, 2, 6, 10, \ldots\}$; $[3] = \{\ldots, -1, 3, 7, 11, \ldots\}$.

Section 1.8

1. R is not a function; R' is a function.
2. R is a function; not one-to-one.

Section **1.9**

1. (a) $\{(1, -1), (2, 2), (4, -1), (1, 2)\}$; not a function.
   (b) $\{(0, -2), (1, 2), (8, 4), (-2, 6)\}$; a function.
2. $f^{-1} = \{(2, -3), (0, -2), (-1, -1), (-3, 0)\}$.
3. f is a function; not one-to-one; f is defined at zero; because zero is divisible by 2, it is classified as even; the inverse relation is not a function.
4. $f^{-1} = \{(x, y) \mid y = 2x + 6\}$.
5. (a) $D: -\infty < x < \infty$; $R: 0 \leqslant y < \infty$. (c) Not a function. (d) Redefined, $f = \{(x, y) \mid y = x^2, x \geqslant 0\}$.
11. (a) $g[f] = \left\{(x, z) \mid z = \dfrac{1}{1 - x}\right\}$.
    (b) $f[g] = \left\{(x, z) \mid z = \dfrac{x - 1}{x}\right\}$.
12. (a) $g[f] = \{(x, z) \mid z = x\}$.
    (b) $f[g] = \{(x, z) \mid z = x\}$.
14. $f(1, 1) = -1, f(1, 0) = 1, f(0, 1) = -2, f(0, 0) = 0$.

Section **2.2**

1. (a) Use De Morgan's first law and $(a')' = a$.
   (c) $x \vee (x' \cdot y) = (x \vee x') \cdot (x \vee y)$. Now simplify.
   (e) $(x' \cdot y')' \vee (x' \cdot y)' = (x \vee y) \vee (x \vee y') = (x \vee x) \vee (y \vee y') = x \vee 1 = 1$.
3. (a) 0. (b) $(x' \vee y') \cdot z$. (c) $x \cdot y' \cdot z'$.
4. (a) Note that the tables are symmetric about the main diagonal.
   (b) The main diagonals are a, b, c, d.
   (c) $4 \cdot 4 \cdot 4 = 64$.
   (d) a and b behave as 0 and 1, respectively.
   (e) $a' = b, b' = a, c' = d, d' = c$.

Section **2.5**

1. (a) $p \vee q$, where p is "A prime number is 2" and q is "A prime number is odd."
   (b) $p \rightarrow q$, where p is "n is an even integer" and q is "$(n + 1)$ is an odd integer."
   (d) $p \leftrightarrow q$, where p is "A triangle is equilateral" and q is "A triangle is equiangular."
   (f) $p \rightarrow q$, where p is "$4x = 3$" and q is "$x = 0.75$."
   (g) $p' \wedge q'$, where p is "The course is difficult" and q is "The grades are low."

   (j) $p \wedge q \rightarrow r$, where p is "Early to bed," q is "Early to rise," and r is "Jack is alert in class."

2. (a) $p \rightarrow q$.   (b) $p' \wedge q'$.   (c) $q' \wedge p'$.   (d) $p' \wedge q$.   (e) $q \rightarrow p$.

Section 2.6

1. If $p \rightarrow q$ and q is true, one cannot logically conclude that p is true; therefore the argument is not valid.

2. If $p \rightarrow q$ and q' is true, then p' is true by use of the contrapositive; conclusion is therefore valid.

3. If taxes have been cut, the market is down. If the market is down, no further conclusion can be reached. The contrapositive of (a) is "If it is not time to sell stocks, then the market is down," and the contrapositive of (b) is "If taxes are not high, it is not time to sell stocks."

4. Since $p \rightarrow q$ and $q' \rightarrow r$ do not imply $p \rightarrow r'$, the conclusion is not valid.

6. For (b_1) the conclusion "Smith is not married" is valid. Use the contrapositive. For (b_2) no logical conclusion other than the premise, "John Smith is not married," can be reached.

7. The conclusion is valid.

8. The points of a radius lie within and on the boundary of the circle.

9. (a) $\forall_a \forall_b \exists_y [ay = b]$.
   (b) $\exists_x [p(x) \vee q(x)]$.
   (c) $\exists_x [p(x)] \rightarrow [\exists_x p(x) \vee \exists_y q(y)]$.

10. (a) Every nonzero real number has a multiplicative inverse.
   (b) For an arbitrary nonzero real number z there exists a nonzero real number y such that $yz = 1$.
   (c) For all nonzero real numbers x and y, if $xy = x$, then $y = 1$.

11. (a) Not every man's home is his castle.
   (b) All numbers are greater than δ.
   (c) There exists a real number that is neither even nor odd.
   (d) All numbers have positive absolute values.

Section 2.7

1.

$\bar{x} \vee (x \cdot y)$ $\bar{x} \cdot (x \vee y)$

(a)

x	y	Circuit
1	1	closed
1	0	open
0	1	closed
0	0	closed

(b)

x	y	Circuit
1	1	open
1	0	open
0	1	closed
0	0	open

$$x \vee (\bar{x} \cdot y)$$

(c)

x	y	Circuit
1	1	closed
1	0	closed
0	1	closed
0	0	open

$$(x \cdot y) \vee \bar{x} \cdot (x \vee y)$$

(d)

x	y	Circuit
1	1	closed
1	0	open
0	1	closed
0	0	open

SECTION 3.2

1. $f(\varnothing) = 0; f(U) = 1.$

2. $\dfrac{165 + 172 + 167 + 171 + 167 + 158}{1000} = 1.$

3. $f(E_1 \cup E_2) = 165 + 172 + 167 + 158 = (165 + 172) + (167 + 158) = f(E_1) + f(E_2).$

4. $\bar{E} = \{2, 4, 6\}; \dfrac{f(\bar{E})}{1000} = 0.501 = 1 - \dfrac{f(E)}{1000}.$

5. Larger; 50%.

6. (a) $\{K_s, K_h, K_d, K_c, Q_s, Q_h, Q_d, Q_c\}$.
   (b) $\{A_d, K_d, \ldots, 3_d, 2_d\}$.
   (c) $\{K_d, Q_d\}$.
   (d) $\{K_d\}$.

7. (a) $U = \{A, B, C, \ldots, Z\}$.
   (b) $E = \{A, E, I, O, U\}$.
   (c) $\bar{E} = U - E$.
   (d) $\{Z\}$.

8. 0.35, 0.28, 0.12, 0.10, 0.08, 0.07.

9. 0.50, 0.228, 0.272, compared with 0.563, 0.187, 0.250.

SECTION 3.3

1. (a) $A \cap B \neq \varnothing$. (b) $A \cap \bar{B} \neq \varnothing$. (c) $A \subseteq B$. (d) $A \subseteq \bar{B}$.
   (e) $\bar{A} \cap \bar{B} \cap \bar{C} \neq \varnothing$. (f) $A \cap \bar{B} \cap \bar{C} \neq \varnothing$.
   (g) $(A \cap \bar{B} \cap \bar{C}) \cup (\bar{A} \cap B \cap \bar{C}) \cup (\bar{A} \cap \bar{B} \cap C) \neq \varnothing$.

2. (a) A set of 20 sets of the type $\{A, B, C\}, \{A, B, D\}, \ldots, \{D, E, F\}$.
   (b) 10. (c) 1/2. (d) 1/5. (e) 1/20.

3. (a) 21/26. (b) 5/26. (c) 7/26. 2/26.

4. (a) 4/36. (b) 32/36. (c) 6/36. (d) 6/36.

5. (a) 3/8. (b) 7/8. (c) 3/8. (d) 7/8. (e) 4/8. (f) 1/8.

6. (a) $\{r, g, b\}, \{r, g, y\}, \{r, b, y\}, \{g, b, y\}$ $p = 1/4$.
   (b) A set of 24 ordered triples is the sample space. There will be 6 possible outcomes in the event "red marble first," namely (r, g, b), (r, b, g), (r, g, y), (r, b, y), (r, y, b), (r, y, g); $p = 6/24$.
   (c) $p = 2/24$.

7. (a) $\{\{1, 5\}, \{1, 10\}, \{1, 25\}, \{5, 10\}, \{5, 25\}, \{10, 25\}\}$. (b) 1/2. (c) 1/3.
   (d) 1/2. (e) 1/2.

8. Yes, because $p_i \geqslant 0$ and $\sum p_i = 1$. Each coin favors heads.

9. (a) $p\{1\} = 1/21$, $p\{2\} = 2/21$, $p\{3\} = 3/21$, $p\{4\} = 4/21$, $p\{5\} = 5/21$, $p\{6\} = 6/21$.
   (b) $p\{2, 4, 6\} = 12/21$.
   (c) $1 - 12/21 = 9/21$.
   (d) $1 - 4/21 = 17/21$.

10. $p\{f\} = 1/7$, $p\{c\} = p\{r\} = p\{s\} = 2/7$.

Section 3.4

1. (a) 7%. (b) 50%.
2. (a) 1/6. (b) 2/11. (c) 5/11.
3. (a) 5/24. (b) 19/24.
4. 1/6.
5. (a) 15%. (b) 47.6%.
6. 3/10.
8. 29/90.
9. $p(A) = 2/8$, $p(B) = 3/8$, $p(D) = 3/8$.
10. (a) 5/34; 10/34; 4/34. (b) 10/34; 30/34. (c) 10/22; 5/22.

Section 3.5

1. 6/16.
2. $6(0.6)^2(0.4)^2$.
3. $(1/4)^4 + 4(1/4)^3(3/4)$.
4. (b) $(5/17)^k(12/17)^{3-k}$, where k is the number of girls in the sample;
   (c) $(12/17)^3 + 3(5/17)^1(12/17)^2$.
5. (a) $6(1/3)^5(2/3)^1$.
   (b) $6(1/3)^5(2/3)^1 + (1/3)^6$.
6. $(99/100)^{120}$, approx. 0.3.
7. $(0.5)^3 + 3(0.5)^2(0.3) + 3(0.5)^2(0.2) = 0.5$.
8. (a) $6(0.3)^2(0.5)^2$. (b) $12(0.3)^2(0.2)(0.5)$.

Section 4.2

1. (a) 1. (b) $(\omega)^{-1} = \omega^2$; $(\omega^2)^{-1} = \omega$.
   (c) Yes, it is a commutative group, although to establish that the system is associative, 27 cases would have to be checked.

2. (a) Identify $R_0 \leftrightarrow 1$, $R_{120} \leftrightarrow \omega$, $R_{240} \leftrightarrow \omega^2$;
   (b) R_0; (c) $R_{-\alpha}$, i.e., a rotation of the same magnitude as that of α, but in the opposite direction.
3. (a) 0. (b) $(-3) = 9$, $(-6) = 6$, $(-9) = 3$. (c) Yes. (d) Yes, it is 9.
   (e) No. (f) The system is a ring.

SECTION 4.3

2. $(1, 7)$.
3. $\alpha + \beta = (0, 2, 5)$.
4. $(2, 2, 4), (-3, -3, -6)$.
5. $(6, -14)$.
6. $(3, 1)$.
9. $(-2/7, -5/7, 9/7), (-1/7, 8/7, 1/7)$.
10. $(1, 1, 2), (-1, 1, 1), (0, 1, 1)$.

SECTION 4.4

1. $(8, 0, -2, -5); (9, -4, 3, 3); (4, -8, 6, 13)$.
3. $\alpha = (7/11, 5/11, -7/11); \beta = (1/11, 7/11, -12/11)$.
6. $\alpha = (2, 0, 1); \beta = (0, 0, 1); \gamma = (0, 1, 2)$.
7. $\alpha = (2, 1, 0); \beta = (2, 2, 2)$.
8. $\alpha = (1, 1 + i, -i); \beta = (1 + 2i, 4i, 2 + i)$.
9. $\alpha = (1 - i, 2 + i, -2); \beta = (-2i, 2 - 6i, -2 - 2i)$.

SECTION 4.5

2. $\beta = 2\alpha_1 - \alpha_2$.
3. $\alpha_3 = -2\alpha_1 + \alpha_2$.
5. $2\alpha_1 + 0\alpha_2 + \alpha_3 = \theta$.
7. $\varepsilon_1 = \frac{3}{4}\alpha_1 + \frac{1}{4}\alpha_2; \varepsilon_2 = -\frac{1}{4}\alpha_1 + \frac{1}{4}\alpha_2$.
8. $x = -\frac{4}{3}$.
9. $\alpha = (1, -1, 2); \beta = (2, 0, 1); \gamma = (0, 1, -1)$.

SECTION 4.6

1. Two-dimensional; one basis is $\{\alpha_3, \alpha_4\}$.
2. $\langle 2, -3 \rangle$.
3. Show that β cannot be expressed as a linear combination of the given vectors.
5. $\langle -1, -1, 2 \rangle$.
6. $\langle i, -1 - i \rangle$.
7. $\{\alpha_1, \alpha_2, \alpha_4\}$ constitute a basis.

9. $\langle -i, 1, \frac{1}{2}, -\frac{1}{2}i \rangle$; that $\varepsilon_1 \in V_3(\mathscr{C})$.

10. $\alpha_1 = \varepsilon_1 - \varepsilon_2$, $\alpha_2 = \varepsilon_1 + \varepsilon_3$, $\alpha_3 = \varepsilon_1 + \varepsilon_2 - \varepsilon_3$; $\varepsilon_1 = \langle \frac{1}{4}, \frac{1}{4}, \frac{1}{4} \rangle$, $\varepsilon_2 = \langle -\frac{3}{4}, \frac{1}{4}, \frac{1}{4} \rangle$, $\varepsilon_3 = \langle -\frac{1}{2}, \frac{1}{2}, -\frac{1}{2} \rangle$.

11. $\rho_3 = i\rho_1 - \rho_2$.

13. Two-dimensional; a basis is $\{(1, 1, 1, 0), (-1, 0, 2, 1)\}$.

14. No.

15. $\langle 3, 2 \rangle$, $\langle 1, 0 \rangle$, $\langle 0, 1 \rangle$.

SECTION 4.7

1. (a) 0. (b) 0. (c) 9. (d) 0.

2. (a) 11. (b) 19.

4. $\langle 3k, 7k, 2k \rangle$, where k is any scalar in the field.

5. A, \$70; B, \$58.

6. Spray 1, \$26.40; spray 2, \$24.96.

8. (a) $\sqrt{x^2 + y^2 + z^2}$. (b) 3. (c) $\sqrt{6}$.

9. (a) $\sqrt{7}$. (b) 4. (c) $\sqrt{11}$.

12. (a) $\left(\dfrac{2}{\sqrt{30}}, \dfrac{-3}{\sqrt{30}}, \dfrac{1}{\sqrt{30}}, \dfrac{4}{\sqrt{30}} \right)$.

   (b) $\left(\dfrac{1-i}{2\sqrt{5}}, \dfrac{2+2i}{2\sqrt{5}}, \dfrac{3}{2\sqrt{5}}, \dfrac{-i}{2\sqrt{5}} \right)$.

SECTION 5.3

1. $\begin{bmatrix} a_{11} & a_{12} \\ a_{21} & a_{22} \\ a_{31} & a_{32} \end{bmatrix}$.

2. $[3, 1, 1, 2]$, $[-1, 2, 0, 1]$, $[3, 1, -1, 4]$.

3. $x = -23/5$, $y = -22/5$.

4. $\begin{bmatrix} 1 & -\frac{1}{3} \\ 1 & -\frac{1}{3} \end{bmatrix}$, $\begin{bmatrix} 0 & -\frac{2}{3} \\ 1 & \frac{4}{3} \end{bmatrix}$.

5. $x = -1$, $y = 2$.

6. (a) $A = 0$. (b) $B = \begin{bmatrix} 0 & 0 & 2 \\ 2 & 1 & 0 \\ 0 & 1 & 1 \end{bmatrix}$.

8.

	p	st	sc
p	0	1	-1
st	-1	0	1
sc	1	-1	0

9.
$$\begin{array}{ccc} & 1 & 2 & 3 \end{array}$$
$$\begin{array}{c} 1 \\ 2 \\ 3 \end{array}\begin{bmatrix} 0 & -2 & 4 \\ 2 & 0 & -2 \\ -4 & 2 & 0 \end{bmatrix}.$$

10.
$$\begin{bmatrix} 0 & 1 & 1 \\ 0 & 0 & 1 \\ 1 & 1 & 0 \end{bmatrix}.$$

SECTION 5.4

1.
$$AB = \begin{bmatrix} 0 \\ -1 \end{bmatrix}, \qquad CA = \begin{bmatrix} 1 & -2 & 1 \\ 4 & -4 & 8 \end{bmatrix}, \qquad C'A = \begin{bmatrix} 1 & 3 & 6 \\ -1 & 1 & -2 \end{bmatrix}.$$

2.
$$AB = \begin{bmatrix} 2 & 0 \\ 2 & 0 \\ 1 & 2 \end{bmatrix}, \qquad AC = \begin{bmatrix} 2 \\ 1 \\ 0 \end{bmatrix}, \qquad C'A = \begin{bmatrix} 2 & 0 & 1 \end{bmatrix}.$$

3.
$$\begin{bmatrix} 110 & -48 \\ -32 & 14 \end{bmatrix}.$$

7.
$$B = \begin{bmatrix} 1 & -1 \\ -3 & 4 \end{bmatrix}.$$

SECTION 5.5

1. (a) 2.   (b) 3.   (c) 2.   (d) 1.   (e) 1.   (f) 2.
2. All are equivalent to N_2 of dimensions 3×4.
3.
$$\begin{bmatrix} 1 & 0 & 0 \\ 0 & 1 & 0 \\ 0 & 0 & 1 \end{bmatrix}, \quad \begin{bmatrix} 1 & 0 & 0 \\ 0 & 1 & 0 \\ 0 & 0 & 0 \end{bmatrix}, \quad \begin{bmatrix} 1 & 0 & 0 \\ 0 & 0 & 0 \\ 0 & 0 & 0 \end{bmatrix}, \quad \begin{bmatrix} 0 & 0 & 0 \\ 0 & 0 & 0 \\ 0 & 0 & 0 \end{bmatrix}.$$

4. $F_{12} = \begin{bmatrix} 0 & 1 \\ 1 & 0 \end{bmatrix}, \qquad F_1(k) = \begin{bmatrix} k & 0 \\ 0 & 1 \end{bmatrix}, \qquad F_2(k) = \begin{bmatrix} 1 & 0 \\ 0 & k \end{bmatrix},$

$F_{21}(k) = \begin{bmatrix} 1 & k \\ 0 & 1 \end{bmatrix}, \qquad F_{12}(k) = \begin{bmatrix} 1 & 0 \\ k & 1 \end{bmatrix}.$

SECTION 5.6

1. (a) $x_1 = -1$, $x_2 = 1$, $x_3 = 2$.
   (b) $x_1 = -7/5 + k/5$, $x_2 = 1/5 + 2k/5$, $x_3 = k$, where k is an arbitrary real number.
   (c) System is inconsistent.

2. (a) $x_1 = -k/16$, $x_2 = 13k/16$, $x_3 = -3k/16$, $x_4 = k$, where k is an arbitrary real number.
   (b) Trivial solution only.
   (c) $x_1 = 3k - 2m$, $x_2 = k$, $x_3 = 5k - 3m$, $x_4 = m$, where k and m are arbitrary real numbers.

SECTION 5.7

1. $I(I) = (I)I = I$. Since inverse is unique when it exists, we have $I^{-1} = I$.
2. $A^{-1}A = AA^{-1} = I$. Since inverse is unique when it exists, we have $A = (A^{-1})^{-1}$.
3. $\begin{bmatrix} \frac{3}{2} & -\frac{1}{2} \\ -2 & 1 \end{bmatrix}$.
5. $\begin{bmatrix} 1 & -1 & 2 \\ -1 & 2 & -3 \\ -1 & 1 & -1 \end{bmatrix}$.
7. $X = \begin{bmatrix} 1 & -17 \\ 0 & -12 \end{bmatrix}$, $Y = \begin{bmatrix} -7 & 4 \\ 10 & -4 \end{bmatrix}$.
9. $\begin{bmatrix} 2 & 2 & 1 \\ 2 & 0 & 2 \\ 2 & 2 & 2 \end{bmatrix}$.

SECTION 6.1

1. (a) $[-2, 1, 3]\xi$. (b) $[1, -4, -2]\xi$. (c) $[3, 1, -1]\xi$.
   When $\xi = \text{col}\,(2, -1, 2)$, then: (a) 1, (b) 2, (c) 3.

2. (a) $\xi' \begin{bmatrix} -2 & 1 & -2 \\ 1 & 1 & -3 \\ -2 & -3 & -3 \end{bmatrix} \xi$; when $\xi = \text{col}\,(1, -2, 3)$, the value is -5.

   (b) $\xi' \begin{bmatrix} 1 & \frac{3}{2} & -2 & 0 \\ \frac{3}{2} & 4 & 0 & \frac{1}{2} \\ -2 & 0 & -1 & -2 \\ 0 & \frac{1}{2} & -2 & -2 \end{bmatrix} \xi$; when $\xi = \text{col}\,(2, 1, 0, -2)$, the value is 4.

3. (a) $\xi'\begin{bmatrix} 2 & -3 & 2 \\ -1 & -2 & -3 \end{bmatrix}\eta$; has value 39 for the given vectors.

   (b)

$$\xi'\begin{bmatrix} 1 & 2 \\ 0 & -1 \\ -4 & 2 \\ -2 & 0 \end{bmatrix}\eta$$; has value -51 for the given vectors.

5. (a) 2. (b) 5. (c) -8. (d) $ad - bc$.

6. (a) 19. (b) 0. (c) 16.

7. (a) -1. (b) 1. (c) -1.

8. (a) 1. (b) 24. (c) $+a_{14}a_{23}a_{32}a_{41}$.

SECTION 6.2

1. (b), (c), and (f).

2. $\begin{bmatrix} 2 & 1 & 3 \\ 1 & 0 & 3 \\ 3 & 0 & 0 \end{bmatrix}$; $T(\xi_1) = \begin{bmatrix} 18 \\ 16 \\ 3 \end{bmatrix}$, $T(\xi_2) = \begin{bmatrix} -5 \\ -5 \\ 3 \end{bmatrix}$, $T(\xi) = \begin{bmatrix} 2x_1 + x_2 + 3x_3 \\ x_1 + 3x_3 \\ 3x_1 \end{bmatrix}$.

3. $T(\xi_1) = \begin{bmatrix} -1 \\ 1 \\ 4 \end{bmatrix}$, $T(\xi_2) = \begin{bmatrix} 26 \\ -5 \\ -6 \end{bmatrix}$, $T(\xi) = \begin{bmatrix} 3x_1 + 4x_2 \\ -x_2 \\ 2x_1 - 2x_2 \end{bmatrix}$.

4. $\begin{bmatrix} 1 & -1 & 0 \\ 0 & 0 & 1 \\ 6 & 0 & 1 \end{bmatrix}$, $T(\xi): \begin{matrix} y_1 = x_1 - x_2 \\ y_2 = x_3, \\ y_3 = 6x_1 + x_3 \end{matrix}$ $T^{-1}: \begin{matrix} x_1 = -y_2 + \frac{1}{6}y_3 \\ x_2 = -y_1 - y_2 + \frac{1}{6}y_3. \\ x_3 = y_2 \end{matrix}$

5. $T: \begin{bmatrix} 1 & 1 & 2 & 0 \\ -1 & 0 & -1 & 0 \\ 0 & 1 & 2 & 0 \\ 0 & 0 & 1 & 1 \end{bmatrix}$, $T^{-1}: \begin{bmatrix} 1 & 0 & -1 & 0 \\ 2 & 2 & -1 & 0 \\ -1 & -1 & 1 & 0 \\ 1 & 1 & -1 & 1 \end{bmatrix}$.

SECTION 6.3

2. The encoded message is given by the columns of the matrix

$$\begin{bmatrix} -77 & -91 & -60 & -47 & -72 & -73 & -52 \\ 56 & 75 & 44 & 42 & 54 & 68 & 39 \\ -22 & -39 & -23 & -19 & -21 & -38 & -25 \end{bmatrix}.$$

3. The message is "Good luck on your quiz."

Section 6.4

1. (a) $\mathscr{S}$ is three times as likely to change from state s_1 to s_2 as it is to remain in state s_1. It cannot change to state s_3.
   (b) If $\mathscr{S}$ is in state s_2 it cannot remain in that state.
   (c) No.

2.
$$
\begin{array}{c}
\quad\ \text{fp}\ \ \text{s}\ \ \text{c}\ \ \text{bh} \\
\begin{array}{c}\text{fp}\\ \text{s}\\ \text{c}\\ \text{bh}\end{array}
\begin{bmatrix}
1 & 0 & 0 & 0 \\
0 & 0 & \frac{1}{2} & \frac{1}{2} \\
0 & 0 & \frac{1}{2} & \frac{1}{2} \\
\frac{1}{3} & \frac{1}{3} & \frac{1}{3} & 0
\end{bmatrix}.
\end{array}
$$

3.
$$
\begin{array}{c}
\quad\ \text{F}\ \ \text{G}\ \ \text{N} \\
\begin{array}{c}\text{F}\\ \text{G}\\ \text{N}\end{array}
\begin{bmatrix}
\frac{1}{2} & \frac{1}{4} & \frac{1}{4} \\
\frac{1}{4} & \frac{1}{2} & \frac{1}{4} \\
\frac{1}{2} & \frac{1}{2} & 0
\end{bmatrix}.
\end{array}
$$
$p_0 T^3 = (\frac{77}{192}, \frac{77}{192}, \frac{38}{192})$. The fixed vector is $(0.4, 0.4, 0.2)$.

4.
$$
\begin{array}{c}
\quad\ s_1\ \ s_2\ \ s_3\ \ s_4 \\
\begin{array}{c}s_1\\ s_2\\ s_3\\ s_4\end{array}
\begin{bmatrix}
1 & 0 & 0 & 0 \\
\frac{1}{2} & 0 & \frac{1}{2} & 0 \\
0 & \frac{1}{2} & 0 & \frac{1}{2} \\
0 & 0 & 0 & 1
\end{bmatrix}.
\end{array}
$$
$p_0 T^2 = (\frac{7}{16}, \frac{1}{16}, \frac{1}{16}, \frac{1}{2})$. The fixed vector is $(\frac{1}{2}, 0, 0, \frac{1}{2})$.

5.
$$
\begin{array}{c}
\quad\ \text{d}\ \ \text{h}\ \ \text{r} \\
\begin{array}{c}\text{d}\\ \text{h}\\ \text{r}\end{array}
\begin{bmatrix}
1 & 0 & 0 \\
\frac{1}{2} & \frac{1}{2} & 0 \\
0 & 1 & 0
\end{bmatrix}.
\end{array}
$$

Section 6.5

1. (a) $\hat{\xi} = [1, 0]$, $\quad \hat{\eta} = \begin{bmatrix} 1 \\ 0 \end{bmatrix}$, $\quad v = 1$.

   (b) $\hat{\xi} = [1, 0]$, $\quad \hat{\eta} = \begin{bmatrix} 1 \\ 0 \end{bmatrix}$, $\quad v = 1$.

   (c) $\hat{\xi} = [\frac{2}{5}, \frac{3}{5}]$, $\quad \hat{\eta} = \begin{bmatrix} \frac{4}{5} \\ \frac{1}{5} \end{bmatrix}$, $\quad v = \frac{13}{5}$.

   (d) $\hat{\xi} = [\frac{2}{7}, \frac{5}{7}]$, $\quad \hat{\eta} = \begin{bmatrix} \frac{6}{7} \\ \frac{1}{7} \end{bmatrix}$, $\quad v = \frac{16}{7}$.

   (e) $\hat{\xi} = [1, 0]$, $\quad \hat{\eta} = \begin{bmatrix} 0 \\ 1 \end{bmatrix}$, $\quad v = 2$.

   (f) $\hat{\xi} = [0, 1]$, $\quad \hat{\eta} = \begin{bmatrix} 0 \\ 1 \end{bmatrix}$, $\quad v = 1$.

2.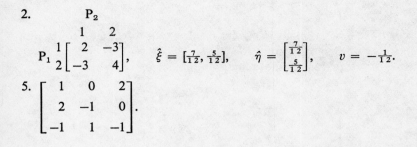

5. $\begin{bmatrix} 1 & 0 & 2 \\ 2 & -1 & 0 \\ -1 & 1 & -1 \end{bmatrix}$.

LIST OF SYMBOLS

Symbol	*Definition*	*Page*
A	the matrix A	161
A^p	p^{th} power of matrix A	176
A^{-1}	inverse of matrix A	194
A'	transpose of matrix A	169
det A	determinant of matrix A	202
$[A, \beta]$	augmented matrix	187
$A = (a_{ij})$	matrix A with element a_{ij} in row i and column j	161
$A = [\alpha_1, \alpha_2, \ldots, \alpha_n]$	matrix A with column vectors α_i	161
$A = \begin{bmatrix} \beta_1 \\ \beta_2 \\ \vdots \\ \beta_n \end{bmatrix}$	matrix A with row vectors β_i	161
A	the set A	2
2^A	power set of set A	7
A'	complement of set A	9
$\bar{A}$	complement of set A	9

251

a'	complement of element a	55
B	the set B of elements in a Boolean algebra	54
$\mathscr{B}$	Boolean algebraic system, as:	

$$\mathscr{B} = \{B, \cap, \cup, '\},$$

	the Boolean system of set B and operations	54
C	set of complex numbers	3
$\mathscr{C}$	field of complex numbers	132
col $(b_1, b_2, \ldots, b_n)$	column vector of dimension n	170
D	domain	29
diag $(d_1, d_2, \ldots, d_n)$	diagonal matrix of order n	175
E	probability event	101
F	set of fractions; set of elements in a field	3; 131
$\mathscr{F}$	field	131
$f; f(x)$	function; function with argument x	29; 30
f^{-1}	inverse function	40
$f: D \to R$	function with domain D and range R	29
$f: X_1 \times X_2 \times \cdots$ $\times X_n \to Z$	function f maps the n-tuple $(x_1, x_2, \ldots, x_n)$ into a unique element z of the range Z	48
$f(E)$	frequency of event E	101
$f(\xi, j)$	expected gain	228
$g[f]$	composite of functions f and g	47
$\mathscr{G}$	game	222
I	set of integers; identity matrix; identity transformation	3; 171; 205
I_n	identity matrix of order n	171
$K = (k\delta_{ij})$	scalar matrix	175
$m \times n$	dimensions of a matrix with m rows and n columns	161
$[N_r]$	equivalence classes of matrices of rank r	173
O	zero matrix	166
p	probability	105
$P(t)$	status vector of system $\mathscr{S}$ at time t	218
P_1	maximizing player in two-player game	223
P_2	minimizing player in two-player game	223
$p(E)$	probability measure of the event E; probability of event E	105
$p(A \mid B)$	conditional probability of the occurrence of the event A given the occurrence of the event B	111
$p_i(t)$	probability that $\mathscr{S}$ is in state s_i at time t	217
Q	set of rational numbers	3

q_{ij}	probability of event S_{ij}	215
$Q = (q_{ij})$	transition matrix	216
R	set of real numbers; range	3; 29
R	in relation, as: $a\,R\,b$, "a is in relation R to b"	20; 22
$\mathscr{R}$	ring, real field	130; 132
$\mathbb{R}$	not in relation, as: $x_i\,\mathbb{R}\,x_j$, "x_i is not relation R with x_j"	169
$\mathscr{S}$	biological or physical system	215
S/R	factor set of set S with respect to relation R	26
$s_i(t)$	state of system $\mathscr{S}$ at time t	217
S_{ij}	the event "$\mathscr{S}$ is in state $s_i(t-1)$ and in state $s_j(t)$"	217
$T: V_n(\mathscr{F}) \to V_m(\mathscr{F})$	linear transformation on a vector space $V_n(\mathscr{F})$	204
$T(\xi)$	image of vector ξ with respect to the transformation T	205
U	universal set; sample space	4; 101
$V_n(\mathscr{F})$	vector space of n-dimensional vectors over a field $\mathscr{F}$	141
z	additive identity in algebraic system	130
Z^+	set of positive integers	3
Z^-	set of negative integers	3
Z_{ij}	zero submatrix	167
$\alpha, \beta, \gamma, \xi, \eta$	algebraic vectors	141
δ_{ij}	Kronecker delta	174
ε_i	unit vector	145
θ	zero vector	142
$\hat{\xi}, \hat{\eta}$	optimal mixed-strategy vectors	230
$\pi = \begin{pmatrix} 1 & 2 & 3 \\ 3 & 2 & 1 \end{pmatrix}$	element of a permutation group	128
ω	$-1/2 + \sqrt{3}\,i/2$	126; 133
ω^2	$-1/2 - \sqrt{3}\,i/2$	126; 133
$\rho: B \times B \to B$	binary operation on set B	54
$(\ldots, \ldots)$	ordered pair, as: (a, b)	15
$\{\ldots\}$	set defined by its elements	3
$[\ldots]$	equivalence class, as: $[x]$; the function "bracket x"	24; 32

$\{x \mid p(x)\}$	set of all elements x with property $p(x)$; set defined by the open statement $p(x)$	4
$\lvert \ldots \rvert$	absolute value, as: $\lvert x \rvert$, absolute value of x	4; 31
$-$	complement, as: $\overline{A}$, complement of set A	9
	complement, as: A', complement of set A, and a', complement of element a; negation of a logical proposition; partial ordering relation; transpose, as A', transpose of matrix A	9; 55; 169
$\dotplus$	direct sum; symmetric difference of sets	14
$-$	relative difference, as: $A - B$, relative difference of sets A and B	9
$\times$	product set, as: $A \times B$, Cartesian product of sets A and B	15
$\cdot$	inner, or dot, product of vectors α, β	156
$\sim$	equivalence, matrices, as: $A \sim B$	179
$\equiv$	congruence, as: $a \equiv b \pmod{m}$, "a is congruent to b, modulo m"	25
$\in$	belongs to, is a member of, as: $a \in A$, "element a belongs to set A"	2
$\notin$	does not belong to, as: $a \notin A$	2
$\subset$	proper subset, as: $A \subset B$, "A is a proper subset of B"	6
$\subseteq$	subset (not necessarily proper), as: $A \subseteq B$, "A is a subset of B"	6
$\cup$	union, set algebra, as: $A \cup B$, union of sets A and B	8
$\cap$	intersection, set algebra, as: $A \cap B$, intersection of sets A and B	8
$\vee$	disjunction, propositional algebra, as: $a \vee b$, disjunction of logical propositions a and b; union, Boolean algebra, as: $a \vee b$, union of elements a and b	71; 54
$\cdot$	intersection, Boolean algebra, as: $a \cdot b$, intersection of a and b	54
$\wedge$	conjunction, propositional algebra, as: $a \wedge b$ conjunction of logical propositions a and b	71
$\rightarrow$	implication, propositional logic, as: $p \rightarrow q$, "p implies q;" mapping, as in $f: A \rightarrow B$, function with domain A and range B	72; 29
$\leftrightarrow$	equivalence, propositional logic, as: $p \leftrightarrow q$, "p and q are equivalent;" correspondence,

INDEX